Oxfordshire's Threatened Plants:

a register of the rare and scarce plants of the administrative county, and of vice-county 23

by S.E. Erskine, H.J. Killick, C.R. Lambrick and E.M. Lee

piscespublications

Published 2018 by Pisces Publications

First published 2018.

British-Library-in-Publication Data
A catalogue record for this book is available from the British Library.

ISBN 978-1-874357-84-1

Designed and published by Pisces Publications

Visit our bookshop
www.naturebureau.co.uk/bookshop/

Pisces Publications is the imprint of NatureBureau,
36 Kingfisher Court, Hambridge Road, Newbury, Berkshire RG14 5SJ
www.naturebureau.co.uk

Printed and bound by Gomer Press, UK

Front cover: *Fritillaria meleagris* Snake's-head Fritillary; *Hypopitys monotropa* Yellow Bird's-nest; *Parnassia palustris* Grass-of-Parnassus; *Orchis simia* Monkey Orchid [Peter Creed]
Back cover: *Gagea lutea* Yellow Star-of-Bethlehem [Peter Creed]

Susan Erskine has been passionate about wild flowers since childhood. Fortunate to live in North Yorkshire, local excursions with the field club included visits to Upper Teesdale and many more botanical hotspots. She has contributed to two BSBI Atlases, was on the board of Plantlife and is an active member of the Ashmolean Natural History Society of Oxfordshire, Oxfordshire Flora Group (OFG). Susan was chair of the OFG since its inception until 2017. She currently works as a Flora Guardian and organises the Spring Talks for the group, as well as helping with surveying for the 2020 BSBI Atlas.

John Killick read Natural Sciences (Botany) at Cambridge. During three years in Nigeria he wrote *Beginning Ecology* and on return to the UK began 25 years with the Natural Environment Research Council and founded the Cheshunt Natural History Society. He recorded Oxfordshire's plants over 40 years, 30 as County Recorder. He was co-author of *The Flora of Oxfordshire* (1998) and wrote over 900 *Oxford Times* articles. For the 2002 Atlas he collated Oxfordshire records and drafted 80 captions, then turning attention to *Oxfordshire's Threatened Plants*.

Camilla Lambrick, née Huxley, led the Cambridge Conservation Volunteers while reading Natural Sciences at Cambridge University. She then worked in Papua New Guinea studying a symbiosis between ants and epiphytes. Returning to Oxford she obtained a D.Phil. on the taxonomy of these plants. She helped set up the Oxford Conservation Volunteers, and then the Rare Plants Group of the Ashmolean Natural History Society of Oxfordshire. Subsequently she worked for Oxfordshire County Council, and then the Thames Valley Environmental Records Centre, surveying Local Wildlife Sites.

Ellen Lee studied chemistry at Oxford as both undergraduate and post-graduate, emerging with a D.Phil. in Physical Chemistry. After doing research (in the UK and The Netherlands) and teaching for some years, she changed tack, becoming a self-employed computer programmer working on business simulations for training in the hospitality industry. In 2003, she made use of her lifelong interest in all kinds of wildlife by joining the newly formed Thames Valley Environmental Records Centre where she has worked as Biodiversity Services Officer ever since.

Contents

Foreword

Twenty years ago the Botanical Society of the Britain and Ireland (BSBI) suggested that in addition to the County Floras, which traditionally cover all the species in each, it might be valuable to produce a publication setting out the known state of affairs for the rare and threatened species. This would be aimed at everybody, of course, but it was hoped that it would be particularly useful for conservation bodies, such as the local Wildlife Trust, English Nature and the local Biological Record Centre, and would better inform the County planners and consultants working on developments.

Guidelines were drawn up, and each county was encouraged to try to meet at least a minimum disclosure of species and details. But there were two radical proposals, one of which caused heart-searching at the time. That was the recommendation to give six-figure grid references for as many records as possible, arguing that knowledge of where each plant occurred was of more value to conservation and outweighed any risk that the giving of a detailed location would encourage picking or destruction. A quarter of a century on that risk has been triumphantly vindicated, with only a tiny handful of known losses. The other interesting development was the inclusion of the less rare species nationally that were known only from a handful of sites in each county, and it is the inclusion of those that makes these Rare Plant Registers so much more interesting. We know, or think we know, the rarest, but the next tranche are often a revelation.

This long-awaited register for Oxfordshire covers the post-1974 administrative county (including areas added from Berkshire) plus a small area near Reading, then transferred to Berkshire. I'm very pleased indeed that it meets and surpasses the BSBI's original guidelines. For not only does it include all the main categories – rare and scarce nationally together with rare and scarce in the county, but it covers older records that have not been seen since 2000 – the start date of the project – but might still be discovered with fresh pair of eyes, or through a change in cultivation. That last is very important, because of the 63 species that were known between 1968 and 1999, but not seen since, one third, 23 species, are plants of arable or anthropogenic – followers of man – and might re-appear with disturbance or cessation of intensive spraying. There must be less hope for the next biggest category of loss, 14 species found in wetland habitats that have been drained and built on or ploughed.

But the book is more than mere lists. Each species account give succinct and, to me, plausible reasons for change. To take two examples at random – *Gentianella germanica*, Chiltern Gentian, one of the glories of the area, is declining because of the decline in sheep-grazing, and possibly drier spring seasons. And *Ophrys insectifera*, Fly Orchid, declining, here, as elsewhere because of scrubbing over of its woodland edge habitat. Each page leads the reader on into more stories. It would have been so easy just to have a list but this work tries to place the list – and its seemingly inevitable catalogue of losses from a lowland English county – into context.

Each of these accounts also has the rationale for inclusion, a map, a photo (not too small) of many and a little arrow symbol, signifying decline, stability, or glory be, an increase. All this is supplemented and placed into context by introductory chapters on analysis of the data, on habitats and the future.

A model account of an important county, and definitely one of the better of the 60-odd already produced.

David Pearman
January 2018

Preface

"Oxfordshire's Threatened Plants" is designed to alert the public to the widespread losses of wild plants.

However, it has a specific task, the presentation of two related Rare Plants Registers.

- One is for the 360,590 ha of modern Administrative Oxfordshire in response to local demand.
- The other aims to meet the requirements of the Botanical Society of Britain and Ireland (BSBI) for that part of Oxfordshire (193,000 ha) that the BSBI has known as Vice-county 23 (vc23) since it was defined by H C Watson in 1810.

This project is a partnership between John Killick, then County Recorder, and Camilla Lambrick and Susan Erskine of the Oxfordshire Flora Group (OFG, formerly the Rare Plants Group) of the Ashmolean Natural History Society of Oxfordshire. Field work was done by volunteers and is detailed below. Ellen Lee at the Thames Valley Environmental Records Centre (TVERC) extracted and collated the data, and with volunteer help prepared the maps.

Susan Erskine, John Killick and Camilla Lambrick each made initial drafts of about a third of the species accounts, with help from others in a smaller number of species, adding our initials at the end of each account; we then edited the accounts and most of the rest of the text collectively.

The Stoneworts are contributed by Phil Cutt who also took many of the photographs. Finally, Peter Creed of NatureBureau has combined it all and contributed freely from his extensive photograph collection.

Acknowledgements

We thank first our many recorders and their invaluable contributions. Every record is useful and our list of recorders (page 145) includes those not only from our regular, wide-ranging contributors but also the providers of single records. The backbone of our database came from the Thames Valley Environmental Records Centre; we were also able to obtain records from many sources, notably the Floras of Oxfordshire and Berkshire, the BSBI and the local Wildlife Trust (BBOWT). Many local wildlife groups, the OFG and other Flora groups and individuals also helped us seek out old records and revisit localities for the Register. John Campbell gave much help in adding records to TVERC's database, and Graham Hawker quantified the areas of important habitats.

Our species accounts, especially of the scarce and rare species, make abundant use of records by named individuals, and some cite expert confirmation by certain of the BSBI's panel of referees. We noted records from herbaria, the Oxford one with help from Serena Marner. We are grateful for help from others in some of the species accounts, adding their initials at the end of each account.

For the framework of this book and for placing our records in the national context we owe much to recent Red Data Books for Great Britain and for England, to the 2002 Atlas of the British and Irish Flora, and to previous Rare Plant Registers in other counties. Phil Cutt was the lead author for the section on Stoneworts (Characeae).

The conservation of many of our rarer species owes much to Natural England and its predecessors, to BBOWT and to other organisations named in some of the species accounts.

Our selection of photographs was made in collaboration with Peter Creed who contributed a great many from the NatureBureau's collection.

We thank Frances Watkins for managing the website.

Generous financial support has come from the Oxfordshire Flora Group, Jeremy and Janet Welsh, Sally and John Rankin, Sue and Dieter Helm, an anonymous donor and ourselves, as well as Natural England, TVERC, the BSBI and BBOWT.

Finally, and far from least, we owe our grateful thanks to Peter and Barbara Creed and their colleagues in NatureBureau for their hard work and expertise in designing the layout and figures for the work and seeing it through the final stages.

Abbreviations

Many of our abbreviations relate to the names of Recorders, tabulated separately. Important ones are noted here but do not include N, E, S, W, NE, NW, SE, SW, Celsius or Fahrenheit.

Abbreviations used in the tables for individual species are defined at the beginning of the species accounts.

ANHSO	Ashmolean Natural History Society of Oxfordshire
ANS	Abingdon Naturalists' Society
BBONT	Berkshire, Buckinghamshire and Oxfordshire Naturalists' Trust, now BBOWT
BBOWT	Berkshire, Buckinghamshire and Oxfordshire Wildlife Trust, formerly BBONT
BI	British Isles – Britain and Ireland
BOS	Banbury Ornithological Society
BSBI	Botanical Society of Britain and Ireland (formerly Botanical Society of the British Isles)
c.	circa, approximately
CRPG	Cotswold Rare Plants Group, now Wychwood Flora Group
CWS	County Wildlife Site, now Local Wildlife Site, a county designation
E	Herbarium specimen held at Edinburgh University
EN	English Nature, now Natural England
FlBe	Flora of Berkshire, M J Crawley 2005
FlOx	Flora of Oxfordshire, John Killick, Roy Perry and Stan Woodell 1998
Fm	Farm
OFG	Oxfordshire Flora Group of the ANHSO, formerly RPG
GB	Great Britain (excludes Northern Ireland)
IUCN	International Union for the Conservation of Nature
LNR	Local Nature Reserve
LWS	Local Wildlife Site, local site designation in Oxfordshire and Berkshire
NCC	Nature Conservancy Council, earlier name for Natural England
NEng	Natural England, formerly English Nature
NMW	Herbarium specimen in the National Museum of Wales
NNR	National Nature Reserve
nr	near
NT	National Trust

OPT	Oxford Preservation Trust
OUBG	Oxford University Botanic Garden
OXF	Fielding Druce Herbarium, Oxford University Dept. of Plant Sciences
PA	Pond Action, now the Freshwater Habitats Trust
pLWS	Proposed Local Wildlife Site
RDG	Herbarium specimen at Reading University
RPG	Rare Plants Group of the ANHSO, now its Oxfordshire Flora Group
RSPB	Royal Society for the Protection of Birds
RVNR	Road Verge Nature Reserve
s. 41	Section 41 species from the Natural Environment and Rural Communities Act 2006; formerly UKBAP priority species
SAC	Special Area of Conservation, an European designation
SSSI	Site of Special Scientific Interest
Sched. 8	Schedule 8 species from Wildlife and Countryside Act 1981
TVERC	Thames Valley Environmental Records Centre
UK	United Kingdom, = GB plus Northern Ireland
UK BAP	UK Biodiversity Action Plan Priority species, now Section 41
vc	Vice-county, see Preface
WER	West Oxfordshire Recorders
WFG	Wychwood Flora Group, formerly the Cotswold Rare Plants Group

Symbols

⬇ Decline in number of localities

⬆ Increase in number of localities

➡ No significant change in number of localities

< Less than, or before a date: the record was made before that date

> More than, or later than, of a date

Introduction

Wild flowers were widely known until the 20th century:

In a cowslip's bell I lie
  Shakespeare, *The Tempest*, 1611

Drowsed by the fume of poppies
  Keats, *Ode to Autumn*, 1821

There grew pied windflowers [Wood Anemone] and violets
  Shelley, *The Question*

A host of golden daffodils
  Wordsworth, *Daffodils*

Celandine, the little children's dower
  Browning, *Home thoughts*

(Peter Creed)

Orchis purpurea **Lady Orchid**

Wild flowers are treasured for their beauty, appearing vividly in literature and poetry; but many of them are now rare and threatened. Oxfordshire, with its varied landscape, enjoys a rich heritage of plants, but this study shows that over a quarter of the total are at risk and over 50 that were present in 1970, are now gone. How are these endangered plants faring? Are the places where they exist being protected? How can we help them to survive? And why are some now lost? This Rare Plants Register addresses these questions by assessing the current threat to our flora, and also aims to assist nature conservation by providing evidence which can direct the planning of land-use and land management. This is vital not only for the plants themselves, but for the diversity of other wildlife dependent on them and not least for the clean air and water which we enjoy.

First of all, a list of potentially threatened species was accumulated – a daunting 450 kinds of plant. A spreadsheet of localities where they had been seen was provided by the Thames Valley Environmental Records Centre. Then, following national guidelines, and aided by many keen volunteers, we searched for 12 years. The results are alarming – we have listed 63 species last recorded between 1968 and 1999, and 274 species found to be either nationally or locally rare or scarce or at risk because their populations are declining sharply. Analysis of the data uses novel mapping which puts the recent, former and negative records against backgrounds showing soil types and the river network. This reveals patterns of loss and mobility of species as well as their sensitivity to the environment. Habitat analysis shows many arable

flowers now relegated to waste ground and quarries, while the decline of aquatic and acid-loving plants is of particular concern.

By adding historical, ecological and experimental detail, we show how conservation, when guided by up-to-date evidence, can sometimes succeed in retaining wild flowers in the landscape. Three examples are: *Viola persicifolia* Fen Violet is nearly lost at its two other sites in the UK, but spreading in the RSPB reserve at Otmoor, *Galium tricornutum* Corn-cleavers has been re-introduced after an absence of 30 years, and is again scrambling in unimproved arable at Wytham, while *Pulsatilla vulgaris* Pasqueflower flourishes if grazing is appropriately managed on the chalk downs. It is also good that *Himantoglossum hircinum* Lizard, *Orchis militaris* Military and *Orchis purpurea* Lady orchids have all appeared spontaneously at new localities, though sometimes have not persisted.

In future, factors such as climate change will make many places unsuitable for their current species, and diseases and new arrivals will alter populations, as happens naturally.

(Peter Creed)

Himantoglossum hircinum Lizard Orchid

(Peter Creed)

Pulsatilla vulgaris Pasqueflower

Our report covers plants found from 2000–2011 in the administrative county of Oxfordshire; this approximately comprises the Botanical Society of Britain and Ireland's (BSBI's) vice-county 23 (vc23) plus the part of Berkshire (vc22) which was added to Oxfordshire in 1974.

The listed plants follow the order in Stace (2010). We describe their selection, their habitats, and how their abundance compares with previous floras. The first three authors have each written over 100 accounts using our new records from 2000 to 2011, with Ellen Lee managing the Thames Valley Environmental Records Centre (TVERC) 2000–2011 database and the maps.

We had **three aims**:

1. **To help conservation**

    Plants are an essential part of natural systems, providing habitat and food for the animals, insects and fungi that exploit them. We document the populations of over 300 of them

(the main British sites of some are in Oxfordshire), the rate of loss of species and many habitats, and actions to mitigate the ill-effects. The decline of a quarter of the 1,485 plant species cited in *The Flora of Oxfordshire* (Killick *et al.* 1998; FlOx) p. 71 has been dramatic; the county (vc23) may have lost 63 species since 1968.

This book will place in context many plant conservation projects, assessing the ecological requirements of many species, and the effects of protected sites and some conservation actions.

2. **To inform Local Authorities considering planning applications, and developers selecting sites**. Our chapter on habitats should make clear that planning applications likely to influence fragile, species-rich habitats should be refused.

3. We hope that the overwhelming case for plant conservation will **inform the public** about the fragile floral heritage of our county and encourage volunteers and community action.

Methods

THE SPECIES CHOSEN FOR STUDY

Following BSBI guidelines, the selection comprises nationally rare, nationally scarce and locally rare, scarce and near-scarce species. Most are native in Oxfordshire or the long-established aliens, naturalised by 1500, defined in the *Atlas of the British and Irish Flora* (Preston *et al.* 2002) (Atlas 2002) as archaeophytes. Only a few species naturalised post-1500 (termed neophytes) are included, a few subspecies and no hybrids.

An alphabetical list of most candidate species was compiled in 2005; Frances Watkins put this on the website. A small number were added over time and by 2014 it included:

■ All the species that were listed by 2005 at a national level. *A Red List for Great Britain* by Cheffings and Farrell (2005) used categories from extinct EX through Extinct in the wild EW, Critically endangered CR, Endangered EN, Vulnerable VU (e.g. *Fritillaria meleagris* Fritillary, *Papaver argemone* Prickly Poppy) and Near Threatened NT, to many of least concern (LC)[1].

Additionally plants found in 1–15 10 × 10 km squares between 1987 and 1999 were categorised as Nationally Rare, and those in 16–100 10 × 10 km squares between 1987 and 1999 as Nationally Scarce.

■ Eleven locally or nationally scarce species studied from 1993 and in some cases managed by the Rare Plants Group of the Ashmolean Natural History Society of Oxfordshire, (ANHSO).

■ At a local level we usually chose plants in fewer than 20 of the 2 km × 2 km (tetrad) records out of a maximum 596 in FlOx and they included many in heathland, acid grassland, sandy habitats and calcareous fens of which vc23 has few.

■ We also studied two categories of species which had been recorded in over 20 tetrads. One comprised species in various habitats believed to be declining sharply. Many plants of wetlands were known to be decreasing even before FlOx was written, so we looked at *Zannichellia palustris* Horned Pondweed, which was in 32 tetrads, *Cirsium dissectum* Meadow Thistle in 36, *Valeriana*

---

1 (We do not wish the reader to infer from LC that there are **no** grounds for concern, because many species in this category have been decimated. For example the cowslip, cited above, was a major feature of a meadow habitat that occupied tens of square miles, but is now a refugee in field margins, lawns, set-aside, nature reserves and motorway verges.)

(Peter Creed)

Fritillaria meleagris Snake's-head Fritillary

(Peter Creed)

Valerianella dentata Narrow-fruited Cornsalad

(Peter Creed)

Moenchia erecta Upright Chickweed

dioica in 76, and most *Carex* Sedges, *Potamogeton* Pondweeds and aquatic *Ranunculus* Water Crowfoots. In arable land the steep decline had barely started in 1968 when FlOx began recording so we looked at, for example, *Valerianella dentata* Narrow-fruited Cornsalad in 25, *Clinopodium acinos* Basil Thyme in 75, *Stachys arvensis* Field Woundwort in 82, *Spergula arvensis* Corn Spurrey in 95 and even *Glebionis* (*Chrysanthemum*) *segetum* Corn Marigold in 186. In unimproved grassland hitherto widespread species had included *Petroselinum segetum* Corn Parsley in 36 and *Arabis hirsuta* Hairy Rock-cress in 40.

- Another, smaller group comprised species which John Killick had believed to be over-recorded in FlOx – *Salix aurita* Eared Willow in 53, *Glyceria declinata* Small Sweet-grass in 46, *Viola canina* Heath Dog-violet in 40, as well as *Agrostis canina* Velvet Bent and *Anthemis arvensis* Corn Chamomile for which many records submitted for FlOx were rejected before publication.
- We added some newly found species – *Agrostis curtisii* Bristle Bent and *Poa infirma* Early Meadow-grass, not recorded in FlOx, and in vc22 (Oxon) *Teesdalia nudicaulis* Shepherd's Cress, *Bolboschoenus maritimus* Sea Club-rush and *Moenchia erecta* Upright Chickweed.

In 2014 we took advantage of the Red List for England (Stroh *et al.*, 2014) to place our records in a more recent and specifically English context. This attached differing levels of threat to some of those in the GB list, so some re-drafting was necessary. Many species it added to the previous list had not been studied and could not be commented on. Table 6 lists the more threatened ones, Vulnerable (VU) and then Near Threatened (NT), with numbers of records previously in FlOx, some surprisingly large.

We found, as did French (2014), that this List is "better suited to the needs of nature conservation" than the GB one.

ASSESSMENT OF THE CHANGED FREQUENCY: THE PAST HISTORY AND FLORAS

Previous Floras reveal the abundance of the selected species. Those of Oxfordshire were by Druce in 1886 and 1927, and by Killick *et al.* in 1998, and those of Berkshire by Druce in 1897, by Bowen in 1968 and by Crawley in 2005. Careful examination of these Floras has helped our assessment of the changing frequency of these species.

Druce's *Flora of Oxfordshire* (1927) was compiled by one of the leading botanists of his day, and as many records were his, the standard of identification was high. Our only caveats were cited in FlOx. The native flora was rich, then only moderately affected by agriculture. However, being written before the plants were systematically recorded in 2 × 2 km grid squares (tetrads), the Flora had tended to concentrate on rich "honeypot" sites and to underemphasise unexciting areas. It likewise listed many sites for the species deemed more interesting (including many now in our Register) but to make only general comments on others. Geographically it was based on "botanical districts" based on river catchments.

Similar comments apply to his **Flora of Oxfordshire** (1886) and **Flora of Berkshire** (1897).

Bowen's *Flora of Berkshire* (1968) was a pioneer in seeking fuller, more uniform geographical coverage by dividing the county, some of which is now in Oxfordshire, into squares based on the national grid. He was a highly competent botanist and again many records were his and the standard of identification was high. Unfortunately for present purposes he used squares of 5 × 5 km, before tetrads were adopted.

Work on **The Flora of Oxfordshire (FlOx)** began in 1968 and dot maps were compiled based on 596 2 × 2 km squares (tetrads), giving comprehensive geographical coverage. Because 75% of the tetrad records were first noted in 1968–73, many dot maps give a snapshot of the county's flora before modern agriculture began seriously to erode it. More generally plants, particularly of wetlands, unimproved grasslands, heaths and arable land, were lost from some of the sites we had recorded, between then and the Flora's publication in 1998.

The survey in FIOx involved more recorders than most county floras, so it was very thorough, even in the marginal, distant and dull tetrads, and comprised a huge number, 184,000, of tetrad records, including very many good ones by Humphry Bowen, Richard Palmer and Richard Fitter.

The FIOx tetrad records are important for this Register for three reasons.

- First, their number was a key criterion in selecting candidates for it.
- Secondly, FIOx remains our most comprehensive source for pre-1996 records, albeit mostly only at tetrad level. Many but not all of these records have been added to the Thames Valley Environmental Records Centre (TVERC) database.
- Also, very many of the selected species are declining, and the tetrad records give the most accurate picture of how far this decline had got by the 1970s, and act as a benchmark for plotting the continuing decline of many species and the effects in some cases of active management.

Unfortunately, tetrad records are not precise enough to be easily re-found, so we could not update as many as we would have wished.

FIOx recording cards used a rather long "tick list" which simplified their assembly in master cards and dot maps. Unfortunately it included many species we regard as rare or scarce, from which one could infer that their finding was unremarkable, and the FIOx records contain all too few six-figure grid references. John Killick did not receive the original cards until after FIOx was written, but did have a comprehensive set of master cards showing what records were added, year on year, and added to them.

Crawley's *Flora of Berkshire* (FIBe) is a comprehensive study with many useful tips for distinguishing the species from closely related species, a practice that has been adopted here.

The author argued that the use of tetrads was misleading on the grounds that many species would have been under-recorded, and did not use them or publish dot maps. In this respect FIBe resembles Druce's Floras and the geographical coverage for West Berkshire, which contains the area now in Oxfordshire is less comprehensive than in FIOx.

Many records are undated and usually, and by inference, not recent, but some from the 1990s onwards are detailed, including six-figure grid references. The names of recorders are evident only when the records have entered the TVERC database.

FIBe contains an extremely comprehensive account of habitats (very useful in summarising habitats for the Register) and local information. It includes data on extinctions, and lists species found in Berks but not Oxon and vice-versa.

RELIABILITY OF DATA

Wrong records can occur in any survey and every record could not be validated among the 184,000 in FIOx or in the Thames Valley Environmental Centre (TVERC) database. However, the name of the recorder and the plausibility of the habitat can be useful guides; among the many recorders for FIOx, BBONT (now BBOWT) and TVERC were a few who produced implausible records. Where the names of recorders are not given, it can be harder to judge their reliability.

Where FIOx received more locations for a native species than Druce had had, e.g. in *Agrostis canina*, many were rejected.

There was concern about possible errors in transcribing data from individuals' records into the databases of both FIOx and TVERC. The master cards compiled by Roy Perry in the years 1968–72, and the transcription of records from FIOx master cards to FIOx dot maps by him and John Killick are of least concern; elsewhere errors are harder to rule out.

Not every relevant record in FIOx is in TVERC. TVERC also had records, mostly plausible, that had not got into FIOx, but they included some records that John Killick had rejected for FIOx. Ideally, suspect records need to be annotated as such.

The current survey has involved many fewer recorders and records (20,000) than did the Flora; it is to be hoped that this implies a lower proportion of errors.

The original aim was to get all the relevant pre-2000 records into the TVERC database, which from 1996 onwards is the main source for post-FIOx records in most species. In writing up this account, relevant FIOx tetrad records have mostly been imported to TVERC to add to those previously sent in. A few species had so many records that it was found easier to refer the reader to the tetrad records and maps in FIOx.

Results: analysis of data

NUMBERS OF RECENT RECORDS COMPARED WITH OLDER ONES

Key to our assessment of the decline of the scarcer species is the ratio between the number of FlOx tetrad (2 x 2 km square) records between 1968 and 1995, and the numbers we found from 2000 to 2011. The number of pre-2000 records from the period 1996–1999, vc22 and other sources was relatively small.

The pre-2000 count was nearly always greater, sometimes much greater, than our post-2000 count. This was for a number of reasons.

- Firstly, we recorded for 12 years rather than 28.
- Because tetrad (2 × 2 km square) records are imprecise we could not re-find as many as we would have wished.
- The present survey involved far fewer recorders than did FlOx.
- Distance from the recorder's home can cause bias in recording (Amphlett 2013). Because the three botanist authors all live in former Berkshire (vc22), and few of our other recorders live north of Burford and Oxford, it has been hard to do justice to the North of the county. Fortunately the River Swere catchment was reported by Meagher and Sheasby (2005). We have identified some species under-recorded in the North, and hope future botanists will fill the gaps.

HOW OUR REGISTER SPECIES HAVE DECLINED

To define the extent to which species have declined (or increased) **at a national level** since the 1962 Atlas (Perring and Walters 1962), the 2002 Atlas (Pearman, Preston and Dines 2002) used a "change index". For simplicity we have referred to a change index worse than -1.0 as a huge, severe or steep, decline, -0.5 to -0.99 as a big decline, and smaller changes as decline.

In assessing abundance changes between the 1962 and 2002 Atlases, allowances had to be made because Atlas 2002 was based on more records than the older one. We in contrast have had to allow for a lesser recording effort in this work than in FlOx.

Therefore we sometimes interpret a smaller number of recent records than that in FlOx as "no change" rather than a decline. Perhaps two-thirds of the number of tetrads is a fair expectation overall, but the proportion varies with species.

We added where applicable the recent update in Braithwaite et al. (2006). Here the BSBI recordings of local change between 1987–8 and 2003–4 have been analysed. Some of their conclusions figure in our species accounts.

THE WORST-AFFECTED SPECIES

Drainage, fertilisers and the other adverse factors noted below under "Causes" have harmed Oxfordshire's plant species to differing extents. Two ways of looking at this are cited here.

1. In Grime et al., (1988) established plants have three basic strategies based on factors which affect photosynthetic production:
   - Fast-growing Competitors (C) such as Urtica dioica Common Nettle and Pteridium aquilinum Bracken exploit ideal conditions of nutrients, light, acidity and temperature.
   - Where sites are disturbed, Ruderals (R) such as Stellaria media Chickweed, Poa annua Annual Meadow-grass, and Papaver rhoeas Common Poppy can spread rapidly.
   - Both these cope less well with a shortage of light or minerals, too much or too little water, high acidity or alkalinity, sub-optimal temperatures, or excessive shade, giving opportunities for small, slow-growing Stress tolerators (S); examples are Calluna vulgaris Heather, Gentianella gentians and some Orchis orchids.

Among the many species (from common to rare) in Grime et al. Table 6.2 (pp 629–637) are 17 competitors, 55 stress-tolerators and 37 ruderals; the rest are in various combinations – CR (Competitor-ruderal), CS, SR, CSR or the intermediates between these e.g. C/CS.

The subset that is found in our Register contains no competitors, only 10 ruderals and 36 of the 55 stress-tolerators; we had to deduce the strategies of a few of these from closely related species in the same genus. Thus our Register has disproportionately more stress-tolerators.

2. In Braithwaite et al. (2006) the habitats/species worst affected included:
   Non-conifer woodland – plants preferring lower temperatures
   Arable, horticultural – northern species
   Most grassland – northern species and species of nutrient-poor places
   Neutral and calcareous grassland – perennials
   Dwarf shrub, heath and bog – species of warmer, drier areas
   Wetlands – annuals and species of nutrient-poor places.

These correlations are not all causal but it is likely that eutrophication was the driving factor for grasslands and wetlands. Warmer winters may have influenced woodlands, and other factors including land-use have played a part. The very hot summer of 2003 may have influenced records in 2003–4.

THE LOST SPECIES
The dates "lost" species were last seen in vc23
Table 1 (p. 8) lists the last records, mostly in FlOx, for species not seen recently in vc23, year by year. Some species lost before 1928 are not in the Register. It omits 13 species mostly recorded in FlOx only once or twice and not recorded since, eg *Dactylorhiza purpurella* Northern Marsh-Orchid. It also omits *Chrysosplenium alternifolium* Alternate-leaved Golden-saxifrage, *Draba muralis* Wall Whitlowgrass, *Euphorbia platyphyllos* Broad-leaved Spurge, *Orchis militaris* Military Orchid and *Rumex palustris* Marsh Dock which were believed lost, but re-found between 2012 and 2015.

Table 7 (p. 22) lists the losses between 1968 and 1999 alphabetically with habitats; non bold print shows where the species is still found in 2000–11 in vc22 (Oxon).

The conclusion is stark. Eleven species were lost by 1900, another 14 by 1967. Then two were lost after 1968, 21 in the 1970s, 25 in the 1980s and 15 in the 1990s. The last 63 from 1968 to 1999 is 8% of the 834 species qualifying as natives in FlOx (p. 71).

This dire conclusion is subject to caveats. After intensive recording for a Flora, one would expect some rare or scarce species not to be re-found for a while. We may not have re-visited relevant colonies or re-recorded in enough of the right habitats. Also, the nearer the last record is to the present, the more likely it is that a new record will turn up. Our findings are based on 2000–2011, but we have records (added to the text) of five subsequent single records – of *Chrysosplenium alternifolium*, *Euphorbia platyphyllos*, *Orchis militaris* Military Orchid, *Rumex palustris* and in vc22 (Oxon) *Torilis arvensis* Spreading Hedge-parsley. In the late 1990s a very thorough survey of some arable farms compared the flora of organic and non–organic farms. Where these farms were not re-visited, 'lost' species may have survived.

Because of dramatic changes to arable and wetland areas, 44% of the 63 listed species have been from these habitats, see Figure 1 p. 8.

(Peter Creed)

Orchis militaris Military Orchid

(Peter Creed)

Chrysosplenium alternifolium Alternate-leaved Golden-saxifrage

Table 1. Loss of species in vc23 classified by date of last record.

Last record	Species	Common name
1830	Drosera rotundifolia	Round-leaved Sundew
1834	Pulicaria vulgaris	Small Fleabane
1880	Pulsatilla vulgaris	Pasqueflower
1881	Littorella uniflora	Shoreweed
1881	Radiola linoides	Allseed
1884	Botrychium lunaria	Moonwort
1886	Moenchia erecta	Upright Chickweed
1887	Gymnocarpium dryopteris	Oak Fern
1887	Huperzia selago	Fir Clubmoss
1882	Teesdalia nudicaulis	Shepherd's Cress
1886	Salix myrsinifolia	Whortle-leaved Willow
1907	Trifolium subterraneum	Subterranean Clover
1910	Sonchus palustris	Marsh Ragwort
1911	Antenaria dioica	Mountain Everlasting
1914	Hypochaeris glabra	Smooth Cat's-ear
1914	Vaccinium myrtilus	Bilberry
1924	Apera interrupta	Dense Silky-bent
1927	Genista anglica	Petty Whin
1927	Filago lutescens	Red-tipped Cudweed
1927	Juncus ranarius	Frog Rush
1927	Silene conica	Sand Catchfly
1927	Viola palustris	Marsh Violet
1931	Bromus interruptus	Interrupted Brome
1948	Lythrum hyssopifolium	Grass-poly
1965	Thelypteris palustris	Marsh Fern
1968	Equisetum sylvaticum	Wood Horsetail
1968	Eleocharis multicaulis	Many-stalked Spike-rush
1970	Cephalanthera longifolia	Narrow-leaved Helleborine
1970	Myriophyllum alterniflorum	Alternate Water-milfoil
1970	Pilularia globulifera	Pillwort
1971	Fumaria purpurea	Purple Ramping-fumitory
1972	Pyrola minor	Common Wintergreen
1973	Potamogeton friesii	Flat-stalked Pondweed
1974	Ulmus plotii	Plot's Elm
1975	Lycopodium clavatum	Stag's-horn Clubmoss
1975	Potamogeton praelongus	Long-stalked Pondweed
1976	Galeopsis speciosa	Large-flowered Hemp-nettle
1976	Potamogeton obtusifolius	Blunt-leaved Pondweed
1977	Lolium temulentum	Darnel
1978	Fumaria bastardii	Tall Ramping-fumitory
1978	Eleocharis acicularis	Needle Spike-rush
1978	Lepidium ruderale	Narrow-leaved Pepperwort
1978	Medicago polymorpha	Toothed Medick
1979	Epipogium aphyllum	Ghost Orchid

Last record	Species	Common name
1979	Fumaria parviflora	Fine-leaved Fumitory
1979	Herminium monorchis	Musk Orchid
1979	Potamogeton compressus	Grass-wrack Pondweed
1979	Potamogeton polygonifolius	Bog Pondweed
1980	Fumaria capreolata	White Ramping-fumitory
1980	Valerianella rimosa	Broad-fruited Cornsalad
1981	Dianthus armeria	Deptford Pink
1981	Turritis glabra	Tower Mustard
1981	Fallopia dumetorum	Copse-bindweed
1981	Minuartia hybrida	Fine-leaved Sandwort
1982	Neotinea ustulata	Burnt Orchid
1983	Centunculus minimus	Chaffweed
1983	Chamaemelum nobile	Chamomile
1983	Lepidium heterophyllum	Smith's Pepperwort
1983	Schoenus nigricans	Black Bog-rush
1984	Oreopteris limbosperma	Lemon-scented Fern
1985	Sagina nodosa	Knotted Pearlwort
1985	Ranunculus hederaceus	Ivy-leaved Crowfoot
1986	Epilobium lanceolatum	Spear-leaved Willowherb
1986	Galium tricornutum	Corn Cleavers
1987	Convallaria majalis	Lily-of-the-valley
1987	Nardus stricta	Mat-grass
1988	Carum carvi	Caraway
1988	Lathyrus aphaca	Yellow Vetchling
1988	Vicia sylvatica	Wood Vetch
1989	Persicaria minor	Small Water-pepper
1989	Vicia lathyroides	Spring Vetch
<1990	Chenopodium murale	Nettle-leaved Goosefoot
<1990	Silene gallica	Small-flowered Catchfly
1990	Pinguicula vulgaris	Common Butterwort
1991	Agrostemma githago	Corncockle
1992	Marrubium vulgare	White Horehound
1993	Rumex maritimus	Golden Dock
1993	Trifolium scabrum	Rough Clover
1993	Utricularia australis	Bladderwort
1994	Clinopodium calamintha	Lesser Calamint
1995	Cystopteris fragilis	Brittle Bladder-fern
1995	Jasione montana	Sheep's-bit
1995	Potentilla argentea	Hoary Cinquefoil
1995	Salix repens	Creeping Willow
1997	Schoenplectus tabermontani	Grey Club-rush
1998	Anisantha madritensis	Compact Brome
1998	Apera spicata-venti	Loose Silky-bent
1999	Torilis arvensis	Spreading Hedge-parsley

Figure 1. The areas of Oxfordshire's main habitats.

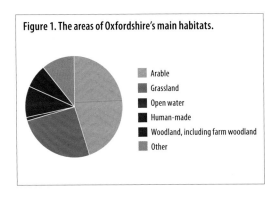

- Arable
- Grassland
- Open water
- Human-made
- Woodland, including farm woodland
- Other

The habitats of our Register species

THE MAIN HABITATS IN OXFORDSHIRE

This account relates the main habitats to be found in Oxfordshire to the occurrence (and also recent losses) of our Register species. It reveals a striking contrast between the two, and then summarises the importance of each of the main habitats for our Register species.

Table 2 classifies the habitats and the areas they occupy; the data are mostly as of 2013; we made some adjustments to earlier data to allow for likely changes.

Table 2. Areas of certain habitats in Oxfordshire (ha).

Source	Land use	area ha		%
Total farmland [1]2013	cereal	70,511	117,437	45.1
	other crops	46,926		
	temporary grass	14,094	66,654	25.6
	permanent grass	52,560		
	other farmland	-	3,503	1.3
	farm woodland	-	9,393	3.6
		Total	**196,987**	**75.6**
Woodland [2]1998	ancient	4,770	19,400	7.4
	plantation	2,740		
	secondary	7,870		
	wood pasture	4,020		
Human-made# [3]2001	built-up	3,659	22,576	8.7
	gardens	9,657		
	roads	5,246		
	other	4,014		
[3]2001	water		2,770	1.1
	Total of non-farmland (includes farm woodland)		44,746	17.2

Total of non-farmland (includes farm woodland)		44,746	17.2
Farm, less woodland		187,594	72.0
Other, see text		28,250	10.8
	Total for county	**260,590**	**100**

Sources: [1]DEFRA 2013, [2]Wicks & Cloughley 1998, [3]www.VisionofBritain.org.uk 2001 + 10%. #We have increased the human-made data in 3 by 10% in line with increased population.

OVERALL CLASSIFICATION OF OUR REGISTER SPECIES BY HABITAT

In parallel with the assessment of the areas of the main habitats, we have assigned to each of our 274 Register species their commonest habitat in Oxfordshire. This is a difficult and subjective matter and with a few species, almost impossible. Other botanists might have classified some of them differently but after lengthy debate we arrived at the numbers and percentages in Table 3.

The Register species and habitats are detailed in Table 5 (p. 18). We similarly classified the species "lost" in vc23 from 1968 to 1999 inclusive and give details in Table 7; these do not figure in the vc23 Register.

Table 3. Numbers of "lost" and Register species in main habitats. The "lost" 63 species are those in vc23 last recorded in 1968–1999.

Habitat	No. lost	%	In Register	%
Arable land	12	19.4	35	12.8
Grassland – neutral	5	6.4	18	6.6
Grassland – calcareous	4	6.5	32	11.7
Grassland – acid plus heath	7	11.3	29	10.6
Anthropogenic	11	17.7	33	12
Woodland	9	14.5	38	13.9
Wetland – mires	3	4.8	45	16.4
Wetland – verges	5	8.1	24	8.7
Wetland – open water	7	11.3	20	7.3
Total	**63**	**100**	**274**	**100**

The percentages in Table 2 are shown in Figure 1. Figure 2 uses the Oxfordshire Register data from Table 3.

REVIEW OF THE MAIN HABITATS

Arable land

This, our most widespread land use, accounts for 45% (27% cereals and 18% non-cereals) of Oxfordshire. When recording for FlOx began it supported many wild flowers (*Glebionis segetum* was in 186 tetrads) but by 2005 farming, herbicides and fertilisers had turned most of Berkshire's arable land into a "wildlife desert" (FlBe), and the same has happened in Oxfordshire. Arable accounts for a fifth of the "lost" species but only 13% of our Register species (Table 3). Most wild flowers of cereals are restricted to field margins, or have become infrequent "refugees" in waste ground, railway ballast, quarries or gardens. Our surviving arable flowers are highly dependent on sympathetic management in a small minority of places where a marginal strip is left unsprayed, a headland is sown with plants deemed valuable for birds and other wildlife, or where, from the 1990s, some arable fields became "set-aside" or funded through other agri–environment schemes.

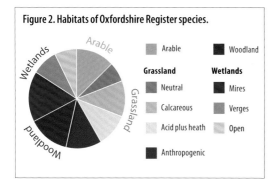

Figure 2. Habitats of Oxfordshire Register species.

Arable
Wetlands
Grassland
Woodland

■ Arable	■ Woodland
Grassland	**Wetlands**
■ Neutral	■ Mires
■ Calcareous	■ Verges
■ Acid plus heath	■ Open
■ Anthropogenic	

Grassland

Agricultural grassland, our second most widespread land use, accounted in 2013 for nearly 66,700 ha – a quarter of Oxfordshire, with 20% being permanent, and 5% botanically dull temporary grass.

It was traditionally used as pasture for grazing cattle or sheep, or as meadows with the grass cut for hay; both were species-rich. A quarter of the species "lost" in vc23 between 1968 and 1999 and 28% of our Register species are from grassland. Now the grass is increasingly cut for silage. There are three categories of priority habitats (Table 4):

- Of the former permanent grassland, most was **neutral grassland**. This was mostly (a commonly cited figure is 97%) destroyed by fertilising, re-seeding, weedkilling and ploughing; of what little is left, most is now in nature reserves or SSSIs. Oxfordshire's UK priority neutral grassland now comprises only 4,989 ha of coastal and floodplain grazing marsh and 1,142 ha of neutral meadows.
- **Calcareous grassland** had existed for hundreds of years up to World War Two. Chalk grassland is now sparse, fragile and declining, following ploughing and loss of grazing by sheep and, after 1953's myxomatosis, that by rabbits. In vc23, after a huge decline due mainly to scrub growth, only nine sites exceed 10 ha; more survives in vc22 (Oxon), especially at Aston Upthorpe, Hackpen, White Horse Hill and above Ashbury. Oxfordshire's UK priority chalk grassland now totals only 775 ha, only 0.3% of the County's area. Four species were lost from vc23 in 1969–1999, but the habitat is still species rich and has 32 Register species. Limestone grassland has declined even more, supports fewer rarities and is highly fragmented. Many recent surveys of Local Wildlife Sites reveal the loss of species known a few years ago.
- **Acid grassland**. Much of our acid grasslands and heaths were cleared and farmed at various times during the enclosures (1750–1880); only a few small enclaves on sands and gravels remained and were further reduced by scrub growth, plantations, fertilising, and developments for building, playing fields and golf courses. Oxfordshire's UK priority acid grasslands and heath now comprises a mere 58 ha, one fortieth of one percent of the county's area. This tiny area is still species rich and has, amazingly, 29 Register species, over 10% of our total.

Anthropogenic habitats

Arguably practically all Oxfordshire habitats are now anthropogenic (human-made) but this account includes only those cited under this heading in FlOx. In 2001, 20,523 ha (www.VisionofBritain.org.uk 2001) comprised gardens 8,779 ha, buildings 3,326 ha, roads 4,769 ha and other items 3,649 ha. We added 10% to this to reflect further development after 2001, giving 22,576 ha – 8.7% of the county.

At first sight, few of our Register species would be expected in anthropogenic habitats, which account for a fifth of the species lost. However, over at least the last 30 years recorders have found it easier to get a good species count by devoting effort to suburban areas and villages rather than the wider countryside. Gardens, churchyards, road verges, quarries, railway land and parks each contain many ecological niches and our expanding built-up areas yield a surprising number of rare or scarce species. We estimated that they were the commonest habitat for 33 (12%) of our Register species. Among these, 26 have been seen at least once from roadsides, 24 from quarries, 20 from pits, 17 from railways, 15 from churchyards and cemeteries, and 15 from (under-recorded) gardens. Some figure in a new Priority Habitat: Open Mosaic Habitats on Previously Developed Land (DEFRA 2010).

Woodland

Woodland (19,400 ha) accounted in 1998 for 7.4% of Oxfordshire (Wicks and Cloughley, 1998). Of this area, DEFRA identified 9,393 ha as farm woodland.

Within Oxfordshire there were 7510 ha of ancient semi-natural woodland, which had been woodland continuously since 1600, but 2740 ha of this has been replaced by plantations. It is spread between 163 FlOx tetrads, but it is most abundant in the Chilterns. Wood pasture and parkland (4020 ha) and relatively species-poor secondary woodland (7870 ha) make up the 19400 ha. It seems possible that some of the 3800 ha of conifers in 1980, detailed in FlOx (p60) may be additional to this total.

Our woodland area will have increased since 1998 with tree planting and scrub growth, though these are no substitute for ancient woodland. Including a few from hedgerows it accounts for 14% of the species lost, and 38 (14%) of our Register species; the woodlands in the larger estates can support scarce species, e.g. those reported by Dunn at Ditchley (FlOx p. 66).

Oxfordshire's UK priority woodland so far mapped comprises 7,939 ha (Table 4) two fifths of the woodland total.

Included here are Oxfordshire's three common **Scrub** communities, characterised by: 1) *Crataegus* and *Hedera* Hawthorn and Ivy; 2) *Prunus spinosa* Blackthorn and *Rubus fruticosus* agg. Bramble; or 3) *Rubus fruticosus* agg. Bramble and Yorkshire-fog. They have often arisen in grassland that has been neglected or no longer grazed, on cleared woodland or on old railway lines; as they comprise all stages of succession from grass to secondary woodland, their area is hard to compute. Most **hedgerows** belong in (1) and (2).

Wetland habitats

These account for a quarter of the species lost, and a third of our Register species; they divide into open water, waterlogged habitats (mires) and also a group of plants typical of the verges of water bodies, often muddy.

- **Open water.** The area of open water is tricky to compute and depends on how small a water body can be included. We use the 2,770 ha (just over 1% of the county) in 2001 data provided through www.VisionofBritain.org.uk. Of this Oxfordshire's UK priority mesotrophic standing waters account for only 117 ha, and ponds only 10.7 ha. Druce (1927) described a rich variety of water plants including *Ranunculus fluitans* River Water-crowfoot all along the Thames from Kelmscott to Sonning. However, many aquatic species notably water-crowfoots and pondweeds, had already severely declined by the time of FlOx. Our rivers and streams (121 ha) now support few rare plants because of nutrient enrichment, and boats, pollution and dredging; FlBe describes the Thames as "comprehensively degraded". Plants in the Oxford Canal have suffered severely from boat traffic. Ponds, particularly with fluctuating water levels, had been a good habitat but their value depends critically on their catchment and therefore its nutrient richness and pollutants. Most are lost or degraded through filling-in, tidying-up, and overgrowth. Lakes notably at Eynsham Park and Blenheim, many wet gravel pits (some new) e.g. between Witney and Cassington and especially new water bodies in Otmoor, provide some redeeming features. Their value depends on the above factors and also on their use for e.g. angling, boating and nature conservation. Seven species, notably pondweeds, figure among the losses, and open water is the main habitat for 20 Register species.

- The tiny area of **Mires** contrasts with its species richness – after losing three species, it supports 45 Register species, the highest for any category. Oxfordshire's UK priority habitats (Table 4) comprise 164 ha of lowland fens (one fifteenth of one percent of the county's area), 14 ha of *Molinia caerulea* Purple Moor-grass and *Juncus* rush pasture and 27 ha of reedbeds. Lowland fens include many Register species, but also and more widespread in them, are swamps. These usually have tall monocotyledons – grasses, pond-sedges, bulrush and club-rush). Also found are tall-herb fens (often nutrient-rich with reeds, other grasses, *Epilobium hirsutum* Great Willowherb, *Eupatorium cannabinum* Hemp-agrimony, *Filipendula ulmaria* Meadowsweet and Nettles) that can suppress smaller plants. Fen meadows are often dominated by *Filipendula ulmaria* and *Angelica sylvestris* Wild Angelica. Fens and bogs often overly peat; despite the use of the word as in Bullingdon Bog, we lack true bogs which are nutrient poor and acidic, but do have

Ranunculus fluitans River Water-crowfoot

(Peter Creed)

(Peter Creed)

Juncus subnodulosus Blunt-flowered Rush

(Peter Creed)

Limosella aquatica Mudwort

fens which are richer in lime. It is the very small low-nutrient areas, at e.g. Cothill, Lye Valley, Otmoor and Sydlings Copse with *Juncus subnodulosus* Blunt-flowered Rush and *Cirsium palustre* Marsh Thistle, or *Molinia caerulea* and *Cirsium dissectum* Meadow Thistle, that, if suitably maintained, support a wealth of Register species (Huxley-Lambrick 2002).

■ The **Mud/verges** category includes rooted plants that grow along the margins of water bodies including ditches, canals, ponds and seasonal pools. The substrate is often mud, affected more in the past than now by cattle. In marginal vegetation and seasonally wet mud, six species were lost, but 24 Register species including *Apium inundatum* Lesser Marshwort, *Apium repens* Creeping Marshwort, *Baldellia ranunculoides* Lesser Water-plantain, *Bidens cernua* Nodding Bur-marigold, *Limosella aquatica* Mudwort and *Sium latifolium* Greater Water-parsnip survive. The species in this category persist more often in the wider countryside outside protected sites than do those of mires.

Other areas (10.6% of the total)

This category comprises areas not officially itemised. Its area is obtained first by deducting farmland and forestry areas from the total.

DEFRA refers to this residue as: "urban land and not otherwise specified", and "other purposes e.g. transport, recreation, non-agricultural semi-natural environment, non-agricultural grass and inland waters". Among these are the anthropogenic and water areas already cited above.

Among the remaining major components in Oxfordshire are likely to be golf courses (perhaps 10,000 ha in all), sports grounds, recreational areas, orchards, conifers, areas of the major estates not under farming and forestry; and scrubland.

Overall these would add mainly to the amount of improved grassland, recently planted woodland, scrub and trees. They could also add tiny amounts to the heathland and mire habitats.

AREAS OF UK PRIORITY HABITATS IN OXFORDSHIRE

TVERC has been mapping the UK's priority habitats for conservation as found in Oxfordshire, and we are grateful for the data in Table 4. The table includes most of Oxfordshire's mires and ponds, but only 10% of its grasslands and 41% of its woodland.

Details of our Register species classified by habitat

Our assignment of 274 Register species to habitats is given in more detail in Table 5 (p. 18).

Table 4. Areas of UK Priority Habitats in Oxfordshire, 2016.
* underestimate, not fully mapped yet.

UK priority habitat	Area mapped in ha	
Grassland		6,964.7
Coastal and floodplain grazing marsh	4,989.6	
Lowland dry acid grassland	54.6	
Lowland heathland	3.5	
Lowland grassland calcareous	775	
Lowland meadows	1,142	
Woodland		7,939.5
Lowland beech and yew woodland	829.1*	
Lowland mixed deciduous woodland	4,801.1*	
Wood pasture and parkland	2,175.2	
Wet woodland	134.1	
Wetland		1,479.4
Lowland fens	164.1	
Mesotrophic standing water	117	
Ponds	10.7	
Purple Moor-grass and rush pasture	14.9	
Reedbeds	27.7	
Rivers	121.7	
Eutrophic standing waters	1,023.3	
Traditional orchards	259.9	
Open mosaic on previously developed land	210.2	

Causes of the decline of our Register species

Oxfordshire has always been an agricultural county; arable production and animal husbandry have greatly intensified recently. The greatest and most widespread effects on the County's flora have been due to changing farming practices, (FlOx, pp 68–70). At the time of Druce (1927) these resembled those of 1794 much more than those of 1997.

- The area of grassland halved between 1910 and 1988 to 24% of the County and is now 25.6%. The meadows described by Young (1813) are now mostly "improved" so only a few survive, mainly in nature reserves. During the same period the area of cereals nearly doubled to 40%. The dominant in the 10% non-cereals is now oilseed rape. With the advent of tractors, agricultural horses had decreased by 72% by 1950 and have now almost disappeared, together with the crops grown to feed them. The decrease in sheep has permitted scrub growth.
- Modern herbicides were developed from 1942, spreading rapidly from 1950 and routinely used in most arable crops by 1960, meaning that the arable flowers other than grass weeds, found when Flora recording began in 1968, were often absent later.
- Mechanisation, drainage and the widespread use of agricultural chemicals (herbicides, pesticides and fertilisers) reduced the proportion of very wet, dry, basic, acidic and poor soils, and the wild plants associated with them. Further inroads into the native flora followed improved seed cleaning.

The result from the floristic standpoint has thus been massive losses in many habitats. Some causes are given above. Fertilisers have greatly improved crop yields but at the site of application and where wind or water have carried (wasted) fertiliser to other places their effects on our flora have been dire and pervasive. Woods, wildlife sites and even nature reserves now have nettles and coarse vegetation near their edges, especially where facing the prevailing wind.

Because the flora of rivers and of ponds depends on their catchment, many water-loving plants have also suffered from fertiliser runoff. Even treated tap water is too nutrient-rich for use in garden ponds.

The effects of pesticides are equally pervasive. Other changes are due to ploughing, re-seeding, drainage, and urban, industrial and road developments. The road verge flora has suffered from car emissions and uncollected cuttings.

The feature most noted by many people is the increase in population (FlOx pp. 70–1); in the pre-1974 county (vc23) the increase from 275,000 in 1951 to 382,000 in 1971 exceeded the County's entire population of 1801. By 1996 the population of Oxford was twice that of 1901, Banbury three times, Witney six times and Bicester nearly eight times. The new Oxfordshire in 2013 had 653,800 people, Oxford 154,800, Banbury 46,853, Witney 27,500, Bicester 35,902, and Abingdon 33,130.

Paradoxically the plant diversity in built-up areas is often high and very much higher than that in the open countryside; if you are recording plants and want a high score a village or market town is often the place to look.

THE CONSERVATION OF RARE SPECIES IN OXFORDSHIRE

People have made much use of the natural landscape. Agriculture occupies the greatest area of land, covering the clay vale and much of the chalk and limestone downland. There are no large lakes in Oxfordshire, but there are a significant number of worked out gravel pits. Large tracts of deciduous woodland are mostly confined to large estates in the Chilterns and Cotswolds.

The species accounts often include a map showing either the natural character areas or the main rivers of the County (see p. 22). Of the natural areas, the clay vales occupy the greatest area, with the chalk and limestone downland the second largest. The much smaller Corallian Ridge running from Beckley to Faringdon gives rise to acidic sandy and alkaline soils. In addition, there are small areas of calcareous fens and peat areas reflecting specific geological events. So with a diversity of underlying rock types and subsequent surface geology, there are a wide variety of habitats in Oxfordshire, though acid soils and fens are scarce.

Nature conservation in Oxfordshire comprises three aspects:
- the designation and management of specific areas;
- attempts to conserve individual species; and
- attempts to conserve the wider countryside.

1. Specific areas

The **designation of nature reserves** began with the purchase in 1902 of the Ruskin Reserve, a small fen that is part of the Cothill complex. Other key events were the founding in 1949 of the Nature Conservancy (later The Nature Conservancy Council, English Nature, and now Natural England) and in 1959 that of the Berkshire, Buckinghamshire and Oxfordshire Naturalists Trust (BBONT), now the

Berkshire, Buckinghamshire and Oxfordshire Wildlife Trust (BBOWT).

A county-wide survey of areas of wildlife interest, undertaken using money from the Manpower Services Commission, enabled sites to be designated as Local Wildlife Sites (originally County Wildlife Sites). The Thames Valley Environmental Records Centre, set up in 2003, undertook further surveys.

The importance of some special habitats has been recognised on a European scale as well as at a local level. Protected sites range from those with the highest degree of protection SAC (Special Area of Conservation) of which Oxfordshire has seven, to LWS (Local Wildlife Sites) which are numerous and may be as small as 100 metres of road verge. In between are NNRs (National Nature Reserves), SSSIs (Sites of Special Scientific Interest) and BBOWT reserves of which some are also SSSIs. As can be seen from chart (Figure 3), many of our rare species rely almost wholly on these areas. Alarming is the number of species growing in locations which have no protection at all. Many of these are arable flowers which are extremely vulnerable.

LWS unlike SACs, NNRs, and SSSIs do not have legal protection, but Local Authorities are expected 'to have regard for' LWS in their policies and planning guidance. Sites are designated not just for their biodiversity, but for their importance in linking similar areas, to help prevent fragmentation, as well as for historical and educational reasons.

The maintenance of all protected sites is often by volunteers: either in practical management, monitoring results or alerting landowners to the needs of species. Wildlife Trusts (e.g. BBOWT) play an important role here as do wildlife groups such as Oxfordshire Flora Group, Wychwood Flora Group and Oxford Urban Wildlife Group.

Many areas of ancient woodland are often protected either as SSSIs, LWS or BBOWT reserves.

As Peter Marren noted some plants are rare because their habitats are rare; this certainly applies to many Oxfordshire rarities. The Corallian Ridge (beige on the maps), has a unique blend of sandstones and limestone (Coral Rag). On the Corallian Ridge, mainly in vc22, there are some species e.g. *Anthriscus caucalis* Bur Chervil which are not scarce in Oxon, but are scarce in vc23. Some species in the Register e.g. *Teesdalia nudicaulis* are only found in vc22.

The importance of acid heaths and calcareous fens, found mostly along the Corallian Ridge is emphasised by the number of SSSIs along the Ridge plus the SAC at Cothill which includes a NNR and BBOWT reserves. The chalk and limestone areas also have four SACs and numerous SSSIs. The other habitat which has attracted SAC status is the floodplain meadows around Oxford. This is one of only two locations for *Apium repens* Creeping Marshwort in the UK.

Such protection is vital for our natural environment and areas which have protection of the law are critical, but pitiably small, some 2% of land in Oxfordshire.

2. Conservation of species

Many BBOWT reserves contain Register species. Their Rare Species Group collected data on Red Data List species notably *Daphne mezereon* Mezereon, *Orchis simia* Monkey Orchid and *Orchis anthropophora* Man Orchid. More recently BBOWT focused on species – *Juniperus communis* Juniper, *Pulsatilla vulgaris* Pasqueflower and *Carex vulpina* True Fox Sedge. It also commissioned a local group, The Oxfordshire Conservation Volunteers, set up in 1977, to do habitat management work.

Jo Dunn, working with the Nature Conservancy Council, studied *Stachys germanica* Downy Woundwort leading to a Biological Flora of the species (Dunn, 1997). This species, and also *Salvia pratensis* Meadow Clary were taken on by the Cotswold Rare Plants Group, now the Wychwood Flora Group.

Much work on individual species has been done by The Rare Plants Group of the Ashmolean Natural History Society of Oxfordshire (from 2013 The Oxfordshire Flora Group). This was formed in 1993 and has since monitored certain species in the county, in partnership with landowners and conservationists.

The group started work on species for different organisations, most notably for English Nature on *Apium repens* and *Gentianella anglica* Early Gentian, but also for Plantlife on *Salvia pratensis* Meadow Clary, *Filago pyramidata* Broad-leaved Cudweed, and *Microthlaspi perfoliata* Cotswold Pennycress. With the co-operation of landowners, fields in which *Adonis annua* Pheasant's Eye, *Lythrum hyssopifolia* Grass-

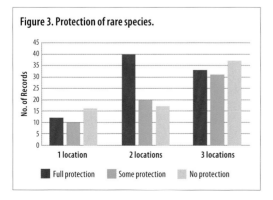

Figure 3. Protection of rare species.

No. of Records

1 location   2 locations   3 locations

■ Full protection   ■ Some protection   ■ No protection

Lythrum hyssopifolia **Grass-poly**

poly and *Apium graveolens* Wild Celery (all single site species in Oxfordshire) are cultivated to benefit these rare species. Habitat monitoring for an SSSI management plan is also being done at Frilford for Natural England.

The Rare Plants Group has done a small amount of experimental work, notably on seed set of *Apium repens* Creeping Marshwort and *Cynoglossum germanicum* Green Hound's-tongue; in both species limited self-compatibility was found. Survival of *Apium repens* under different water depths was studied at the Oxford University Botanic Garden. This showed that under water during the summer plants became detached from the soil and were thus free to float away and become established elsewhere.

The field conditions of *Viola persicifolia* Fen Violet were studied rigorously in connection with its translocation onto RSPB land at Otmoor for English Nature. A local hydrologist Curt Lamberth was contracted to study the water soil conditions and compare them with water levels for existing

populations. *Apium repens* Creeping Marshwort was also translocated, with a successful colony now flourishing on Oxford Preservation Trust land at South Hinksey near its main site on Port Meadow, Oxford. At Aston Upthorpe *Pulsatilla vulgaris* was successfully reinforced and subsequently established at Hartslock BBOWT reserve. The population of *Carex vulpina* True Fox Sedge was reinforced at Murcott Meadow SSSI, Asham Meads BBOWT Reserve. Most recently *Galium tricornutum* Corn Cleavers was re-introduced at Wytham SSSI in conjunction with the BSBI, the Oxford University Botanic Garden and Natural England.

The Group also puts out information through lectures and workshops. A series of four spring lectures is held each year and workshops have been held on *Apium repens*, *Salvia pratensis*, *Viola persicifolia* Fen Violet and *Carex vulpina*. Other species studied include *Lythrum hyssopifolia*, *Aristolochia clematitis* Birthwort and *Veronica praecox* Breckland Speedwell.

3. Protection of the wider countryside has been more difficult and often unsuccessful, as evidenced by our comments on the Thames and arable land. The areas which have least protection are arable, consequently arable flowers are amongst the hardest hit. Many plants have become 'refugees' elsewhere, e.g. in wasteland.

The best-known successes, for example the banning of DDT and organochlorine insecticides, followed the observation of harmful effects on birds of prey, not on plants.

But FlOx, p. 76 noted progress; the Rio de Janeiro summit in 1992 encouraged action for species conservation by local authorities and conservation groups. Wild Oxfordshire (formerly The Oxfordshire Nature Conservation Forum) was set up, and a Biodiversity Action Plan (BAP) was put together listing species and habitats. Environmentally Sensitive Areas have been designated for attention, including for the Upper Thames.

Since the government signed up to the Rio declaration of 1992 to protect the natural environment more attention has been given to conservation; some farmers have signed up for Higher Level Funding schemes to conserve wildlife on their land. *Apium graveolens* Wild Celery is one species which is protected in this way.

The future, including climate change

H.J. Killick

Some Register species could become increasingly threatened by a warming climate; the fact of human-made climate change is now accepted in 95% of scientific papers published in refereed journals.

Some **animals**, especially with short generation times e.g. Comma and Peacock butterflies can often quickly adapt to it (Butterfly Conservation 2014). However, many **plants**, especially perennials, tend now to be mismatched to their changing environments.

This must be increasingly true of rare plants, confined to specific habitats and dependent on successful colonisation of similar habitats by seeds or vegetative means. However, such habitats can be far distant, e.g. habitats similar to some wet areas near Cothill are not found nearer than North Wales or East Anglia. Many other local habitats that support rare species are like islands in an ocean of unsuitable ground. If climate change annihilates the rare plants where they stand, there may be no accessible place for colonisation.

A recent paper by Amano *et al.* (2010) has studied plants' response to the effects of climate change in terms of earlier flowering and/or movements in latitude.

Increasing carbon dioxide in the atmosphere ought to affect ecosystems, including ancient woodlands, directly.

If the climate gets warmer by 3°C this is for a plant equivalent to descending 300 m in altitude or to moving approximately 700 km nearer the equator (Rackham 2008). He argued that this may show little effect on native trees; damage by heat or drought is mostly limited to planted trees e.g. beeches on thin chalk.

But if coolness is a factor in the habitat preference of a chalk-loving herb at 200 m in Oxfordshire, it cannot move upwards, and 700 km north of here there is probably no comparable habitat.

Inability to self-pollinate is likely to slow northward migration, as isolated populations (e.g. on calcareous grassland) may be unable to set seed. (Moser and Thompson 2014).

In England, in addition to general warming, there is a forecast reduction in rainfall and a shift in the maximum rainfall from early summer to winter (Mitchell *et al.* 2007). Heavy rain in winter could potentially flood key habitats with water that contains too much nutrient or pollutants.

England and Wales has a climatic gradient from west (oceanic) to east (continental). Hot dry summers might threaten the eastern outliers of woodland plants with an oceanic distribution; *Primula vulgaris* Primrose has markedly declined after hot summers (Rackham 1999).

Global warming may allow parasites and invasive aliens to extend their range. It may already have helped the proliferation of deer, which in the past were limited by starvation in cold winters.

What can our readers do?

Updates to this book will be made via the website. The register page is on the OFG website: www.anhso-ofg.org.uk. We hope that, like us, our readers are very concerned at the threats to and losses from our wildflower heritage. For those that would like to get involved, here are some possible actions:

■ Join the Botanical Society of Britain and Ireland, Plantlife, and at a local level, BBOWT and societies such as the Ashmolean Natural History Society of Oxfordshire.

■ Look for some of the species and localities (six-fig. grid references should help). Take care to get permission on private land.

■ Note how many of the species are confined to tiny areas of their chosen habitat.

■ Send in new records, with data ideally as in our tables, to vc23 County Recorder, David Morris, david.m.morris1989@gmail.com. Likewise, records that update by several years those we have presented.

■ Help with the groups that count the populations of threatened species (an example is Snake's-head Fritillary).

■ Help with the groups that manage some of the threatened species for their conservation (an example is Meadow Clary).

■ Become a Flora Guardian with the Oxfordshire Flora Group.

■ Extend the work of counting and management to new locations and species.

■ Attend the annual Recorders and Conservation Conference organised by Thames Valley Environmental Records Centre.

■ Comment on planning applications, especially those likely to threaten our chosen species – to local authorities, MPs, the press and the internet.

■ Raise issues concerning Oxfordshire's Threatened Plants using blogs, Facebook and Twitter.

■ Observe how agriculture, development and climate change have affected the chances of our threatened plants' survival, and how they will affect them in future.

■ Suggest new ways of addressing the problems.

The Register

As a result of our recording, 274 of the species chosen for study, and nine stoneworts, qualify for the Register (Table 5). Twenty-four other species were added to the Register in 2014, too late to study (Table 6).

Table 7 lists the 63 species "lost" from vc23 since 1968. They are mostly not in the Register but are an important part of our account.

Table 5. The Register Species for Oxfordshire, studied by us and classified by habitat. The species in **the vc23 Register** are in **bold type**; species not in bold type are only wild in parts of Oxon outside vc23.

Register species are those which were found after 2000 and are either nationally listed, scarce or rare (p3) or locally rare (found in 1–3 sites) or scarce (in 10 or fewer localities in the county). Stoneworts (Characeae) are added at the end.

Species	Common name	Habitat
Adiantum capillus-veneris	Maidenhair Fern	Anthropogenic
Adonis annua	Pheasant's-eye	Arable
Agrostis canina	Velvet Bent	Grass, Acid/Heath
Agrostis curtisii	Bristle Bent	Grass, Acid/Heath
Agrostis vinealis	Brown Bent	Grass, Acid/Heath
Aira caryophyllea	Silver Hair-grass	Grass, Acid/Heath
Aira praecox	Early Hair-grass	Grass, Acid/Heath
Alchemilla filiformis ssp. vestita	Hairy Lady's-mantle	Grass, Neutral
Alisma lanceolatum	Narrow-leaved Water-plantain	Wetland, Mud/Verges
Alopecurus aequalis	Orange Foxtail	Wetland, Mud/Verges
Anacamptis morio	Green-winged Orchid	Grass, Acid/Heath
Anagallis foemina	Blue Pimpernel	Arable
Anagallis tenella	Bog Pimpernel	Wetland, Mud/Verges
Anthemis arvensis	Corn Chamomile	Arable Refugee
Anthriscus caucalis	Bur Chervil	Woodland, Hedges
Apera interrupta	Dense Silky-bent	Arable Refugee
Apera spica-venti	Loose Silky-bent	Arable
Aphanes australis	Slender Parsley-piert	Anthropogenic
Apium graveolens	Wild Celery	Wetland, Mud/Verges
Apium inundatum	Lesser Marshwort	Wetland, Mud/Verges
Apium repens	Creeping Marshwort	Wetland, Mires
Arabis hirsuta	Hairy Rock-cress	Grass, Calcareous
Aristolochia clematitis	Birthwort	Woodland, Hedges
Artemisia absinthium	Wormwood	Anthropogenic
Astragalus danicus	Purple Milk-vetch	Grass, Calcareous
Baldellia ranunculoides	Lesser Water-plantain	Wetland, Mud/Verges
Berberis vulgaris	Barberry	Woodland, Hedges
Bidens cernua	Nodding Bur-marigold	Wetland, Mud/Verges
Blechnum spicant	Hard Fern	Woodland
Blysmus compressus	Flat-sedge	Wetland, Mires
Bolboschoenus maritimus	Sea Club-rush	Wetland, Mires
Bromopsis benekenii	Lesser Hairy-brome	Woodland
Bromus secalinus	Rye Brome	Arable
Calamagrostis canesens	Purple Small-reed	Woodland
Callitriche brutia	Intermediate Water-starwort	Wetland, Open water
Callitriche obtusangula	Blunt-fruited Water-starwort	Wetland, Open water
Calluna vulgaris	Heather	Grass, Acid/Heath
Campanula latifolia	Giant Bellflower	Woodland
Carduus tenuiflorus	Slender Thistle	Anthropogenic
Carex binervis	Green-ribbed Sedge	Grass, Acid/Heath
Carex demissa	Common Yellow-sedge	Wetland, Mires
Carex dioica	Dioecious Sedge	Wetland, Mires
Carex distans	Distant Sedge	Wetland, Mires

Species	Common name	Habitat
Carex divulsa ssp. leersii	Leers' Sedge	Woodland
Carex echinata	Star Sedge	Wetland, Mires
Carex elata	Tufted-sedge	Wetland, Mud/Verges
Carex filiformis	Downy-fruited Sedge	Grass, Calcareous
Carex hostiana	Tawny Sedge	Wetland, Mires
Carex lepidocarpa	Long-stalked Yellow-sedge	Wetland, Mires
Carex muricata ssp. muricata	Prickly Sedge	Grass, Acid/Heath
Carex oederi	Small-fruited Yellow-sedge	Wetland, Mires
Carex pallescens	Pale Sedge	Woodland
Carex pulicaris	Flea Sedge	Wetland, Mires
Carex rostrata	Bottle Sedge	Wetland, Open water
Carex strigosa	Thin-spiked Wood-sedge	Woodland
Carex vesicaria	Bladder-sedge	Wetland, Mires
Carex vulpina	True Fox-sedge	Wetland, Mires
Catabrosa aquatica	Water Whorl-grass	Wetland, Mud/Verges
Centaurea cyanus	Cornflower	Arable
Centaurium pulchellum	Lesser Centaury	Anthropogenic
Cephalanthera damasonium	White Helleborine	Woodland
Cerastium pumilum	Dwarf Mouse-ear	Anthropogenic
Ceratocapnos claviculata	Climbing Corydalis	Woodland
Chenopodium bonus-henricus	Good-King-Henry	Anthropogenic
Chenopodium ficifolium	Fig-leaved Goosefoot	Anthropogenic
Chenopodium hybridum	Maple-leaved Goosefoot	Anthropogenic
Chrysosplenium alternifolium	Alternate-leaved Golden-saxifrage	Wetland, Mires
Cirsium dissectum	Meadow Thistle	Grass, Calcareous
Clinopodium acinos	Basil Thyme	Grass, Calcareous
Clinopodium calamintha	Lesser Calamint	Grass, Neutral
Coeloglossum viride	Frog Orchid	Grass, Calcareous
Cuscuta epithymum	Dodder	Grass, Calcareous
Cuscuta europaea	Greater Dodder	Woodland, Hedges
Cynoglossum germanicum	Green Hound's-tongue	Woodland
Cynoglossum officinale	Hound's-tongue	Grass, Calcareous
Dactylorhiza traunsteinerioides	Narrow-leaved Marsh-orchid	Wetland, Mires
Daphne mezereum	Mezereon	Woodland
Descurainia sophia	Flixweed	Arable Refugee
Dianthus deltoides	Maiden Pink	Grass, Neutral
Diplotaxis tenuifolia	Perennial Wall-rocket	Anthropogenic
Dipsacus pilosus	Small Teasel	Woodland, Hedges
Draba muralis	Wall Whitlow-grass	Anthropogenic
Drosera rotundifolia	Round-leaved Sundew	Wetland, Mires
Eleocharis quinqueflora	Few-flowered Spike-rush	Wetland, Mires
Eleocharis uniglumis	Slender Spike-rush	Wetland, Mires
Epilobium palustre	Marsh Willowherb	Wetland, Mires
Epilobium roseum	Pale Willowherb	Anthropogenic

Table 5, cont'd. The Register Species for Oxfordshire, classified by habitat. The species in **the vc23 Register** are in **bold type**; species not in bold type are only wild in parts of Oxon outside vc23.

Species	Common name	Habitat
Epipactis leptochila	**Narrow-lipped Helleborine**	**Woodland**
Epipactis palustris	**Marsh Helleborine**	**Wetland, Mires**
Epipactis phyllanthes	**Green-flowered Helleborine**	**Woodland**
Equisetum variegatum	Variegated Horsetail	Wetland, Mires
Erica cinerea	**Bell Heather**	**Grass, Acid/Heath**
Erica tetralix	**Cross-leaved Heath**	**Grass, Acid/Heath**
Eriophorum angustifolium	**Common Cottongrass**	**Wetland, Mires**
Eriophorum latifolium	**Broad-leaved Cottongrass**	**Wetland, Mires**
Euphorbia exigua	**Dwarf Spurge**	**Arable**
Euphorbia platyphyllos	**Broad-leaved Spurge**	**Arable**
Fallopia dumetorum	Copse-bindweed	Woodland
Festuca filiformis	**Fine-leaved Sheep's-fescue**	**Grass, Acid/Heath**
Filago minima	**Small Cudweed**	**Grass, Acid/Heath**
Filago pyramidata	**Broad-leaved Cudweed**	**Anthropogenic**
Filago vulgaris	**Common Cudweed**	**Arable Refugee**
Frangula alnus	**Alder Buckthorn**	**Woodland, Hedges**
Fritillaria meleagris	**Fritillary**	**Wetland, Mires**
Fumaria capreolata	White Ramping-fumitory	Anthropogenic
Fumaria muralis	**Common Ramping-fumitory**	**Anthropogenic**
Fumaria vaillantii	**Few-flowered Fumitory**	**Arable**
Gagea lutea	**Yellow Star-of-Bethlehem**	**Woodland**
Galeopsis angustifolia	**Red Hemp-nettle**	**Arable Refugee**
Galeopsis bifida	**Bifid Hemp-nettle**	**Arable Refugee**
Galium pumilum	**Slender Bedstraw**	**Grass, Calcareous**
Genista tinctoria	**Dyer's Greenweed**	**Grass, Calcareous**
Gentianella anglica	**Early Gentian**	**Grass, Calcareous**
Gentianella germanica	**Chiltern Gentian**	**Grass, Calcareous**
Geum rivale	**Water Avens**	**Woodland**
Glebionis segetum	**Corn Marigold**	**Arable**
Glyceria declinata	**Small Sweet-grass**	**Wetland, Mud/Verges**
Gnaphalium sylvaticum	**Heath Cudweed**	**Grass, Acid/Heath**
Groenlandia densa	**Opposite-leaved Pondweed**	**Wetland, Open Water**
Gymnadenia conopsea	**Chalk Fragrant-orchid**	**Grass, Calcareous**
Gymnadenia densiflora	**Marsh Fragrant-orchid**	**Wetland, Mires**
Gymnocarpium robertianum	**Limestone Fern**	**Anthropogenic**
Helleborus foetidus	**Stinking Hellebore**	**Woodland**
Himantoglossum hircinum	**Lizard Orchid**	**Grass, Calcareous**
Hottonia palustris	**Water-violet**	**Wetland, Mud/Verges**
Hydrocharis morsus-ranae	**Frogbit**	**Wetland, Open Water**
Hydrocotyle vulgaris	**Marsh Pennywort**	**Wetland, Mires**
Hyoscyamus niger	**Henbane**	**Anthropogenic**
Hypericum montanum	**Pale St John's-wort**	**Grass, Calcareous**
Hypochaeris glabra	Smooth Cat's-ear	Grass, Neutral
Hypopitys monotropa	**Yellow Bird's-nest**	**Woodland**
Iberis amara	**Wild Candytuft**	**Grass, Calcareous**
Inula helenium	**Elecampane**	**Anthropogenic**
Juncus bulbosus	**Bulbous Rush**	**Wetland, Mud/Verges**
Juncus compressus	**Round-fruited Rush**	**Wetland, Mires**
Juncus squarrosus	**Heath Rush**	**Grass, Acid/Heath**
Juniperus communis	**Juniper**	**Grass, Calcareous**
Lathyrus linifolius	**Bitter-vetch**	**Woodland**
Lemna gibba	**Fat Duckweed**	**Wetland, Open Water**
Lepidium ruderale	Narrow-leaved Pepperwort	Anthropogenic
Leucojum aestivum	**Summer Snowflake**	**Wetland, Mires**
Limosella aquatica	**Mudwort**	**Wetland, Mud/Verges**
Lithospermum arvense	**Corn Gromwell**	**Arable**
Lotus tenuis	**Narrow-leaved Bird's-foot-trefoil**	**Grass, Neutral**
Luzula sylvatica	**Great Wood-rush**	**Woodland**
Lythrum hyssopifolia	Grass-poly	Wetland, Mud/Verges
Lythrum portula	**Water-purslane**	**Grass, Acid/Heath**
Medicago polymorpha	Toothed Medick	Anthropogenic
Medicago sativa ssp. falcata	**Sickle Medick**	**Grass, Acid/Heath**
Melampyrum pratense	**Common Cow-wheat**	**Woodland**
Mentha pulegium	**Pennyroyal**	**Wetland Mud/Verges**
Menyanthes trifoliata	**Bog-bean**	**Wetland, Mires**
Microthlaspi perfoliatum	**Cotswold Penny-cress**	**Arable Refugee**
Misopates orontium	**Weasel's-snout**	**Arable Refugee**
Moenchia erecta	Upright Chickweed	Grass, Acid/Heath
Molinia caerulea	**Purple Moor-grass**	**Wetland, Mires**
Montia fontana	**Blinks**	**Wetland, Mires**
Muscari neglectum	**Grape-hyacinth**	**Anthropogenic**
Myosurus minimus	**Mousetail**	**Arable Refugee**
Myriophyllum verticillatum	**Whorled Water-milfoil**	**Wetland, Open Water**
Neotinea ustulata	Burnt Orchid	Grass, Calcareous
Neottia nidus-avis	**Bird's-nest Orchid**	**Woodland**
Nepeta cataria	**Catmint**	**Anthropogenic**
Nymphoides peltata	**Fringed Water-lily**	**Wetland, Open Water**
Oenanthe aquatica	**Fine-leaved Water-dropwort**	**Wetland, Mud/Verges**
Oenanthe fistulosa	**Tubular Water-dropwort**	**Wetland, Mires**
Oenanthe fluviatilis	**River Water-dropwort**	**Wetland, Open Water**
Oenanthe lachenalii	**Parsley Water-dropwort**	**Wetland, Mires**
Oenanthe silaifolia	**Narrow-leaved Water-dropwort**	**Grass, Neutral**
Onobrychis viciifolia	**Sainfoin**	**Grass, Calcareous**
Ononis spinosa	**Spiny Restharrow**	**Grass, Calcareous**
Ophrys insectifera	**Fly Orchid**	**Woodland**
Orchis anthropophora	**Man Orchid**	**Grass, Calcareous**
Orchis militaris	**Military Orchid**	**Grass, Calcareous**
Orchis purpurea	**Lady Orchid**	**Grass, Calcareous**
Orchis simia	**Monkey Orchid**	**Grass, Calcareous**
Ornithopus perpusillus	**Bird's-foot**	**Grass, Acid/Heath**
Orobanche hederae	**Ivy Broomrape**	**Anthropogenic**
Papaver argemone	**Prickly Poppy**	**Arable**
Papaver hybridum	**Rough Poppy**	**Arable**
Parnassia palustris	**Grass-of-Parnassus**	**Wetland, Mires**
Pedicularis palustris	**Marsh Lousewort**	**Wetland, Mires**
Pedicularis sylvatica	**Lousewort**	**Grass Acid/ Heath**
Persicaria mitis	**Tasteless Water-pepper**	**Wetland, Mud/Verges**
Pimpinella major	**Greater Burnet-saxifrage**	**Anthropogenic**
Pinguicula vulgaris	Common Butterwort	Wetland, Mires
Platanthera bifolia	**Lesser Butterfly-orchid**	**Woodland**
Platanthera chlorantha	**Greater Butterfly-orchid**	**Woodland**
Poa angustifolia	**Narrow-leaved Meadow-grass**	**Grass, Neutral**
Poa humilis	**Spreading Meadow-grass**	**Grass, Neutral**
Poa infirma	**Early Meadow-grass**	**Anthropogenic**
Polygala calcarea	**Chalk Milkwort**	**Grass, Calcareous**
Polgala serpyllifolia	**Heath Milkwort**	**Grass, Acid/ Heath**
Polygonatum multiflorum	**Solomon's-seal**	**Woodland**
Polygonum rurivagum	**Cornfield Knotgrass**	**Arable**
Polypodium interjectum	**Intermediate Polypody**	**Anthropogenic**
Polypogon monspeliensis	**Annual Beard-grass**	**Wetland, Mud/Verges**

Table 5, cont'd. The Register Species for Oxfordshire, classified by habitat. The species in the vc23 Register are in bold type; species not in bold type are only wild in parts of Oxon outside vc23.

Species	Common name	Habitat
Potamogeton coloratus	Fen Pondweed	Wetland, Open Water
Potamogeton lucens	**Shining Pondweed**	**Wetland, Open Water**
Potamogeton pusillus	**Lesser Pondweed**	**Wetland, Open Water**
Potamogeton trichoides	**Hair-like Pondweed**	**Wetland, Open Water**
Potentilla anglica	**Trailing Tormentil**	**Grass, Acid/Heath**
Potentilla argentea	Hoary Cinquefoil	Grass, Neutral
Prunus cerasus	**Dwarf Cherry**	**Woodland, Hedges**
Pulsatilla vulgaris	**Pasqueflower**	**Grass, Calcareous**
Pyrus pyraster	**Wild Pear**	**Woodland, Hedges**
Ranunculus arvensis	**Corn Buttercup**	**Arable**
Ranunculus circinatus	**Fan-leaved Water-crowfoot**	**Wetland, Open water**
Ranunculus fluitans	**River Water-crowfoot**	**Wetland, Open water**
Ranunculus hederaceus	Ivy-leaved Crowfoot	Wetland, Mud/Verges
Ranunculus lingua	**Greater Spearwort**	**Wetland, Mud/Verges**
Ranunculus parviflorus	**Small-flowered Buttercup**	**Arable**
Ranunculus peltatus	**Pond Water-crowfoot**	**Wetland, Open water**
Ranunculus sardous	Hairy Buttercup	Grass, Neutral
Ranunculus trichophyllus	**Thread-leaved Water-crowfoot**	**Wetland, Open water**
Rumex palustris	**Marsh Dock**	**Wetland, Mud/Verges**
Sagina apetala	**Annual Pearlwort**	**Anthropogenic**
Salix aurita	**Eared Willow**	**Woodland**
Salix myrsinifolia	Dark-leaved Willow	Woodland
Salvia pratensis	**Meadow Clary**	**Grass, Calcareous**
Salvia verbenaca	**Wild Clary**	**Anthropogenic**
Sambucus ebulus	**Dwarf Elder**	**Anthropogenic**
Samolus valerandi	**Brookweed**	**Wetland, Mud/Verges**
Scandix pecten-veneris	**Shepherd's-needle**	**Arable**
Schoenplectus tabernaemontani	**Grey Club-rush**	**Wetland, Mud/Verges**
Schoenus nigricans	Black Bog-rush	Wetland, Mires
Scirpus sylvaticus	**Wood Club-rush**	**Wetland, Mires**
Scleranthus annuus	**Annual Knawel**	**Arable Refugee**
Senecio sarracenius	**Broad-leaved Ragwort**	**Woodland**
Senecio sylvaticus	**Heath Groundsel**	**Woodland**
Serratula tinctoria	**Saw-wort**	**Wetland, Mires**
Silene conica	Sand Catchfly	Grass, Acid/Heath
Silene noctiflora	**Night-flowering Catchfly**	**Arable Refugee**
Sium latifolium	**Greater Water-parsnip**	**Wetland, Mud/Verges**
Smyrnium olusatrum	**Alexanders**	**Anthropogenic**
Solidago virgaurea	**Goldenrod**	**Grass, Acid/Heath**
Spergula arvensis	**Corn Spurrey**	**Arable**
Spergularia rubra	**Sand Spurrey**	**Grass, Neutral**
Spiranthes spiralis	**Autumn Lady's-tresses**	**Grass, Calcareous**

Species	Common name	Habitat
Spirodela polyrhiza	**Greater Duckweed**	**Wetland, Open water**
Stachys arvensis	**Field Woundwort**	**Arable**
Stachys germanica	**Downy Woundwort**	**Grass, Calcareous**
Stellaria pallida	**Lesser Chickweed**	**Grass, Neutral**
Stellaria palustris	**Marsh Stitchwort**	**Wetland, Mires**
Teesdalia nudicaulis	Shepherd's-cress	Grass, Neutral
Tephroseris integrifolia	Field Fleawort	Grass, Calcareous
Thesium humifusum	**Bastard Toadflax**	**Grass, Calcareous**
Torilis arvensis	Spreading Hedge-parsley	Arable
Trifolium arvense	**Hare's-foot Clover**	**Grass, Acid/Heath**
Trifolium fragiferum	**Strawberry Clover**	**Grass, Neutral**
Trifolium scabrum	Rough Clover	Grass, Acid/Heath
Trifolium striatum	**Knotted Clover**	**Grass, Neutral**
Trifolium subterraneum	Subterraneum Clover	Grass, Neutral
Triglochin palustre	**Marsh Arrow-grass**	**Wetland, Mires**
Tulipa sylvestris	**Wild Tulip**	**Anthropogenic**
Ulex gallii	**Western Gorse**	**Grass, Acid/Heath**
Ulex minor	**Dwarf Gorse**	**Grass, Acid/Heath**
Umbilicus rupestris	**Wall Pennywort**	**Anthropogenic**
Utricularia australis	Bladderwort	Wetland, Open water
Utricularia vulgaris	**Greater Bladderwort**	**Wetland, Open water**
Valeriana dioica	**Marsh Valerian**	**Wetland, Mires**
Valerianella dentata	**Narrow-fruited Cornsalad**	**Arable**
Valerianella rimosa	Broad-fruited Cornsalad	Arable
Veronica praecox	**Breckland Speedwell**	**Anthropogenic**
Veronica scutellata	**Marsh Speedwell**	**Wetland, Mires**
Vicia lathyroides	Spring Vetch	Grass, Acid/Heath
Vicia parviflora	**Slender Tare**	**Arable**
Vicia sativa ssp. nigra	**Narrow-leaved Vetch**	**Grass, Acid/Heath**
Vicia sativa ssp. sativa	Common Vetch	Arable
Viola canina	**Heath Dog-violet**	**Grass, Neutral**
Viola persicifolia	**Fen Violet**	**Wetland, Mires**
Viola tricolor	**Wild Pansy**	**Arable Refugee**
Vulpia unilateralis	**Mat-grass Fescue**	**Grass, Calcareous**
Zannichellia palustris	**Horned Pondweed**	**Wetland, Open water**
Chara hispida	**Bristly Stonewort**	**Wetland, Open water**
Chara curta	**Lesser Bearded Stonewort**	**Wetland, Open water**
Chara globularis	**Fragile Stonewort**	**Wetland, Open water**
Nitella flexilis	**Smooth Stonewort**	**Wetland, Open water**
Nitella opaca	**Smooth Stonewort**	**Wetland, Open water**
Nitella mucronata	**Pointed Stonewort**	**Wetland, Open water**
Tolypella intricata	**Tassel Stonewort**	**Wetland, Open water**
Tolypella prolifera	**Great Tassel Stonewort**	**Wetland, Open water**
Tolypella glomerata	**Clustered Stonewort**	**Wetland, Open water**

Table 6. The species added to the Register following Stroh *et al*. (2014) — too late for us to study.

Species	Common name	Status	FlOx tetrads	Species	Common name	Status	FlOx tetrads
Anthemis cotula	Stinking Chamomile	Vulnerable	187	Lepidium campestre	Field Pepperwort	Near Threatened	55
Briza media	Quaking grass	Near Threatened	253	Mentha arvensis	Corn Mint	Near Threatened	252
Campanula rotundifolia	Harebell	Near Threatened	161	Oxalis acetosella	Wood-sorrel	Near Threatened	129
Carlina vulgaris	Carline Thistle	Near Threatened	84	Plantago media	Hoary Plantain	Near Threatened	460
Cerastium arvense	Field Mouse-ear	Near Threatened	88	Potentilla erecta	Tormentil	Near Threatened	163
Cichorium intybus	Chicory	Vulnerable	100	Ranunculus flammula	Lesser Spearwort	Vulnerable	99
Cruciata laevipes	Crosswort	Near Threatened	149	Sanicula europaea	Sanicle	Near Threatened	224
Erysimum cheiranthoides	Treacle-mustard	Near Threatened	150	Senecio aquaticus	Marsh Ragwort	Near Threatened	107
Fragaria vesca	Wild Strawberry	Near Threatened	297	Silene flos-cuculi	Ragged Robin	Near Threatened	282
Gentianella amarella	Autumn Gentian	Near Threatened	63	Succisa pratensis	Devil's-bit Scabious	Near Threatened	129
Helianthemum nummularium	Rock-rose	Near Threatened	138	Valeriana officinalis	Common Valerian	Near Threatened	227
Knautia arvensis	Field Scabious	Near Threatened	478	Veronica officinalis	Heath Speedwell	Near Threatened	128

Table 7. The species 'lost' from vc23. This lists the 63 species recorded in vc23 between 1968 and 1999 but NOT re-found in 2000–2016. The species not in bold type are still wild in vc22 (Oxon).

Species	Common name	Habitat	Species	Common name	Habitat
Agrostemma githago	Corncockle	Arable	Medicago polymorpha	Toothed Medick	Anthropogenic
Anisantha madritensis	Compact Brome	Anthropogenic	Minuartia hybrida	Fine-leaved Sandwort	Grass, Calcareous
Apera spica-venti	Loose Silky-bent	Arable	Myriophyllum alterniflorum	Alternate Water-milfoil	Wetland, Open water
Carum carvi	Caraway	Arable	Nardus stricta	Mat-grass	Grass, Acid/heath
Centunculus minimus	Chaffweed	Grass, Acid/heath	Neotinea ustulata	Burnt Orchid	Grass, Calcareous
Cephalanthera longifolia	Narrow-leaved Helleborine	Woodland	Oreopteris limbosperma	Lemon-scented Fern	Woodland
Chamaemelum nobile	Chamomile	Grass, Acid/heath	Persicaria minor	Small Water-pepper	Wetland, Mud/verge
Chenopodium murale	Nettle-leaved Goosefoot	Anthropogenic	Pilularia globulifera	Pillwort	Wetland, Mud/verge
Clinopodium calamintha	Lesser Calamint	Grass, Calcareous	Pinguicula vulgaris	Common Butterwort	Wetland, Mires
Convallaria majalis	Lily-of-the-valley	Woodland	Potamogeton compressus	Grass-wrack Pondweed	Wetland, Open water
Cystopteris fragilis	Brittle Bladder-fern	Anthropogenic	Potamogeton friesii	Flat-stalked Pondweed	Wetland, Open water
Dianthus armeria	Deptford Pink	Grass, Neutral	Potamogeton obtusifolius	Blunt-leaved Pondweed	Wetland, Open water
Eleocharis acicularis	Needle Spike-rush	Wetland, Mud/verge	Potamogeton polygonifolius	Bog Pondweed	Wetland, Open water
Eleocharis multicaulis	Many-stalked Spike-rush	Wetland, Mires	Potamogeton praelongus	Long-stalked Pondweed	Wetland, Open water
Epilobium lanceolatum	Spear-leaved Willowherb	Anthropogenic	Potentilla argentea	Hoary Cinquefoil	Grass, neutral
Epipogium aphyllum	Ghost Orchid	Woodland	Pyrola minor	Common Wintergreen	Woodland
Equisetum sylvaticum	Wood Horsetail	Woodland	Ranunculus hederaceus	Ivy-leaved Crowfoot	Wetland, Mud/verge
Fallopia dumetorum	Copse-bindweed	Woodland: hedge	Rumex maritimus	Golden Dock	Grass, Neutral
Fumaria bastardii	Tall Ramping-fumitory	Arable	Sagina nodosa	Knotted Pearlwort	Grass, Neutral
Fumaria capreolata	White Ramping-fumitory	Arable	Salix repens	Creeping Willow	Grass, Acid/heath
Fumaria parviflora	Fine-leaved Fumitory	Arable	Schoenoplectus tabernaemontani	Grey Club-rush	Wetland, Mud/verge
Fumaria purpurea	Purple Ramping-fumitory	Arable	Schoenus nigricans	Black Bog-rush	Wetland, Mires
Galeopsis speciosa	Large-flowered Hemp-nettle	Arable	Silene gallica	Small-flowered Catchfly	Anthropogenic
Galium tricornutum	Corn Cleavers	Arable	Torilis arvensis	Spreading Hedge-parsley	Arable
Herminium monorchis	Musk Orchid	Grass, Calcareous	Trifolium scabrum	Rough Clover	Grass, Neutral
Jasione montana	Sheep's-bit	Grass, Acid/heath	Turritis glabra	Tower Mustard	Anthropogenic
Lathyrus aphaca	Yellow Vetchling	Anthropogenic	Ulmus plotii	Plot's Elm	Woodland, hedge
Lepidium heterophyllum	Smith's Pepperwort	Arable	Utricularia australis	Bladderwort	Wetland, Open water
Lepidium ruderale	Narrow-leaved Pepperwort	Anthropogenic	Valerianella rimosa	Broad-fruited Cornsalad	Arable
Lolium temulentum	Darnel	Anthropogenic	Vicia lathyroides	Spring Vetch	Grass, Acid/heath
Lycopodium clavatum	Stag's-horn Clubmoss	Grass, Acid/heath	Vicia sylvatica	Wood Vetch	Woodland
Marrubium vulgare	White Horehound	Anthropogenic			

The species accounts

THE FORMAT OF THE SPECIES ACCOUNTS

Oxfordshire's 274 Register species listed in Table 5 and the species "lost" from vc23 since 1968 listed in Table 7 are presented in the order of Stace (2010) in the larger point size with status given in line 2.

The **top line** usually starts with an arrow, most often down indicating decline but also up (increasing) or level (little change). Then the scientific and English names, and sometimes older scientific names in brackets. ***Papaver argemone*, Prickly Poppy**, is a typical example.

The left of **Line 2** has status (native, archaeophyte = introduced before 1500, neophyte = human introductions arriving after 1500); then endemic or iconic, where applicable.

Next, where applicable, the European Schedule 8 and Section 41 of the Countryside and Rights of Way Act 2000 (s. 41) precede the England Red List

categories: Near Threatened NT, Vulnerable VU, Endangered EN, Critically Endangered CR, Extinct in the Wild EW, or Extinct EX. (We have not cited the unresolved ones which are Data Deficient DD and Waiting List WL). We then give GB Red List categories in a few cases. Then Nationally Rare and Nationally Scarce defined respectively as 1–15 and 16–100 10 km squares in Great Britain in Atlas 2002.

To the right is a note on rarity in Oxfordshire (Rare, Scarce, or the date of the last record in Oxon). There is a similar note on its status in vc23. Plants found to have 1–3 sites (sites must usually be >500 metres apart) count as locally rare, and those with 4–10, locally scarce.

The **text from Line 3** onwards may include identifying features. It cites habitat, changes in abundance nationally and locally, and past abundance in FlOx and elsewhere, and often factors

Oxfordshire

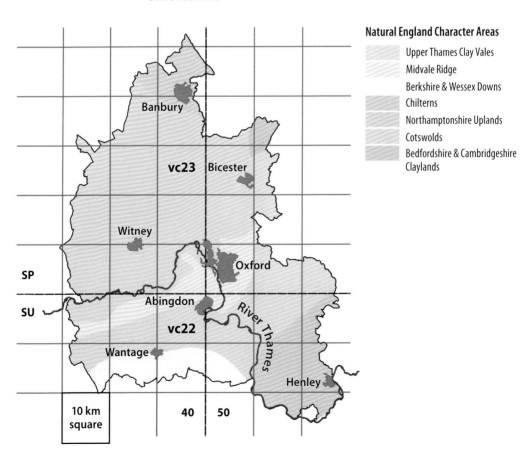

Natural England Character Areas

- Upper Thames Clay Vales
- Midvale Ridge
- Berkshire & Wessex Downs
- Chilterns
- Northamptonshire Uplands
- Cotswolds
- Bedfordshire & Cambridgeshire Claylands

affecting survival, good sites for it, and management to protect it. The reliability of records is sometimes discussed.

There is often a **table** citing:
- vice-County (vc22 formerly Berks, vc23 formerly Oxon) and District (C Cherwell, O Oxford City, S South Oxfordshire, V Vale of White Horse, W West Oxfordshire; rarely 23 Be = vc23 now in Berkshire or 23 Bu = vc23 now in Buckinghamshire).
- localities, newest first; 2000–2011 but not 1968–1999 shown bold. Records not re-found are in italics. Sometimes older records are omitted or the reader is referred to FlOx for fuller details. For nationally scarce species, unless they are far from scarce in vc23, all localities are shown;
- the site's conservation status – SAC Special Area of Conservation, SSSI Site of Special Scientific Interest, NR nature reserve, LWS Local Wildlife Site;
- grid reference; our survey mostly used 6-figure or more precise grid references; for brevity only six figures appear in the tables. Grid references for a few confidential records are less precise or omitted. Tetrad (2 km x 2 km square) records are in the form 21A = grid reference 2010, 21B = 2012 etc; the year;

- the recorder's initials (for a summary see p. 145); and
- a remarks column including numbers, or, failing that, abundance; abs. = absent, det. = determined by, conf. = confirmed by. For some records not re-found the searcher's initials and year are given. Some herbarium specimens are noted.

Many species have a map, explained below, and/or a photo.

The remaining species in our original selection, which proved to be Not Scarce, or in a few species deemed extinct before 1968, are also reported briefly using a smaller point size. They lie within the main text and also in the index.

Key to Species Maps

●   Post 2000, species present, location known to 100m

X   Last known location to 100m

●   Pre 2000, species present, location known to 100m

▪   Pre 2000, species present, location tetrad (2 km)

Lycopodium clavatum
Native

Stag's-horn Clubmoss
Last Oxon and vc23 record 1975

This evergreen prostrate pteridophyte is usually a plant of northern and western wet moors, very acidic with low nitrogen, but sometimes base-rich, soils. It had declined pre 1930 in the S. Druce listed Shotover (extinct) and three sites in the Chilterns and FlOx two tetrads. It was at Nettlebed (SU6886) Paul and Fitter, 1975, and thought to have been introduced with ballast on the Wardington railway (SP5044) where it has been looked for but not re-found. CRL

Equisetum variegatum
Native

Variegated Horsetail
Nationally Scarce ■ Rare in Oxon, absent in vc23

E. variegatum is a wintergreen perennial with slender prostrate shoots and tiny cones. Known only from Dry Sandford Pit, abundant in 1959; in FlBe; still there in 2009 (768 shoots, 38 with cones, CRL+, SU465996) but since threatened by *Carex disticha*. At the edge of clear shallow water, among lime-encrusted mosses and short vegetation; it is highly dependent on scrub clearance and grazing. In GB in infertile places – dune-slacks, river shingle and loch shores mainly in the W; our site is 100 km from the nearest site in S Wales. HJK

Equisetum fluviatile
Water Horsetail
We studied this aquatic and semi-aquatic herb because although it was in 100 FlOx tetrads, it had declined since Druce, and Killick doubted many of the records. We found it to be Not Scarce by 2008. HJK

Equisetum sylvaticum
Native

Wood Horsetail
Last confirmed record in Oxon and vc23 1968

This graceful perennial is widespread in Wales, Scotland and the W, but has declined. It requires damp, shady conditions and prefers slightly acidic soils, tolerating raised nutrients. Palmer collected it in a rough pasture corner with alders on Monks Farm, Shotover SP5606 1966 **OXF**. FlOx cited 14 tetrads but suggested that very branched *E. arvense* had been mistaken for it. Druce had it at Bagley, Chilswell, and Boars Hill till 1918; the first two are in FlBe and in SP40 and 50 in 1987–99 in the 2002 Atlas but not seen by us. CRL, HJK

Pilularia globulifera
Native

Pillwort
Vulnerable, Nationally Scarce ■ Last record in Oxon and vc23 1970

This is a peculiar, small, rhizomatous fern that colonises open watersides where the substrate is acidic and very low in nutrients. It is a lowland plant that was always uncommon and has declined probably due to habitat loss and eutrophication. Not known to Druce in vc23. It was recorded in a pond between Peppard and Cane End SU6981 and seen c. 1970 by Paul but not found later by Fitter. FlBe has no records in our area. CRL

Adiantum capillus-veneris
Native and naturalised

Maidenhair Fern
Nationally Scarce ■ Rare in Oxon and vc23

This delightful semi-evergreen fern is frost-sensitive and mostly confined to the S and W. Often cultivated, it requires high lime and low nutrients. It is spreading nationally and has colonised c. 50 m of brickwork supporting the railway platform at Shiplake (SU776796, 2010 JHW). Not mentioned by Druce or FlOx, FlBe has it at Radley College. CRL

Thelypteris palustris
Native

Marsh Fern
Nationally Scarce ■ Last confirmed record in Oxon and vc23 1965

This rhizomatous perennial of moist shady habitats is widespread in England and Wales but has been declining over a long period. It prefers base-rich mires and colonises readily on bare peat. It tolerates raised nitrates and is also long-lived. Druce had it as extinct at Shotover; in vc22 (Oxon) it was at Wytham. FlOx had it at High Wood, Shiplake. It was unconfirmed from Home Wood and Park Wood in 1981. CRL

Oreopteris limbosperma
Native

Lemon-scented Fern
Last reliable record in Oxon and vc23 1984

This fern of shady and damp places often grows beside becks. It is common in the N and W, but has declined in the S. In general it prefers acidic and low-nutrient woodlands. Druce had it on the Corallian Ridge at Shotover and also S of Oxford, but extinct at Ramsden. Bowen reported it in 1964 at Boars Hill. FlOx p. 92 cited Nettlebed Clay Pit (1973 Bevan), Rangers Lawn (1984 SP333194 Saunders). CRL

Gymnocarpium robertianum
Native introduced in Oxon

Limestone Fern
Nationally Scarce ■ Rare in Oxon and vc23

This dainty deciduous fern of limestone rocks and walls was at Cornbury until 1925 and recorded three times in FlOx but not in FlBe. At Heythrop Park in 2008, next to an artificial species-rich pond, it could have been introduced. In GB as a wild plant it is uncommon, mostly in the W; in SE England it has sporadically escaped from gardens; these distributions meet in Oxon. HJK

23	W	Heythrop Park		SP365261	2008	HJK	10 introduced?, new
23	S	Shotridge Wood		SU720939	1981	Doom	was there in 1893
23	W	Holwell		SP2208	1979	ML	
23	C	Newton Purcell		SP6230	1972	RJC+	

Cystopteris fragilis
Native

Brittle Bladder-fern
Last Oxon and vc23 record 1995

This shade-loving fern of the N and W has its eastern limit in Oxon. It requires calcareous rocks or walls. Braithwaite et al. (2006) found that this species decreased significantly between 1987–8 and 2003–4, perhaps not tolerating warmer summers. Druce had it at S Newington Churchyard and Wychwood, FlOx had five tetrads, it was found several times at Taynton. CRL

23	O	Oxford Parks		SP5006	1995	SRJW+	Prob. Intr.
23	O	Wolvercote Churchyard		SP4808	1994	RM	Abs. CRL+
23	W	Taynton Quarries	SSSI	SP236151	1972	HJMB	Rocky hollow

Blechnum spicant
Native

Hard-fern
Scarce in Oxon and vc23

(Peter Creed)

Hard-fern is small and evergreen. Its habitat, shady places and ditch banks on lime-free acid soils, is uncommon in Oxon and has decreased; eight of Druce's localities were lost by 1968. FlOx had tetrad records only at SP2420 and acid Chilterns (SU7086, 7088 and 7092); it has not declined since. FlBe had it "around Wytham". In GB it is widespread outside the Midlands and East Anglia, but reduced by clearance of woods and heaths. HJK

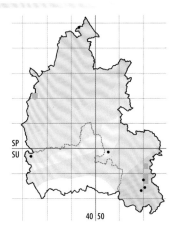

22	V	Buscot Park		SU234969	2009	SG	New
23	S	Nettlebed Common	LWS	SU700874	2009	JHW	4 sites
23	S	Burnt Platt		SU691832	2008	SR	New
23	S	Nuneham Arboretum	LWS	SU554986	2007	JHW	New
23	S	Holly Grove	LWS	SU706844	2007	JHW	New
23	C	Mollington Wood		SP431483	2006	CRL+	New
23	W	Foxholes	SSSI, BBOWT	SP250205	1981	HJMB+	

Polystichum setiferum

Soft Shield-fern

This and P. aculeatum are both ancient woodland indicators, well distributed in Great GB though scarce in the Midlands. In Oxon it is now mostly on the Corallian Ridge and the Chilterns. The populations are generally small. It was known to Druce at six sites (one re-found). FlOx p. 93 gave 20 tetrads, Bowen cited Bagley Wood 1965. In 20 sites in 2000–11, 17 of them in vc23, it is Not Scarce. CRL

Polystichum aculeatum

Hard Shield-fern

This is on more alkaline and less nutrient-rich soils than P. setiferum. In Oxford, it is by a wooded stream and in walls and gratings. Current sites appear to be in small clusters. Druce knew 16 sites; Bowen gave Bagley, FlOx had 25 tetrads. In 2000–11 at 16 sites, 14 of them in vc23, it is Not Scarce. JHW, CRL

Dryopteris affinis agg.

Golden-scaled Male-fern

This group is apogamous – producing spores with unreduced chromosome numbers, which grow into plants genetically identical to the parent. A range of forms occurs from those similar to D. filix-mas (D. borreri) to very scaly (D. affinis ssp. affinis). They grow in slightly acidic woodlands which are not too nutrient-poor, being slightly more common in the Cotswolds than on the Corallian Ridge or Chilterns. FlOx p. 94 had 28 tetrads, and FlBe had Wytham and Bagley. Oxon had 20 localities in 2000–11, of which 13 were in vc23, so it is Not Scarce. CRL

➡ *Dryopteris carthusiana*   **Narrow-leaved Buckler-fern**

This fern of damp, slightly acidic, not particularly low-nutrient, woodlands, in Oxon is mostly on the Chilterns. Druce gave nine sites, and FlOx (p. 94) 32 tetrads. In 2000–11, 19 sites were found so it is Not Scarce. CRL

⬇ *Polypodium interjectum*   **Intermediate Polypody**
Native   **Seemingly Scarce in Oxon and vc23**

This rhizomatous perennial epiphyte is widespread in most areas of the British Isles except central England. The number of records is increasing as it is better recognised – this is also true in Oxon. It grows here in its full range of habitats – in mortar and on trees and shady banks. FlOx p. 91 had 24 tetrads. The relatively small number of recent records may reflect a lack of confident recorders, as all but two are by Edgington. All but one of the 2000–11 records are at new sites, suggesting it is under-recorded. CRL

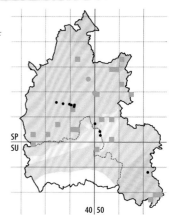

23	W	Ramsden Heath		SP344158	2006	CRL	R, new
23	W	Wilcote Manor		SP371153	2006	JE	Wall mortar, new
23	W	Sturt Copse	SSSI	SP397151	2006	JE	Many
23	W	Abel Wood		SP404148	2006	JE	1, new
23	W	Long Hanborough		SP416142	2006	JE	Many, new
23	W	Evenlode		SP417148	2006	JE	On *Salix*, new
23	O	Walton Well Rd, Oxford		SP502073	2006	JE	Wall mortar, new
22	O	Donnington Bridge Rd		SP522042	2006	JE	Wall mortar, new
22	V	Thames south of Iffley	OPT	SP524027	2006	JE	Many, new
23	S	Warburg	SSSI, BBOWT	SU718879	2002	JHW	1, on bank new
23	C	Dean Plantn, Steeple Aston		SP474250	1969	ARP	

40 50

⬇ *Juniperus communis*   **Juniper**
Native   **s. 41, Near Threatened ■ Not Scarce in Oxon, Scarce in vc23**

(Peter Creed)

Juniper is an evergreen shrub with separate male and female plants. It is widely distributed in the British Isles; but in the S and SE is mostly on chalk grasslands. Druce had eight sites on the Cotswolds including "one tree left on Juniper Hill" and locally common on the chalk. FlOx p. 96 had 23 tetrads, almost all on the chalk, and 12 sites were re-found in 2000–11. FlBe says that in the 19th century it extended from Streatley. The plants have a limited life-span and often fail to establish from seed. Extensive planting was conducted where the M40 cut through Aston Rowant NNR. Most extant localities are on protected sites or ancient trackways. Many sites have only a few senescent plants. BBOWT with the OUBG, had a restoration programme, and Plantlife is currently working on this species in the Chilterns and Wessex Downs. CRL

23	C	Juniper Hill at pub		SP579325	2009	HJK	2
23	S	Chinnor Hill	SSSI, BBOWT	SP766008	2009	JC	49 in 2 areas
22	S	Aston Upthorpe Downs	SSSI	SU543831	2009	RMW	1300
23	S	Hartslock	SAC, SSSI, BBOWT	SU617794	2008	HJK	1
23	S	Swyncombe Downs	SSSI	SU671914	2007	JHW	5
23	S	Shirburn Hill	SSSI	SU715954	2007	JHW	30
23	S	Aston Rowant	SAC, NNR, SSSI	SU724962	2007	HJK	1 + many introduced
23	S	Peppard Common	LWS	SU706817	2006	JHW	5
23	S	Chinnor Chalk Pit	SSSI	SP757000	2003	JMC	
22	V	Blewbury Hill	LWS	SU527823	2002	HJK	Few
23	S	Nuffield Common	LWS	SU673876	2002	JHW	
23	S	Aston Rowant	SAC, NNR, SSSI	SU727973	2002	JMC	
23	S	Kingwood Common	LWS	SU696825	1995	RdA	
22	V	Ridgeway Path		SU525824	1991	PJ	
22	S	Aston Upthorpe Downs	SSSI	SU545835	1991	EN	
22	V	Blewbury Hill	LWS	SU530824	1990	JMC	
23	S	Oakley Hill	LWS, BBOWT	SU758995	1988	RSRF	
22	S	Fairmile to Kingstanding Hill		SU560834	1986	GH	
22	S	Moulsford Downs	SSSI	SU577827	1986	JMC	Destroyed
23	S	Watlington and Pyrton Hills	SSSI	SU703936	1986	JY	
22	V	Aston Upthorpe Downs	SSSI	SU537836	1984	GB	Destroyed
22	V	Chilton Disused railway line	LWS	SU505865	1982	JMC	
23	S	Icknield Way		SU660900	1981	SW	Abs. 2011 CRL
22	S	Aston Upthorpe, Upper Hill Barn track		SU555835	1979		
23	S	Warren Wood (main part)	pLWS	SU652858	1979	GB	

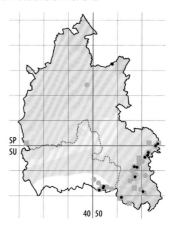

40 50

➡ *Aristolochia clematitis*
Neophyte, Iconic

Birthwort
Rare in Oxon and vc23

(Peter Creed)

This scrambling perennial grows near former habitations, especially monastic sites, where it was grown for its medicinal properties. It was presumably introduced to GB before 1540 (before the Dissolution of the Monasteries), and is found at fewer than 20 sites across lowland GB. It is gradually declining; in Berks it was formerly introduced, but now extinct. In Oxon it grows by the ruins of Godstow Nunnery and in a hedge at the adjacent village of Wytham vc22 (Oxon). At Godstow (vc23 SP484090) it is in a ditch and hedge, where hawthorn protects it from grazing cattle. Monitoring by the RPG since 1993 has shown variation between 63 and 379 shoots. Shoots appear from rhizomes each year, and one attempt to raise it from seed has failed. CRL, SO

➡ *Ceratophyllum demersum*

Rigid Hornwort

Rigid Hornwort was in 29 tetrads in FlOx; many records in rivers were not re-found. It is Not Scarce as we now have 40 2000–11 records in ponds, of which half are in gardens and probably introduced. HJK

⬇ *Papaver hybridum*
Archaeophyte

Rough Poppy
Scarce in Oxon and vc23

(Peter Sheasby)

Rough Poppy grew in dry arable land, mostly lime-rich, often with other poppies. FlOx cited 21 tetrads and we have eight records in vc22 (Oxon). We have not re-visited seven tetrads N of SP4224. Some colonies are on set-aside sites; at one of these, a few appeared four times since 1998 among plentiful *P. rhoeas* and *P. argemone*. In GB most frequent on chalk, especially between Dorset and Norfolk, also on limestone and lime-rich sands; it has declined, probably reduced by herbicides, but its seeds are long-lived. HJK

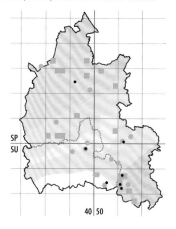

22	S	Aston Upthorpe Downs	(non SSSI)	SU554845	2010	RH-B	Arable margin, >40, new
23	S	South Stoke Footpath		SU610838	2010	JHW	
23	S	Crowmarsh near Sheepcote Farm		SU619874	2010	JHW	31 in fr
23	S	Goring near Grove Farm		SU616822	2009	JHW	3
22	V	Confidential		SU49U	2008	HJK	Arable, few
23	S	Wells Farm	BBOWT	SP624007	2007	RdA	Set-aside, fallow
23	W	Whiteways Quarry	LWS, LGS	SP420246	2002	AW	New
23	S	Ouseley Barn Cottages		SU645836	1999	RWHS	

→ *Papaver argemone*
Archaeophyte

Prickly Poppy
Endangered ■ **Not Scarce in Oxon and vc23**

(Susan Erskine)

This is one of the smaller poppies with prickly seed heads. It is an arable annual and generally found on dry, well-drained, calcareous, sandy or gravelly soils and usually in field margins. It is susceptible to herbicides and thus has declined nationally and in Oxon; though in 2000–11 it has many more than 10 sites. As it is classed as endangered nationally it is included in this register. Like other members of the *Papaver* genus, its seed bank is long lived and it can re-occur in old habitats after many years. Druce 1927 described it as 'not uncommon' and it is still found in many of his sites as well as new ones. FlOx had it in 85 tetrads. In vc22 it is found in many arable and set-aside fields near the Corallian Ridge. SEE

23	C	Horsehay Quarry (West)	LWS	SP455274	2011	HJK	
22	V	Confidential		SU49T	2010	HJK	Abundant in 6 sites
22	S	Aston Upthorpe		SU549841	2010	RH-B	1 plant
23	S	Goring Gorse Farm		SU617829	2010	JHW	2 plants
23	S	S. Stoke Wood		SU618835	2010	JHW	Frequent
23	S	Ipsden Wood		SU636863	2010	JHW	17 plants
23	S	Nuffield Warren Hill		SU657878	2010	JHW	1 plant
23	S	Track to Sydlings Copse		SP557091	2009	RH-B	1 plant
23	S	Elsfield		SP558101	2009	HJK	
23	S	Stanton St John		SP565096	2009	RH-B	1 plant
22	V	Tubney, field by lay-by on A420		SU439966	2009	SEE	At least 6
23	O	Homebase car park		SP557049	2008	RH-B	
22	V	Confidential		SU49N	2008	HJK	25 plants
23	W	Palmers Bank	LWS	SP378179	2007	CRL	Rare
23	W	Ditchley		SP392209	2007	AJD	
23	O	Path through BMW works Cowley		SP557035	2007	JW	
23	S	Wells Farm	BBOWT	SP624007	2007	RdA	
22	V	Barcote Lane		SU326962	2006	SEE	Scattered field margin
23	W	Whiteways Quarry	LWS, LGS	SP420246	2002	AW	
23	S	Coombe End Farm		SU636795	2000	SK	10
23	S	Manor Farm		SU705830	2000	SK+	
23	S	Cowfields Farm		SU737818	2000	SK+	1 plant

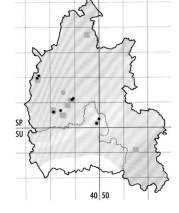

SP
SU

40 | 50

→ *Ceratocapnos claviculata* (*Corydalis claviculata*)
Native

Climbing Corydalis
Scarce in Oxon and vc23

(Peter Creed)

Climbing Corydalis is a delicate scrambling annual. In Oxon only in shady sites on poor acid sandy soils where these factors deter competitors; it can appear after clearing and co-exist with bracken. FlOx had it in eight tetrads, mostly between 1962 and 1970. Not in Bowen (1968), FlBe or the sandy (but lime-rich) soils near Frilford. It is widely scattered but surviving well – at Foxholes, at four sites (sometimes among bracken) in Eynsham Park; and in three new places in vc22 (Oxon), the later at Coxwell Wood (SU257943, 2012 Erskine). In GB it is widely spread and it made gains between 1987 and 2004 by spreading under conifers (Braithwaite *et al.* 2006). HJK

23	W	Cogges Wood	LWS	SP387112	2010	JAW	
23	W	Foxholes	SSSI, BBOWT	SP248198	2009	HJK	New
23	W	Foxholes	SSSI	SP255208	2009	HJK	12 other sites
23	W	Eynsham Park		SP393117	2008	HJK	20, 3 other sites
23	W	Lew Gorse		SP313063	2006	SJH	
22	V	Chilswell Valley	LWS	SP499035	2006	CRL	New
22	V	Foxcombe Wood, Boars Hill		SP490018	2004	RH-B	
23	W	Mouldens Wood and Davis Copse	LWS	SP341069	2001	CRL	New
22	V	Foxcombe Hill		SP490018	1985	RH-B	
23	O	Port Meadow Tip		SP4808	1979	HJMB	

SP
SU

40 | 50

Fumaria   **Fumitories**

Oxfordshire has only one widespread fumitory, *F. officinalis*; it lies on the westward limit of small arable species of chalky fields and to the E of the taller ramping-fumitories. The fumitories are scrambling annuals, germinating in spring and found in spring-sown crops. All can appear as casuals but with their long-lived seeds can then persist. The arable populations have suffered from intensive farming and winter-sown crops.

Fumitories are tricky to identify, but plants with flowers (and in particular sepals) bigger or smaller than those of *F. officinalis* (mostly 7–8 mm long, sepals 1–1.5 mm wide) can be one of our unusual species. Fresh flower length and colour excluding the tips are cited. The records, cited as received, may include errors.

The first four are large ramping-fumitories with a western distribution, in arable land, gardens and hedgerows, often on free-draining acidic soils. Oxon is E of their main range. HJK

⬇ *Fumaria capreolata*   **White Ramping-fumitory**
Native   **Rare in Oxon, last vc23 record 1980**

F. capreolata has broad leaflets, big (10–13 mm) cream flowers and recurved fruit-stalks. It can be a winter annual. Vc23 had eight records pre-1935, one near Goring (SU6181, 1969 anon) and N Oxford tip (4808, 1980 Bowen). Many at Abingdon SU485972 in 2015, Killick. In GB, widespread near the W coast but has declined inland. Our plants are the endemic ssp. *babingtonii*. HJK

22	V	Sunningwell, nr pub	SP497006	2011	HJK	2, garden, new

⬇ *Fumaria bastardii*   **Tall Ramping-fumitory**
Native   **Last Oxon record 1978**

F. bastardii has broad leaflets and 9–11 mm pale pink flowers; dry fruits rugose. It grows in arable land and gardens. Seen only at Bullingdon (Druce), Kidlington in 1938 **OXF**: field records at Ewelme (SP6591, 1970) and Brize Norton (SP3008, 1978 Loukes). In GB, it is widespread near the W coast. HJK

⬇ *Fumaria muralis*   **Common Ramping-fumitory**
Native   **Rare in Oxon and vc23**

F. muralis has broad leaflets and big (9–11 mm) flowers with toothed sepals. Our plant is ssp. *boroei*. Known in Oxon from 1880; in 11 FlOx tetrads in waste places including Oxford, Oxford tip and Sonning Common. In 1993 at North Leigh and re-found 18 years later, suggesting that other previous records may yet be re-found. In vc22 (Oxon) (19th Century, **OXF**), from Hinksey SP50; in SU59 at Culham, Frilford in 1977: in Killick's garden, for 11 years, sometimes non-fruiting, sometimes abundant, it is ousting *F. officinalis*. In 2013 newly at City Farm, Eynsham SP425113, Larkman. GB's commonest large-flowered fumitory, widespread in the W and N, this has spread elsewhere between 1987 and 2004 (Braithwaite *et al.* 2006). The map shows the distributions before and after 2000 differ, despite the persistent seeds. HJK

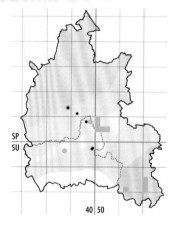

23	W	N. Leigh Churchyard		SP387136	2011	HJK	20
22	V	Park Crescent, Abingdon		SU490975	2011	HJK	Many new
22	V	Wytham Woods	SSSI	SP463080	2005	AWM	
22	V	Cherbury Camp	LWS	SU374963	1986	EC	
23	O	Port Meadow Tip		SP4808	1979	HJMB	

⬇ *Fumaria purpurea*   **Purple Ramping-fumitory**
Native endemic   **Nationally Scarce, s. 41, Vulnerable ■ Last Oxon and vc23 record 1971**

F. purpurea has broad leaflets, big (10–13 mm) purple flowers and recurved fruit-stalks. It grows in hedgebanks, arable land and gardens. Near Cowley in 1886 and at Sturdy's Castle (SP4618, 1971 Theobald). In GB it is local, mostly near the W coast. HJK

The following *Fumaria* species are small, almost always in arable land on chalk in SE England, and increasingly limited to field margins; Oxon is at the W end of their range in GB. HJK

➡ *Fumaria densiflora*   Dense-flowered Fumitory

F. densiflora has channelled leaflets and smallish (6–7 mm) pale pink flowers, with broader sepals and longer bracts than in *F. officinalis*. In 30 tetrads FlOx (p. 107), many repeated in 1999–2000 by the Northmoor Trust (now Earth Trust). There were five records from 2000 onwards and 14 in 1999; *F. densiflora* seems Not Scarce in Oxon. HJK

⬇ *Fumaria parviflora*   Fine-leaved Fumitory
Archaeophyte   Near Threatened, Nationally Scarce ■ Last Oxon record 1992, in vc23 1979

This fumitory has narrow channelled leaflets, long bracts and small (5–6 mm) pale flowers in nearly stalkless flower clusters. Formerly widespread on Lower Chalk, which is now intensively cultivated. In FlOx at SU6892 in 1979 (also 1945, **OXF**); also at Ridgeway Path SU620877, OCMR, undated. The most recent in vc22 (Oxon) were near Aston Upthorpe (reservoir SU5585 in 1988, the Down SU544835 in 1992). HJK

⬇ *Fumaria vaillantii*   Few-flowered Fumitory
Archaeophyte   Endangered, Nationally Scarce ■ Rare in Oxon and vc23

This fumitory has narrow flat leaflets and small (5–6 mm) pale pink flowers with tiny sepals and short bracts. In 22 tetrads (FlOx p. 106), mainly in the Chilterns. It had spread since Druce 1927 but has since greatly declined. In vc22 (Oxon) since 1986 above Wantage (SU347847), Castle Hill Fort (SU381841), Aston Upthorpe (SU545835) and Fair Mile (SU553826). HJK

23	S	Goring		SU6181	2000	HJK
23	S	Crowmarsh Battle Farm		SU657889	1999	SJG+
23	S	Ewelme Park Estate		SU672895	1999	SJG+

⬇ *Berberis vulgaris*   Barberry
Native or Alien   Not Scarce in Oxon, Scarce vc23

This spiny shrub was present in the Neolithic and widely planted in medieval times, but almost eradicated in the 19th Century as it is the winter host of wheat rust. It is widespread in GB especially on lime-rich and nutrient-poor soils but has undergone a big decline. While Druce had 32 sites, FlOx reported it in 56 tetrads; Bowen and FlBe also had several sites. Some 2000–11 records are at new sites so it may be under-recorded. It has been introduced at Barton Fields as it is the food-plant of two moths – the Barberry Carpet and Mottled Pug. CRL

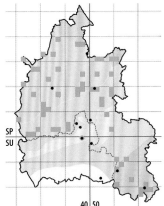

23	C	Weston-on-the-Green		SP521193	2010	HJK	20m
23	S	Crowsley Frieze Farm Lane		SU726796	2010	JHW	
22	V	Dry Sandford Pit	SSSI, LGS, BBOWT	SU468994	2008	HJK	1 + intr
22	V	Radley Gravel Pits	LWS	SU507973	2008	DG	Introduced, new
23	S	North Stoke		SU614864	2008	JHW	1
23	W	Road SE of Black Bourton		SP2903	2007	Ski	South Hedge
22	V	Cumnor		SP461038	2007	HJK	
22	S	Aston Upthorpe Downs	SSSI	SU545835	2007	SR	New
23	C	Cherwell Somerton to		SP490332	2005	CRL	New
		Nell Bridge					
22	V	Farmoor Reservoir	LWS	SP446053	2003	HJK	New
23	O	Fiddlers Island		SP503067	2002	OUWG	New
23	W	Charlbury		SP347194	2000	HJK	New
23	C	Banbury Rd, Kidlington		SP480140	2000	HJK	
23	W	Old Woodstock		SP4417	1998	JT	Balliol Lane
22	V	Denmans Farm, Cumnor		SP465055	1996	HJK	Track

SP
SU

40 | 50

➡️ *Helleborus foetidus*
Native and alien

Stinking Hellebore
Nationally Scarce ■ **Probably Not Scarce in Oxon**

(Peter Creed)

Stinking Hellebore is a perennial, intolerant of competition and of deep shade. As a wild plant it was in 10 vc23 tetrads (FlOx p. 99) in extensive woodlands especially Wychwood, Ditchley, N of Taynton and on lime-rich soils, mostly Oolite; one in the Warburg reserve was transplanted. In vc22 (Oxon) in old woods, chiefly beech. The species is also commonly grown in gardens and churchyards from which it increasingly escapes, so in GB and Oxon it has spread and the native and escaped plants are hard to separate. The recent data are therefore mapped rather than listed. The map shows past and present records do not correspond closely and we did not re-visit beyond Northings 20. HJK

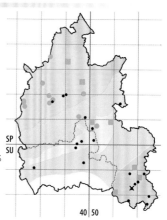

⬇️ *Helleborus viridis*

Green Hellebore

This woodland plant was in 22 FlOx tetrads in the Chilterns and Cotswolds but the vc22 (Oxon) records were mostly garden escapes. With 18 2000–11 records in Oxon (16 in vc23) it is Not Scarce. HJK

⬇️ *Pulsatilla vulgaris*
Native

Pasqueflower

s. 41, Vulnerable, Nationally Scarce ■ **Rare in Oxon Reintroduced in vc23**

(Frances Watkins)

This spectacular perennial is confined to calcareous pasture in central England and has suffered a big decline. It prefers steep S and SW facing slopes with low-nutrient soils and species-rich sward; as Druce says, it is curiously absent from the Chilterns scarp, and also from the western chalk (FlBe). It is vulnerable to grazing, especially the flowers (pheasants are implicated), but it requires short turf. It became extinct in vc23 in the 1880s. A site at Moulsford with thousands of plants was ploughed in the 1960s. Part of the last remaining small population at Aston Upthorpe was rabbit-fenced in the 1970s, but this led to the grass becoming very dense leading to reduction in survival and flowering of the enclosed Pasqueflowers. As it is believed rarely to establish naturally from seed the small population near Aston Upthorpe was reinforced in 1999 with c. 100 plants using seed collected from the same site. Establishment was initially high and the exclosure fencing was opened to allow sheep grazing later in the year. In 2012 51 plants survived from the reinforcement and about 12 natural plants are present. Despite the rabbit-netting a significant number of flowers are grazed off before seedset unless given additional protection (wire hats). A new population was introduced at Hartslock BBOWT NR in 1998 raised from seed from Bedfordshire. In 2012 79 plants survived with naturally arising seedlings making up for initial losses among the original 72 transplants and thus producing a small increase despite a tendency for many of the flowers to be grazed off before seedset. Plants from Hertfordshire were introduced to Warburg Reserve both at Leahill Wildlife Garden (SU720870, eight in 2010) and at Maidensgrove Field (SU717883 five in 2006). CRL, KJW, RDA

➡️ *Ranunculus sardous*
Native

Hairy Buttercup
Rare in Oxon, not recently in vc23

This species is superficially similar to *R. bulbosus* with its reflexed sepals, but it has no 'bulbous' root; the achenes are smooth with a few tubercles inside the border. It is an annual which flourishes in heavy clay soils, mostly in coastal pastures and disturbed ground, around the southern coasts of England and Wales. Found in 1998 on an organic farm, by Erskine and Gimson whilst conducting an arable flowers survey for the Northmoor Trust. Thereafter it has been seen on biannual visits. It is presumed extinct in vc23 (FlOx), very rare (Druce 1897), rare (FlBe and Bowen 1968). SEE

22	V	Step Farm, Faringdon		SU268954	2003	SEE	20+ plants on arable margin, new

➔ *Ranunculus parviflorus*
Native

Small-flowered Buttercup
Scarce in Oxon and vc23

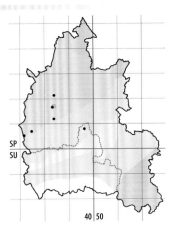

This is an annual of dry, disturbed, neutral to calcareous soils. It has retreated south-westwards to the S and W of England but now appears stable in its core areas. In Oxon, in Druce 1886 and FlOx this was described as decreasing and rare. It has been lost from many locations and has only been recorded from six sites, the most recent being Cherwell Service station (2015 Stanley). It needs disturbed soil to germinate, and can reappear after many years. In some locations e.g. Wytham where it is recorded annually (latest 2015) and Bradwell airfield it can occur in thousands in favourable years. SEE

23	W	Shilton Bradwell Grove Airfield	pLWS	SP248070	2007	HJK	5 sites here
23	W	Wychwood	NNR, SSSI	SP332167	2007	WOR	Occasional
23	W	Manor Farm Meadow, Crawley	LWS	SP338120	2007	WOR	A dry grassy bank
22	V	Wytham Woods	SSSI	SP463080	2005	AWM+	1000+
23	W	Oxleaze Farm		SP217053	2001	HJK	Few
23	W	Dean Common (Dean Sand Pit)	Other	SP339214	2000	CRL	
23	W	Wychwood	NNR, SSSI	SP338170	1984	PS	

⬇ *Ranunculus arvensis*
Archaeophyte

Corn Buttercup
s. 41, Endangered ■ Scarce in Oxon, Rare in vc23

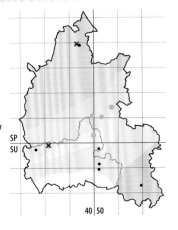

This is an annual which is found in a wide range of soils in arable situations. It was mostly found in lowland S and E England. There has been a huge decline nationwide. It is thought to have a long seed bank, but improved methods of seed cleaning, result in fewer seeds to regenerate. Druce 1927 described it as locally abundant, by FlOx only 55 tetrads had records, with FlBe noting a few sites mainly confined to Upper Greensand. There are only three post-2000 records in vc23. SEE

22	V	Radley Gravel Pits	LWS	SU520977	2010	RdA	
23	C	The Saltway, Banbury	pLWS	SP442390	2004	PS	2 sites
22	S	Didcot Trading Estate, undeveloped plot		SU522916	2004	SEE	20+, V. vulnerable, new
23	S	Kingwood Common	LWS	SU694830	2004	VR	
22	V	Step Farm Faringdon (Organic)		SU263973	2000	SEE	
22	V	Chilswell Farm		SP498030	1996	LH	
22	V	Pucketty Farm		SU314989	1989	SEE	SEE in 2006 nor by MFVC
23	S	Woodeaton		SP532103	1988	NDB	Not seen 2006, SEE, MFVC
23	C	Otmoor	SSSI	SP573142	1983	FlOx	
23	C	The Bretch, Banbury		SP430394	1975	PS	Not re-found HJK 2001

➔ *Ranunculus lingua*
Native and planted

Greater Spearwort
Scarce in Oxon and vc23

This is a stoloniferous perennial frequenting slow-moving or still water: lakes, canals and ditches. The 1962 BSBI Atlas showed a decline in its distribution, but since then it has become popular as a cultivated plant and has been planted in the wild or escaped, so that the original distribution of native plants has become totally blurred. Records from village ponds or similar have been omitted as probably planted or escaped. It has always been scarce in Oxon, Druce 1927 described it as local and rare, FlOx noted only 13 localities and it has been stable since then. SEE

23	W	Moors Lake		SP354086	2009	SEE+	3 clumps
22	V	Wytham Ditches & Flushes	SSSI	SP469100	2009	FHW	1 flower
22	V	Raleigh Park	LWS	SP492052	2009	RH-B	Large patch
23	O	Milhamford Field & Quad	LWS	SP529073	2009	JAW	Abundant
22	V	Dry Sandford Pit	SSSI	SU468995	2009	HJK	150 shoots
23	C	Muswell Hill Fields	LWS	SP636152	2008	CRL	Few
22	V	Hitchcopse Pit	SSSI, BBOWT	SU452997	2008	HJK	>10
23	W	Ditchley Park	pLWS	SP388213	2007	AJD	Few
22	V	Uffington Gorse	WT	SU312898	2006	SEE	Last seen 2000
23	C	Deddington Mill	LWS	SP456327	2000	PS	
22	V	S. of Charney Bassett		SU379932	2000	SEE	Large patch in ditch, new

Ranunculus subgenus *Batrachium*   Water-crowfoots

Identification problems have made water-crowfoots difficult to report in County Floras, Atlas 2002 and now in Rare Plant Registers. It is easy to misidentify some plants; frequent changes in their classification have caused many specimens to be identified differently by different people, including experts, at different times, giving records under two or more names and much over-recording.

Most species have declined greatly and Killick saw more of them between 1946 and 1952 (mostly in Wiltshire) than in any year since.

In rivers and canals the causes could be pollution, eutrophication and turbidity; ponds suffer from these but very many of them are also shaded, overgrown, dried out or filled in. Thus most dot maps in FlOx contain lost colonies. Atlas 2002 reports a decline in *R. hederaceus* since 1950 in areas that are mostly arable; this surely applies in Oxon and to other water-crowfoots.

R. penicillatus survives well in several streams but most species became candidates for our Rare Plants Register; with hindsight we might have also checked on *R. aquatilis*. The plausible records are listed below but relatively few were confirmed by N T H Holmes or C D Preston. Many specimens are in **OXF**.

There are discrepancies in the records of some species; where unresolved, FlOx data are used rather than TVERC's. HJK

⬇ *Ranunculus hederaceus*   Ivy-leaved Crowfoot
Native   Rare in Oxon, Last record 1985

The leaves, all ivy-shaped, and tiny petals (c. 3 mm) are characteristic. It grows in mud, often acid, in ponds and slow streams. Druce (1927) had 23 localities but FlOx only Church Hanborough (SP4212), Drayton St Leonard (SP5894), Yarnton (4612) all 1985 and Nuneham (SP5498, 1985 Bowen). None of Druce's Thames-side plants figure in FlBe. Found at Berkeley Old golf course, N of Boars Hill (22 V, SP494021, 2010, Lambrick). Widespread in GB but most concentrated in the W; Atlas 2002 reports a decline since 1950 in areas in S England that are mostly arable. HJK

(Peter Creed)

⬇ *Ranunculus omiophyllus*   Round-leaved Crowfoot
Native   Only Oxon and vc23 records 1975–6

This has more indented and rounded leaves and longer (5–6 mm) petals than *R. hederaceus*. A plant of acid, non-eutrophic waters recorded, surprisingly, at Launton (SP6222) by Fitter in 1976 and Emmington (SP7402) by Fitter and Woodell (1975). These, not re-found, lie outside the national range; it is widespread but mostly in the W from Glasgow to Wales and Cornwall, but declining at the edges of its range. HJK

⬇ *Ranunculus trichophyllus*   Thread-leaved Water-crowfoot
Native   Not Scarce in Oxon, Scarce in vc23

The leaves are all short and thread-like, the petals small, <6 mm with crescent-moon shaped nectar-pits. This small, early-flowering species of ponds and still water was in 85 tetrads (FlOx p. 100) of which only eight were added after 1986. It has been lost from many places but has been widely reported in Otmoor and repeatedly in Abingdon Common. Killick re-found a colony in a pond by the Cherwell in Oxford (SP523071, 1994 Killick) in 2015. In GB it is very widespread and stable but mostly S of a line Exeter–York. HJK

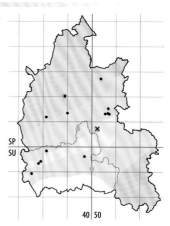

22	V	Abingdon Common		SU470962	2010	HJK	Many, new
23	C	Ardley Cutting and Quarry	SSSI, LGS, BBOWT	SP537272	2009	CRL	1, new
23	W	Minster Lovell Marsh	LWS	SP313119	2007	WOR	Few
23	W	Ditchley Park		SP389202	2007	WOR	Few
23	W	North Leigh Common	LWS	SP400135	2007	WOR	Few, pond, new
22	V	Defence Academy, Shrivenham		SU254893	2007	SEE	Pond, 6
22	V	Wicklesham and Coxwell Pits	SSSI, LGS	SU291942	2007	SEE	¼ of pond
23	C	RSPB Otmoor	pLWS, RSPB	SP555132	2006	RSPB	Ditches
23	C	RSPB Otmoor	pLWS, RSPB	SP566134	2006	RSPB	Drains
22	V	Little Coxwell village pond		SU282934	2006	SEE	Most of pond
22	V	Pucketty Farm		SU314984	2006	SEE	Organic farm
23	C	Otmoor		SP568153	2005	JE	Pond margin
23	C	Otmoor	SSSI	SP572131	2004	JE	Ditches
22	V	Didcot road		SU501912	1999	HJK	Roadside ditch
22	V	Farmoor Reservoir	LWS	SP443072	1997	PA	Pond
23	W	Ditchley Estate		SP387203	1991	AJD	Pool

⬇ *Ranunculus peltatus*
Native

Pond Water-crowfoot
Scarce in ponds in Oxon and vc23

R. peltatus usually has floating leaves and big flowers; told from *R. aquatilis* by petals >10 mm, fruit stalks >5 cm and pear-shaped nectar-pit, and from *R. penicillatus* by finely divided leaves shorter than adjacent internode, with <100 divergent segments. Typically in ponds but much decreased; also in the upper reaches of lime-rich streams.

One past classification and also Druce included some stream plants now placed in *R. penicillatus*, so Druce regarded it as common. There are 13 records from five tetrads in the Windrush in 1996, some cited below. Of 40 widespread tetrad records in FlOx (p. 101), only three were after 1986. In vc22 (Oxon) since 1986 only near Wantage and Wytham; recent pond records are few but garden ponds (Tubney and Abingdon) are helping this species to survive. Nationally it is widespread and mainly lowland, but unrecorded recently in many places. HJK

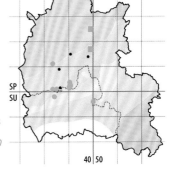

23	S	Aston Rowant	SAC, NNR, SSSI	SU725958	2007	HJK	Not seen 2011
23	W	Ashford Bridge to Combe Cutting (Cotswold Line)	LWS	SP390157	2005	FHW	New
23	C	RSPB Otmoor	pLWS, RSPB	SP564146	2004	RSPB	
23	C	Cutter's Brook Meadows	LWS	SP618218	2004	CRL	New
23	W	Windrush		SP232133	1996	FG	
23	W	Windrush		SP286115	1996	SJW	
23	W	Windrush		SP353104	1996	AJLo	
23	W	Windrush (West Branch)		SP383058	1996	JAT	
23	W	North Leigh		SP382135	1993	HJK	Re-found 2011

⬇ *Ranunculus fluitans*
Native

River Water-crowfoot
?Scarce in Oxon and vc23

R. fluitans, unlike *R. penicillatus,* has glabrous receptacle and leaves longer than the internodes and rarely >4 times forked. In the larger rivers; in Druce (1927) it was 'a characteristic feature in the Thames from Kelmscott to Sonning', but in FlOx the few specimens there were 'mostly scrappy, flowerless and damaged' and its decline in the main Thames is beyond doubt. Although some of the 66 FlOx tetrad records (p. 101) may be correct they are not repeated here; many could have been *R. penicillatus*. It survives in tributaries close to the Thames but the amount is problematical; there are confirmed records from the Lower Windrush in 1996 and others below. The map covers 1990–2011. In GB it is widespread but most concentrated in the W and E Midlands and to Killick's surprise has reportedly increased. HJK

23	W	Combe		SP407150	2006	SEE	Frequent, new
23	C	Kidlington		SP4814	2004	JE	Also 4815,4915,4816
23	W	Witney Lake & Meadows	Other	SP361090	2003	FLY	Quadrat, many
23	W	Chimney Meadows	BBOWT	SP365016	2003	CRL	
23	S	Back Water		SU5096	1999	HJK	Few, leaves only
23	W	Windrush		SP401015	1996	SJW+	Also upstream to SP403038
23	W	Oxon Tetrad 4824		SP4824	1993	HJK	Det. NTHH
23	W	Great Brook		SP334009	1991	HJK	Conf. NTHH, overgrown 2010
23	W	Crawley Mead	LWS	SP334112	1991	HJK	Det. NTHH

⬇ *Ranunculus circinatus*
Native

Fan-leaved Water-crowfoot
Rare in Oxon and vc23

With short finely divided leaves, with short rigid segments all in one plane, *R. circinatus* grows in deep (1–3 m), clear base-rich mostly still water. It is in 41 sites in Druce (1927), but only 19 FlOx tetrads (p. 102), some 'improbable'. The 1978 record is surprising but Ruskin Reserve then had a bigger pond. Atlas 2002 includes 1987–99 records in FlBe from Buscot Lake (SU29), [SP40], Radley (SU59), Kennington pit and South Hinksey (SP50). Killick found floating fragments in Thrupp Lake (22 V, SU599977) in 2013 but not since. In England it is mostly SE of a line Exeter–York; it has declined steadily during the 20th Century following habitat destruction and eutrophication. HJK

23	C	Woodsides Meadow	SSSI, BBOWT	SP556178	2008	JAW	1 m wide in pond, new
23	W	Linch Hill Leisure Park, fishing lake		SP417042	2007	SEE	Wet gravel pit, new
22	V	Ruskin Reserve	SAC, NNR, SSSI	SU459997	1978	HJMB+	
23	C	Oxford Canal		SP489350	1975	PS+	Oxford Canal
23	S	Chinnor Hill	SSSI, BBOWT	SP766007	1968	RSRF	

Myosurus minimus
Native

Vulnerable ■ Scarce in Oxon and vc23

Mousetail

(Phil Cutt)

This is a small annual of seasonally flooded nutrient-rich soils. It flourishes in disturbed areas especially where grazing animals drink. Losses are attributed to better drainage and infilling of ponds, but it is also a poor competitor. In FlOx it is described as rare, with 12 widely scattered sites in vc23. In this survey, most of the records come from the S. SEE

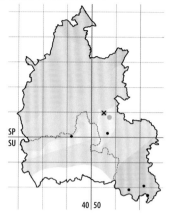

22	V	Marsh Farm, Fyfield	SP418003	2010	PEC+	large patch
23	S	Hardwick	SU655791	2010	JHW	11 plants
23	S	Littlestead Green	SU733769	2010	JHW	5 plants
23	S	Elsfield	SP551096	2009	HJK	Absent
23	S	Toot Baldon	SP566016	2008	RH-B	40 plants
23	S	Sonning	SU732768	2004	JHW	71 plants
23	S	Rotherfield Peppard	SU717807	2000	SK+	1 plant
23	S	Manor Farm	SP573079	1998	SJG+	
23	S	Hill Farm	SP551096	1996	LH	

SP
SU

40 50

Adonis annua
Archaeophyte

s. 41, Endangered, Nationally Rare ■ Rare in Oxon and vc23

Pheasant's-eye

(Phil Cutt)

This glorious annual of chalky arable soils is usually autumn germinating. It occurs in S England but has suffered a huge decline. In South Oxon it has been known since the 1970s from one field margin on a S-facing slope. It prefers autumn sown crops and numbers vary with the crop, weather and cultivation. Management without herbicides enabled the population to reach 110. Threats include over-shading by weeds and grazing by deer and rabbits. RBG Kew has grown on some seed. Druce reported seven sites in vc23 and one in vc22 (Oxon). FlOx had three tetrads, and FlBe two in 1977. CRL

Aquilegia vulgaris
Columbine

This handsome perennial is not only an Ancient Woodland Indicator, but also a popular garden plant which spreads readily, making it difficult to distinguish natural from naturalised populations. Druce – widespread, FlOx (p. 102) had 71 tetrads; in 2000–11 we found 18 sites so it is Not Scarce. CRL

Saxifraga granulata
Meadow Saxifrage

This delicate early-flowering perennial of damp grasslands was known to Druce at 34 sites and in FlOx (p. 150) at 51 tetrads. In 2000–11 we recorded it at 20 sites, 11 of them in vc23, so it is Not Scarce. CRL

Chrysosplenium oppositifolium
Opposite-leaved Golden-saxifrage

This is found in large patches in shady woods, usually on a spring line. Its number of locations has almost halved since FlOx, but there are 17 2000–11 records in Oxon (11 in vc23). It is Not Scarce. SEE

Chrysosplenium alternifolium
Native

Alternate-leaved Golden-saxifrage
Rare in Oxon and vc23

(Peter Creed)

This perennial plant of boggy ground is known only in Sarsgrove Wood SP 301242, in FlOx (SP2822) in 1974, seen by Dawkins in 1974, Dunn in 1987 and Laney in 2013. The less scarce C. oppositifolium, which favours slightly more acidic soil, is with it. No FlBe records in our area. In GB it is mainly in the N and W, often with alkaline water and bryophytes. HJK

⬇ *Umbilicus rupestris*
Native

Wall Pennywort
Scarce in Oxon and vc23

(Peter Creed)

This is a perennial, growing on walls, rocks and on acid substrates. It is at the eastern edge of its range in GB. Nationally it is stable in the SW but declined further east, where the mean January temperature dips below 5°C. It was noted in 11 FlOx tetrads. On the Corallian walls in vc22 there are sites where it has remained for several years. Bowen 1968 had only two extant sites, but only in Dry Sandford is it still found. He describes the species as decreasing. In vc22 it does seem to be declining, with only three recent finds. Erskine found a new site in Little Coxwell in 2002. It disappeared after moss clearance, but re-appeared in 2010 and is still present 2016. SEE

23	W	Finstock		SP361166	2011	HJK	13 small
22	V	Little Coxwell Church roof		SU281935	2010	SEE	First seen 2002, new
23	S	Cuddesdon		SP601030	2009	RH-B	South-facing roadside wall
23	S	Great Haseley Church		SP644017	2007	HJK	About 20
22	V	Dry Sandford		SP467003	2006	JE	Church farm house
22	V	Hinton Waldrist		SU375991	2006	SEE	30 m along top of wall at the Grange
23	S	Culham Manor and Churchyard		SU501949	2006	HJK	Still present 2011
22	V	Littleworth		SU313971	1996	SEE	
22	V	Longworth Churchyard		SU384994	1996	SEE	
23	S	Dorchester Abbey		SU579943	1996	SJG	
22	V	Gozzards Ford		SU467987	1986	AIS	

➔ *Sedum telephium*

Orpine

An Ancient Woodland Indicator of neutral soils tolerating slightly raised nutrients. Now mostly on the Chilterns dip slope. Druce had 27 sites; in 32 FlOx tetrads and in 19 sites 2000–11 all in vc23. CRL

⬇ *Myriophyllum verticillatum*
Native

Whorled Water-milfoil
Near Threatened, Nationally Scarce ■ Scarce in Oxon, Rare in vc23

This submerged aquatic occurs in central, S and E England, but has suffered a big decline. It favours highly calcareous and nutrient-rich, still, or slow-moving, waters. Now absent from the Thames where it was common in Druce's time (26 localities). FlOx had 12 tetrads; it is now in five sites, none in rivers. CRL

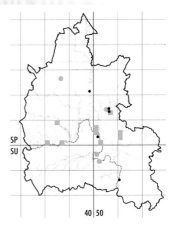

22	V	Kennington Pool	LWS	SP518033	2010	CRL+	New
22	S	Pond North of Cholsey Marsh		SU606862	2006	CRL+	New
23	C	RSPB Otmoor	pLWS, RSPB	SP564146	2004	RSPB	New
23	C	RSPB Otmoor	pLWS, RSPB	SP565134	2004	RSPB	New
23	W	Northbrook Marsh	LWS	SP484215	2001	CRL	New
23	S	Warren Farm Meadow		SU514963	1985	WS	
23	W	Heythrop Park		SP365265	1979	HJMB	Abs. 2008
23	C	Ray		SP554142	1978	FlOx	
22	V	Appleford Holt		SU524935	1976	FlBe	Pond **OXF**

SP
SU

40 50

⬇ *Myriophyllum alterniflorum*
Native

Alternate Water-milfoil
Last Oxon record 1978, in vc23 1970

This submerged aquatic is commonest in the N and W. It flourishes in base-poor water which would account for its loss here. Druce had no records. FlOx had three records by Richards in SP3408, 4202 and 5012 during 1969–70. It was in the River Cole in 1978 (FlBe). CRL

⬇ *Astragalus danicus*
Native

Purple Milk-vetch
s. 41, Endangered ■ **Rare in Oxon and vc23**

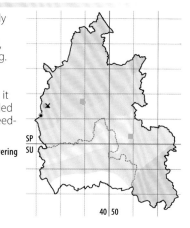

This low-growing perennial prefers lime and very low nitrates. It is curiously distributed, being coastal in the NE of the UK and inland on limestone and chalk in the south. Nationally it has declined greatly since before 1930, especially in the Cotswolds, probably due to ploughing and lack of grazing. It has always been rare in Oxon (four sites in Druce, five FlOx tetrads). The BBOWT reserve is grazed, and was monitored over many years including some of the years 2003–2010; in the best year, 2005, B Betteridge reported it in 92 1 m square quadrats. The roadside LWS, though monitored and tended by the WFG, has become too rank, however there is some evidence the seed-bank is long-lived (BSBI website). FlBe: extinct. CRL

23	W	Westwell Gorse	SSSI, BBOWT	SP219113	2008	HJK	Approx 50, 14 flowering
23	W	*Taynton Down verge*		*SP248149*	*2002*	*HJK 2007*	
23	W	Taynton Quarries	SSSI	SP236151	1997	HJK	
23	W	*Stockey Plantation & Meadows*		*SP398169*	*1979*	*JMC*	*Coniferised*
23	W	Stonesfield		SP394166		BBOWT	
23	S	Garsington		SP599035			

➡ *Onobrychis viciifolia*
Native and Alien

Sainfoin
Vulnerable ■ **Not Scarce in Oxon and vc23**

(Peter Creed)

This is a small to medium perennial, decumbent to erect, which grows on old unimproved calcareous grassland. It was used as a fodder crop and is now extensively found in seed mixes used on road verges, embankments and cuttings. Its natural distribution is therefore obscured, but native plants are usually smaller than those used for fodder or derived from them. It is assumed to be native in old grassland such as found in the Chilterns, Wessex Downs and in North Oxfordshire. There are many records from these areas, the majority of those mapped here are probably native. SEE

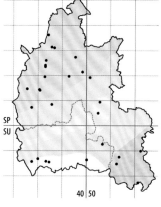

⬇ *Lotus tenuis* (*L. glaber*)
Native

Narrow-leaved Bird's-foot-trefoil
Scarce in Oxon and vc23

L. tenuis is a spreading perennial herb found inland in rough grassland, pits and road verges on various soils, most often clay. In FlOx (p. 166) it is very scattered, often in small numbers, in 18 tetrads; in FlBe local and rather rare with 12 old records. The new records are fewer and mostly elsewhere. It has been sown in ground affected by past quarrying (Stratton Audley) and has appeared on tipped fly-ash (Radley Lakes) and set-aside; it can be a casual. In GB it has stable populations on coastal grazing land, but has declined inland. HJK

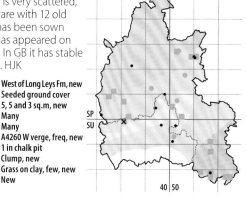

22	V	Cumnor		SP443045	2010	HJK	West of Long Leys Fm, new
23	C	Stratton Audley Quarry	SSSI, LWS	SP601251	2009	BC	Seeded ground cover
22	V	Radley Gravel Pits	LWS	SU526975	2009	HJK	5, 5 and 3 sq.m, new
23	C	Stratton Audley Quarry	LWS	SP605246	2008	PEC+	Many
23	W	Spelsbury		SP343213	2006	anon	Many
23	O	Near Kidlington		SP4810	2006	JE	A4260 W verge, freq, new
23	S	Gutteridge Wood	LWS	SU669792	2006	JHW	1 in chalk pit
22	V	Confidential		SU49T	2004	HJK	Clump, new
22	S	Didcot Power Station		SU513912	2004	SEE+	Grass on clay, few, new
23	W	Old Gravel Pit near Little Faringdon	LWS	SP219017	2002	CRL	New
23	O	Milhamford Field and Quad	LWS	SP531074	1999	JAW	

➡ *Ornithopus perpusillus*
Native

Bird's-foot
Not Scarce in Oxon, Scarce in vc23

This is a prostrate annual, with stems that can grow to 40 cm. It thrives on dry, nutrient-poor sandy soils. Nationally it is a good coloniser of suitable sites and the population is stable. Its habitat preference is rare in the county, hence the species is scarce. Druce described it as local in areas of heath and sandy pastures, in warm sunny spots. It is still found in many of these areas today. SEE

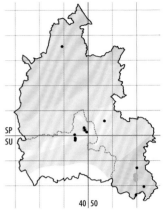

22	V	Jarn Field	OPT	SP486022	2010	CRL	Few
23	S	Caversham Heath Golf Course		SU696763	2010	JHW	40
23	S	Crowsley Park	LWS	SU729796	2010	JHW	4 patches
22	V	Confidential	SSSI	SU49P	2009	HJK	Few
22	V	Birch Copse set-aside	pLWS	SP4803	2008	CRL	100's
23	C	Tadmarton Golf Course		SP392355	2007	HJK	3 sites
22	V	Confidential	SSSI	SU49P	2007	SEE	5 patches
22	V	Confidential	SSSI	SU49P	2007	SEE	Frequent
23	S	Nettlebed Common Cricket Ground		SU7087	2007	JHW	7 patches
22	V	Tubney Woods	LWS	SP445001	2005	FHW	
22	V	Lincombe Lane Field	LWS, OPT	SP494014	2005	IC	
23	S	Brasenose Wood and Shotover Hill	SSSI, LGS	SP567058	2005	HJK	
23	S	Witheridge Hill		SU695840	1995	RdA	
23	S	Kingwood Common	LWS	SU696825	1995	RdA	
22	V	Matthew Arnold Field	OPT	SP485024	1985	HJMB	

⬇ *Hippocrepis comosa*

Horseshoe Vetch

This lime-rich grassland plant has declined in GB and here, with its habitat. However, with 28 2000–11 records in Oxon (15 in vc23) it is Not Scarce. HJK

⬇ *Vicia sylvatica*
Native

Wood Vetch
Last Oxon and vc23 record 1988

Wood Vetch is a climbing or scrambling plant of woods, wood margins and clearings. Before 1989 FlOx (p. 168) had 15 records in vc23; vc22 (Oxon) had three; some of these were re-visited without success. The decline may reflect the cessation of coppicing; Dunn found it after conifer clearance in 1988; in Wiltshire Grose (1957) reported it 'sometimes abundant in newly coppiced woods'. Its survival thus depends on seed viability and renewed coppicing. In GB Wood Vetch has much declined. HJK

23	W	Standridge & Wisdom's Copses		SP316126	1988	Doom+	
23	W	Ditchley Estate		SP381219	1988	AJD	Not seen AJD 2007
23	S	Greenfield and College Woods		SU719910	1988	VP+	
22	V	Whitley Copse		SP440046	1985	HS+	Abs. HJK
23	C	Ardley Cutting and Quarry	SSSI, LGS, BBOWT	SP538273	1984	JMC	Abs. 2011 HJK

⬇ *Vicia parviflora*
Native

Slender Tare
Vulnerable, Nationally Scarce ■ **Rare in Oxon and vc23**

This delicate annual is restricted to the S and E of England and has suffered a huge decline. FlOx (p. 168) says it is introduced in Oxon, but Atlas 2002 has it as mostly native. It prefers woodland rides, dry grassland and arable on winter wet clays. On Wytham it was recorded by C Gibson on Upper Seeds and is monitored annually by the OFG in The Triangle – an area of well-drained former arable which is ploughed annually to maintain populations of arable weeds especially *Fumaria muralis, Euphorbia exigua, Ranunculus parviflorus, Chaenorhinum minus* and *Kickxia* spp. In 2012 it was abundant with many seedpods ripening. This is also an introduction site for *Galium tricornutum*. Spring ploughing was tried in 2009, but proved unsuitable for this suite of species. Druce had seven sites, FlOx three, and FlBe three. CRL

23	W	Stonehenge Farm (Field 5)		SP406019	2005	CRPG
22	V	Wytham Woods	SSSI	SP462080	2005	AWM

➡ *Vicia sativa* ssp. *nigra*
Native

Common (or Narrow-leaved) Vetch
Scarce in Oxon, Rare in vc23

Nearly all Oxon's *Vicia sativa* is ssp. *segetalis*. However a few are ssp. *nigra* with small flowers with petals all dark, narrow leaflets especially near the top of the plant, and small (3 cm) hispid pods; this small annual favours rather bare ground usually on sandy soils. Because Clapham *et al.* (1962) did not separate this from ssp. *segetalis*, some older records are ambiguous, but it is now better recorded here. It was in only five tetrads (FIOx p. 169) but widespread in many other counties in GB including vc22 (Oxon); FIBe called it "widespread in the north" of West Berks. It has colonised set-aside fields from the margins where the grass is not too dense. HJK

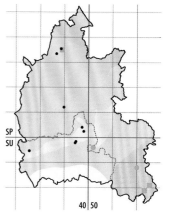

22	V	Boars Hill		SP481025	2011	HJK	Field corner
23	C	Hook Norton		SP367334	2010	HJK	By path and quarry, new
23	W	Eynsham Park		SP398121	2009	HJK	3 sites, new
22	V	Hurst Hill	SSSI	SP474041	2009	HJK	Hill top
22	V	Confidential		SU49P	2009	HJK	20
23	C	Tadmarton Heath		SP386354	2008	HJK	Golf course
22	V	Coxwell Wood	LWS	SU256946	2008	HJK	10
22	V	Confidential		SU49N	2008	HJK	Few
22	V	Confidential		SU49U	2006	HJK	West of field
23	S	Warburg	SSSI, BBOWT	SU7088	1996	HJK	
23	S	N of Culham Laboratory		SU5296	1991	HJK	

⬇ *Vicia sativa* ssp. *sativa*
Archaeophyte

Common Vetch
Rare in Oxon and vc23

Nearly all Oxon's *Vicia sativa* is ssp. *segetalis* but a very few are ssp. *sativa*, formerly a common fodder crop. This declined sharply when farm horses were replaced by tractors (Killick 1975; FIOx.) It is a robust annual with large bi-coloured flowers, big broad leaflets and broad brown (not black) pods with big seeds which give them a bumpy outline. It was in two tetrads in 1968 (SU7294-96) but is now rare in Oxon and, Killick believes, much over-recorded elsewhere. It is (August 2015) at City Farm SP4311. HJK

23	C	Kirtlington Park Lake (south)	LWS	SP513191	2010	HJK	Frequent, field verge by lake, new
23	S	Collins End		SU657788	2007	HJK	Many, sown, new

➡ *Vicia lathyroides*
Native

Spring Vetch
Scarce in Oxon, last vc23 record 1984

(John Killick)

This early-flowering annual is told from *V. sativa* ssp. *nigra* with which it can grow, by small size, small lilac 6–9 mm flowers, lack of tendrils and tuberculate seeds. In Oxon, it is on dry infertile sandy or gravelly soils. Recently to the NE of Frilford in three set-aside fields where small numbers have been seen most years since 1997 except in years after wet weather which had favoured competing grasses; also in three other locations. Before 1991, was in FIBe and four FIOx tetrads. In GB it is mostly on coastal sand dunes; despite better recording recently it has decreased and many inland hectad records near here are pre-1970. HJK

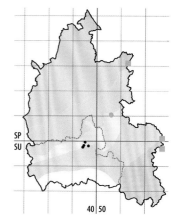

22	V	Confidential		SU49P	2008	HJK	Very few
22	V	Confidential		SU49U	2008	HJK	Very few
22	V	Hitchcopse Pit	SSSI, BBOWT	SU452996	2007	SEE	2
22	V	Confidential	SSSI	SU49N	2006	SEE	Few
23	S	Stow Wood		SP560104	1984	DTS	Was in Druce

Vicia lutea
Native, Casual inland
Yellow-vetch
Vulnerable, Nationally Scarce ■ **Last record in Oxon in 1965–71, in vc23 in 1927**

This annual is a coastal plant and a casual inland. Druce had it twice in Oxford as a casual, FlOx had Sonning, in error. FlBe had it in Kingston Bagpuize 1965–71. CRL

⬇ *Lathyrus linifolius*
Native
Bitter-vetch
Near Threatened ■ **Seemingly Rare in Oxon and vc23**

(Rod d'Ayala)

Bitter-vetch is a perennial herb of moist, rather acid, infertile open woods, wood edges, unimproved grassland and banks. FlOx (p. 169) had 11 tetrads, five in the Chilterns. Few were re-found but new colonies were seen. Five sites N of Oxford were not re-visited. At a steep, sandy woodland site in the Chilterns it benefited from the light after tree clearance. FlBe has no relevant records. In GB it is widespread but has declined in E England and the Midlands with loss of the grassland habitat. HJK, CRL, JHW

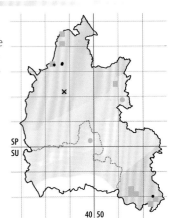

23	C	Cradle and Grounds Farm Banks	LWS	SP369329	2009	SG	Other sites near, new
23	S	Crowsley Estate		SU739801	2006	JHW	New
23	C	Berryfields Farm	LWS	SP337327	2004	PS	
23	W	Ditchley Estate		SP378218	1985	AJD	Not in 2007
22	V	Matthew Arnold Field	OPT	SP485024	1985	HJMB+	Abs. CRL 2010
23	Be	Clayfield Copse	LNR	SU726773	1982	HHC	

⬇ *Lathyrus sylvestris*
Narrow-leaved Everlasting-pea
This Pea, in 34 FlOx tetrads (p. 170), was seen in 20 2000–10 sites in Oxon (16 in vc23) so is Not Scarce. HJK

➡ *Lathyrus nissolia*
Grass Vetchling
With 23 2000–11 records in Oxon (16 in vc23) this slender annual is Not Scarce in Oxon. Unless it is in flower it is very easily overlooked, so may be under recorded. It tolerates high nitrates and is increasing in GB. SEE

⬇ *Lathyrus aphaca*
Archaeophyte
Yellow Vetchling
Vulnerable, Nationally Scarce ■ **Last record in Oxon and vc23 1988**

(Peter Sheasby)

This distinctive annual is often an arable introduction but may be native on dry calcareous banks in central England. It has suffered a huge decline nationally. With us it is probably a casual; in three tetrads in FlOx p. 170 (Foxhole Bottom, Heythrop and Eynsham) and pre-1966 in FlBe. CRL

⬇ *Ononis spinosa*
Native

Spiny Restharrow
Near Threatened ■ Not Scarce in Oxon, Scarce in vc23

A small spiny woody plant, this species favours infertile calcareous grassland. *O. spinosa* has hairs on one side (occasionally on opposite sides) of the main stem, whereas in *O. repens* the stems are equally hairy all over. Its decline nationally and in the county is probably due to agricultural improvements. It is found mainly in protected areas and on old agricultural land. Its stronghold is along the Ridgeway (mainly vc22), from where there are many records, some waiting to be re-found. The site at Oday Hill verge was re-found by Killick in 2013. There has been a sharp decline in vc23 from 40 localities in FlOx to nine 2000–11 records. Druce's records are somewhat problematical in that there was a marked increase between 1886 and 1927, possibly due to the inclusion of some very spiny variants of *O. repens*. SEE

23	C	Frieze Way, Kidlington		SP492111	2010	JAW	Several patches
22	V	Aston Upthorpe Downs (non SSSI)		SU536825	2010	RH-B	5 m patch
22	V	Raleigh Park	LWS	SP492053	2009	RH-B	7 clumps
23	O	Cuttleslowe recreation field		SP512104	2009	JAW	100s
23	O	Barracks Lane		SP539050	2009	JAW	50+
22	V	Ridgeway nr Segsbury		SU379841	2009	HJK	Plentiful
22	S	Little Wittenham	SAC, SSSI	SU567932	2009	RH-B	Several
23	C	Woodsides Meadow	SSSI, BBOWT	SP556178	2008	JAW	Numerous
23	W	Taynton Quarries	SSSI	SP234147	2007	HJK	
22	V	N end of grassy field		SP481019	2007	HJK	A few
22	V	Ridgeway S of Whitehorse Hill		SU297861	2007	HJK	A few
22	V	Whitehorse Hill	SSSI	SU298865	2007	HJK	Plentiful
23	S	Otmoor		SP572124	2006	JE	
22	V	Abbey Fishponds	LNR, LWS	SU513979	2004	HJK	Abs. 2006
22	V	Odstone Coombes	LWS	SU274853	2003	CRL	
22	V	Churn Ecological area		SU312826	2002	CRL	
22	V	Blewbury, Lower Chance Farm		SU523823	2002	CRL	2 sites
23	W	West of Abel Wood	LWS	SP404147	2001	CRL	
23	S	Upper Park Farm		SP572114	2001	CRL	
23	S	Bus Station Playing Field		SP538051	2000	CRL	
23	C	*Buckingham Road field*		*SP591243*	*1999*	*GH*	
22	V	*Pigtrough Bottom*	*LWS*	*SU346855*	*1986*	*EC*	*Abs. SEE 2009*
22	V	*Cherbury Camp*	*LWS*	*SU374963*	*1986*	*EC*	*Abs. SEE 2006*

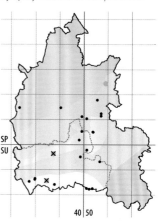

⬇ *Medicago sativa ssp. falcata*
Introduced in Oxon

Sickle Medick
Nationally Scarce ■ Rare in Oxon, last vc23 record 2002

Sickle Medick, a perennial in waste and grassy places on gravels since 1820, was always rare; in Headington, Cowley and Iffley long ago, at South Hinksey (FlBe) in 1965 and tetrads SP4418, SP5226 before 1977, SU7482 in 1991 and SU7498. Bowen's 1977 Marston record may be that below. In GB it is native on grassy heaths and roadsides on sandy and lime-rich soils in East Anglia and a scattered introduction elsewhere. It has declined with loss of habitat and is intolerant of grazing. Its hybrid with ssp. *sativa*, ssp. × *varia*, Sand Lucerne, has not been seen since FlOx records from Sydlings Copse (SP553093, 1978 Fitter), Ewelme (SU6688, 1972) and Goring (1964). HJK

23	*O*	*Marston T-jct N of A40*	*SP533089*	*2002*	*HJK*	*Several, not seen 2006 and 2009*

Medicago minima
Seaside native

Bur Medick
Vulnerable ■ Last Oxon and vc23 record 1963–4

This small annual, a casual here, was seen by Simmonds at Drayton St Leonard (SU5896) in 1963–4 but not since. HJK

⬇ *Medicago polymorpha*
Native in coastal areas

Toothed Medick
Rare in Oxon, Last vc23 record 1978

The stipules of *M. polymorpha* are deeply incised, not entire or denticulate, and the wings are longer than the keel. Introduced in Oxfordshire, this small annual is found in dry sandy or gravelly habitats. It has experienced a decline in both its native and introduced locations. In Druce 1927 it was a rare casual found at Botley (1888) and by the railway at Didcot. For FlOx, Simmonds recorded it at Drayton St Leonard in 1963/4 (**RDG**) and Loukes at Witney in 1978; also Hook Norton (SP3632). SEE

22	S	Didcot Power Station, by gatehouse	SU513912	2004	SEE
22	V	Verge, West Way, Botley	SU484061	2004	FHW

⬇ *Trifolium fragiferum* Strawberry Clover
Native Vulnerable ■ Not Scarce in Oxon and vc23

This clover, of damp meadows on heavy soils, has declined in GB and here through loss of old pastures. It was in 50 FlOx tetrads, but with 26 2000–11 records in Oxon (17 in vc23) it is not yet Scarce. It is scattered in England and S Scotland. HJK, SEE

(Peter Creed)

⬇ *Trifolium striatum* Knotted Clover
Native Scarce in Oxon, Rare in vc23

This and *T. scabrum* are small annual clovers which grow in dry sandy soils, in unimproved grassland. They are very similar but *T. striatum* has pink not white flowers and the lateral veins on the leaflets are straight, not thickened and recurved. It has declined nationally and locally due to the abandonment of poor quality pasture land, which has then scrubbed over or been otherwise developed. Six sites have been recorded in the Frilford Heath complex where it is found in good numbers. However it is much scarcer in vc23. Cole found a large patch on the old football ground at Headington, since lost. It re-appeared at Buckland Warren in 2014, otherwise the most recent finds have been on Nettlebed Common and Kingwood Common.
Described as rare and local in Druce and Bowen 1968; FlOx had 19 tetrad records. SEE

(Peter Creed)

22	V	Hitchcopse Pit	SSSI, BBOWT	SU4599	2010	HJK	Scattered
22	V	Confidential	SSSI	SU49P	2009	SEE	Frequent
22	V	Dry Sandford Pit	SSSI, BBOWT	SU468995	2009	HJK	Few
23	C	Tadmarton Heath		SP398354	2007	HJK	
23	O	Old football ground, Headington		SP554072	2007	EAC	Site now built on
22	V	Abingdon		SU485970	2007	HJK	
23	C	South Newington Meadow	LWS	SP417328	2006	CRL	
22	V	Lincombe Lane Field	LWS, OPT	SP493013	2006	SEE	Frequent
22	V	Buckland Warren	SSSI	SU334963	2009	SEE	8
23	S	Dyke Hills	LWS	SU576936	2006	HJK	
23	S	Kingwood Common	LWS	SU696825	1995	RdA	
23	S	Nettlebed Common	LWS	SU705871	1995	RdA	
23	S	Brasenose Wood and Shotover Hill	SSSI, LGS	SP567057	1981	DTS	

SP
SU
× 40 50

➡ *Trifolium scabrum* Rough Clover
Native Rare in Oxon, last vc23 record 1993

This and *T. striatum* are very similar small annual clovers. *T. scabrum* can be distinguished by its white, not pink, flowers and the lateral veins on the leaflet are thickened and recurved. It requires nutrient-poor dry, sandy soils, and is now almost confined to coastal locations especially in S and E England. Formerly found on suitable inland sites it has declined greatly here, and in Oxon is now found only in the Frilford area, where it is quite widespread (it increased in 2015). The species is particular in its habitat requirements and is susceptible to small changes; where it grows with *T. striatum* and habitat changes take place, *T. scabrum* disappears first. It was described as rare by Druce 1886, Bowen 1968 and in FlOx and FlBe. Found most recently in vc23 (FlOx) by J M Campbell at Lower Windrush in 1993 and by Palmer at N. Newington in 1992 and Dyke Hills in 1985. SEE

22	V	Confidential		SU49P	2007	HJK	
22	V	Confidential	SSSI	SU49N	2005	SEE+	2 plants, not found 2006
22	V	Hills sandpit, Tubney		SP450006	1995	JMC	
23	W	Downs Rd Settlement field		SP386047	1993	JMC	

⬇ *Trifolium arvense*
Native

(Peter Creed)

This perennial is widespread in England and coastal in the W. It grows in neutral grasslands with very low nutrients. Now mostly on the light soils of the Corallian Ridge, formerly more widespread – Druce recorded it in 23 sites, FlOx (p. 173) in 36 tetrads (not tabulated) and FlBe in 12 in our area. We had 15 sites, five of them in vc23. CRL

23	S	Caversham Heath Golf Course		SU692757	2010	JHW	50
23	Be	Caversham Heath Golf Course		SU696763	2010	JHW	With *Ornith per*
23	C	turning off Langford Lane		SP479149	2009	JAW	Lots (verge)
22	V	Confidential		SU49N	2008	HJK	Many in north field
22	V	Confidential		SU49P	2008	HJK	Frequent
22	V	Confidential		SU49U	2008	HJK	Few in north field
23	0	Southfield Golf Course, Oxford		SP543053	2007	MF	
22	V	Tubney Woods	LWS	SP444003	2005	FHW+	
22	V	Confidential	SSSI	SU49J	2005	RPG	Rare
22	V	Carswell Golf Course		SU332964	2004	JMC	
22	V	Tubney Woods	LWS	SU445995	2004	JMC	
23	S	Wells Farm	BBOWT	SP620009	2003	BBOWT	1
22	V	Sita pit, Hatford		SU333954	2003	JMC	
22	V	Besselsleigh		SP460023	2001	JMC	
23	S	Barton		SP560090	1983	RH-B	Roadside verge

⬇ *Trifolium subterraneum*
Native

(John Killick)

This clover is a winter annual forming early-flowering procumbent patches in short, sometimes close mown, turf on infertile rather acid sandy or gravelly soil. In vc23 it was at Shotover and Stow Wood until 1907; in vc22 (Oxon) formerly at Grove and Tubney but not since. Near Frilford, few, scattered at or near the margins of set-aside (Campbell and Killick) from 1998–2012 except 1999 and (after 2003's dry late summer) in 2004; one of the small clumps was found most years, with additional ones more widespread in good years; the absence in 2004 parallels FlBe's Silwood Park populations. Two records are new. In GB it is mostly by the S and SE coasts, with few post-1970 inland records. HJK

22	V	Confidential	SU49P	2010	HJK+	New, 1998–2012, 1 sq.m
22	V	Confidential	SU49U	2009	HJK	New, 2006–9, 1 sq.m, not 2010–12

 *Genista tinctoria*
Native

Dyer's Greenweed
Vulnerable ■ Not Scarce in Oxon, Scarce in vc23

(Rod d'Ayala)

This small leguminous shrub was used in dyeing from Viking times till the early 19th Century. It is characteristic of old meadows and rough pastures and is widely distributed in England and Wales, but has declined considerably, probably through habitat loss and eutrophication. It grows on calcareous, neutral to slightly acidic, heavy soils with very low nutrients. It has declined since Druce had 19 sites and FlOx 18 tetrads; in Oxon half the sites are in hay meadows in the Ray catchment, and the others scattered on the chalk and Corallian (cf *Serratula tinctoria*); one locality has been lost to competition, and some populations are very small or appear to be declining as at Burnt Platt. CRL

23	C	Arncott Bridge Meadows	SSSI		SP608185	2011	JAW	
23	C	Wendlebury Meads and Mansmoor Closes	SSSI		SP562172	2009	HJK	
23	S	Holly Hill (Elmore Park Grassland)	LWS		SU630814	2009	JHW	Lots
23	S	Burnt Platt			SU694833	2009	JHW	6
23	W	Shilton Bradwell Grove Airfield	LWS		SP244068	2008	MMC+	New
23	W	Shilton Bradwell Grove Airfield	LWS		SP245073	2008	MMC+	New
23	C	Woodsides Meadow	SSSI, BBOWT		SP556178	2008	JAW	10
23	S	Otmoor	SSSI		SP572127	2008	CRL+	3 fields
23	C	Asham Meads	SSSI, BBOWT		SP593140	2008	CRL	1
22	V	Parsonage Moor	SAC, SSSI, BBOWT		SU459999	2008	HJK	1
23	S	Reading, Play Hatch quarry			SU744759	2000	JHW	Edge of quarry
23	*S*	*Menmarsh Moat*			*SP592111*	*1985*	*HJMB*	
23	*C*	*Horley*	*LWS*		*SP410430*	*1980*	*AN*	
23	*W*	*Bladon Heath*	*LWS*		*SP455138*	*1978*	*SVH*	
23	*C*	*The Slade, Bloxham*			*SP425355*	*1977*	*SRJW*	*Abs. HJK 2010*

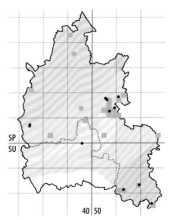

Genista anglica
Native

Petty Whin
Vulnerable ■ Last Oxon record before 2000, last vc23 record 1884

Petty Whin is a small shrub of heathy places and bogs. It was last seen in vc23 at Hardwick Heath in 1884. It has substantially declined in England and is one of the first to disappear owing to cultivation. A FlBe record from "Cothill, [40]" and in SP40 for 1987–1999 in Atlas 2002 could have been *G. tinctoria*. HJK, CRL.

Ulex   Gorses

Ulex minor and *U. gallii* flower in late summer and the fruits mature the next spring. They differ from the common Gorse in small size and their bracteoles (leafy bits at the base of the flower stalk) <1.5 × 1 mm rather than 1.8–4.5 × 1.5–4 mm. *Ulex minor* has smaller flowers – calyx 6.5–9.5 mm rather than 9–13.5 in *U. gallii*; diverging calyx teeth and wing petals straight and shorter than the keels rather than curved and longer than the keels. In *U. minor* the pod is c. 7 mm long; and in *U. gallii* it is c. 10 mm. Both grow on dry heaths with Heather and Gorse, and flourish with extremely low nutrients. Oxon is at the E edge of the range of the Western Gorse and the W limit of the Dwarf Gorse. Hybrids occur. CRL

⇨ *Ulex gallii*   Western Gorse
Native   Rare in Oxon and vc23

The Western Gorse is abundant in Wales and the W of England, and in Norfolk. It flourishes on somewhat acidic and very infertile soils. Druce had the same sites in the NW of the county where it is still just hanging on, as well as Cogges and Woodcote. CRL

23	C	Tadmarton Heath Golf Course		SP385354	2007	HJK	1 new
23	C	Tadmarton Heath Golf Course		SP393353	2007	HJK	1 new
23	W	North Leigh Common	LWS	SP401135	2006	JE	1 old
23	W	Cogges Wood	LWS	SP380110	1985	JMC	

⇨ *Ulex minor*   Dwarf Gorse
Native   Rare in Oxon and vc23

(Peter Creed)

This species is restricted to East Dorset eastwards to Surrey and northwards to Herts. It needs extremely acidic soils. With us it is on the plateau gravels of the Chilterns. Druce had *U. minor* in three sites in the NW of the county as well as two sites in the Chilterns – Peppard and Binfield. CRL

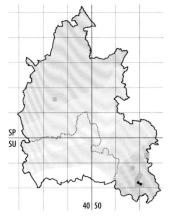

23	S	Peppard Common	LWS	SU704815	2007	JHW	51 x 44 m
23	S	Kingwood Common	LWS	SU694821	2006	JHW	5
23	S	Witheridge Hill		SU695840	1995	RdA	
23	S	Highmoor and Lower Common Wood	LWS	SU702850	1995	RdA	
23	S	Nuffield Common	LWS	SU671879	1990	Doom	

SP
SU

40 50

⬇ *Polygala serpyllifolia*   Heath Milkwort
Native   Near Threatened ■ Scarce in Oxon and vc23

This is a small perennial of acidic, low-nutrient grasslands, moors and heaths. It differs from the commoner *P. vulgaris* in smaller main flower-clusters (<10) and opposite leaves or leaf-scars at the stem base. It is widespread in GB except central S England where it has declined substantially. It struggles when the sward is too tall. Druce had five sites including Shotover, FlOx (p. 182) had 12 tetrads and FlBe only at Bagley Wood. It benefitted from a species recovery programme by Shotover Wildlife. CRL

22	V	Parsonage Moor	SAC, SSSI, BBOWT	SU460998	2010	JAW+	10 new
23	W	North Leigh Common	LWS	SP401136	2009	HJK	>20
23	S	Kingwood Common	LWS	SU697826	2007	JHW	Lots
23	S	Brasenose Wood and Shotover Hill	SSSI	SP561060	2006	ShW	
23	W	Cogges Wood	LWS	SP383110	2005	RdA	
23	S	Maidensgrove Common		SU723890	1995	RdA	
22	V	Confidential	SSSI	SU49P	1986	SW	

Polygala calcarea
Native

Chalk Milkwort
Not Scarce in Oxon, Scarce in vc23

(Peter Creed)

Superficially similar to the blue forms of *P. vulgaris*, *P. calcarea* has a leafless portion of woody stem below the basal rosette and the lower leaves are larger than the upper ones. Also the veins on the inner sepals are not anastomising, (veins joining near the edge to form a loop). This species is confined to S England on low-nutrient chalk grassland, so has always been very local in Oxon. It seems stable in the county though declining elsewhere due to habitat change. Its strongholds remain in the Chilterns and along the Wessex Downs, especially in the White Horse Hill and Hackpen Hill areas where it is seen annually, the latest in 2015. SEE

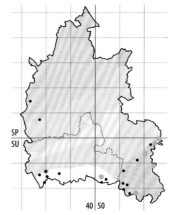

22	V	Hackpen Downs	SSSI	SU354858	2011	SEE
23	S	Holly Hill (Elmore Park Grassland)	LWS	SU631813	2011	JK
23	S	Hartslock	SAC, SSSI, BBOWT	SU617794	2008	HJK
23	W	Taynton Quarries	SSSI	SP235147	2007	HJK
22	S	Aston Upthorpe Downs	SSSI	SU545835	2007	SR
22	V	Kingstone Warren Down (north)	LWS	SU305846	2004	SEE
23	S	Fiddle Hill	LWS	SU614819	2004	JMC
22	V	Odstone Coombes	LWS	SU274853	2003	CRL
22	V	Blewbury Hill	LWS	SU527823	2002	CRL
23	S	Aston Rowant	SAC, NNR, SSSI	SU729973	2002	JMC
23	W	Carterton Grassland	LWS	SP274073	2000	SEE
22	V	Weathercock Down		SU294823	2000	NT
23	S	Mongewell		SU616860	2000	JMC
23	S	The Basin and Bozedown Park	LWS	SU641778	2000	CRL
23	S	Swyncombe Downs	SSSI	SU672912	2000	CRL
22	V	Whitehorse Hill	SSSI	SU300867	1997	SG
23	V	Westford Hill Copse	LWS	SU666779	1997	JMC
23	S	Stonor Park (south west)	LWS	SU739888	1992	NCC
23	S	Kingston Grove		SU744978	1992	NCC
23	S	Oakley Hill	LWS, BBOWT	SU761996	1992	NCC
22	V	Churn		SU525845	1991	SG
23	S	Watlington and Pyrton Hills	SSSI	SU703937	1991	NCC

SP
SU

40 | 50

Prunus cerasus
Archaeophyte

Dwarf Cherry
Near Threatened ■ ?Scarce in Oxon, ?Rare in vc23

P. cerasus is a small tree of hedges, copses and wood borders and also a crop. Told from but often confused with, the common *P. avium* by size (<7 m), by the green leaf-like bud scales beneath the flowers, and by smaller glossier leaves (firm when young) lacking two red glands at the base. Its receptacles are hardly constricted at the top. "Prunu cer" on the FlOx recording cards may have attracted many records belonging to the common *P. cerasifera*. Therefore Killick doubted many of the 113 tetrad records (FlOx p.162), almost none have been re-found; Druce had found it in Chiltern woods. FlBe more plausibly has only three, undated, records. In GB it is widespread but often confused with *P. avium* and has declined. HJK

23	S	Clayhill Wood, Burnt Platt & Threelandboard Wood		SU686835	2011	SR+	Few
23	0	Peasmoor Piece	SLINC	SP534082	2010	CL	Few
22	V	Coxwell Wood	LWS	SU258950	2002	SEE	

Pyrus pyraster
Archaeophyte

Wild Pear
?Scarce in Oxon, Rare in vc23

Only the fruits (hard, round and c. 25 mm rather than larger and pear-shaped) distinguish Wild Pear from the cultivated *P. communis*. FlOx, FlBe and Atlas 2002 combined them. Both may be sought in hedgerows. We have few recent records of the segregate, so are grateful to C A Spinage (2000) whose paper "Pear Trees in the Vale of White Horse" summarised their history there from AD 956 onwards. He has provided much of the following list. Druce's specimen (1915, **RDG**) is perhaps from Radley. Welsh believes "wild" pear may grow from stock of cultivated trees. HJK

22	V	Denchworth, Circourt Rd		SU337914	2013	CAS	1
22	V	Baulking, Old Field Meadow		SU344915	2013	CAS	1
22	V	W Hanney, by path		SU406925	2013	CAS	4
22	V	Road E Hanney – Steventon		SU441928	2013	CAS	1, also SU439930
23	C	Old LNER Railway		SP619336	2010	JK	Few, new
23	C	A41		SP561200	2009	RH-B	New, 1 old tree
23	C	Wigginton		SP389325	2007	HJK	1, new
23	S	Blackhouse Wood	LWS	SU729771	1997	HW	

➡ Sorbus torminalis

Wild Service-tree

This native is widespread in Wales and S of Lancashire, but rarely abundant, though it does form stands by suckering. FlOx had 39 tetrads and it was found in 34 localities 2000–11 so is Not Scarce. >100 localised in Ditchley by Dunn. CRL

⬇ Potentilla argentea
Native

Hoary Cinquefoil
Near Threatened ■ **Scarce in Oxon, last vc23 record 1995**

(Phil Cutt)

This is a small perennial growing on dry acid grassland, and copes well in short turf and longer grassy conditions. The species is commoner in SE England than elsewhere in GB, but nationally has suffered a big decline. This seems to be due to habitat destruction. It survives both in short mown/grazed grassland and in uncut verges, so there is always hope it will reappear at old sites as the seeds have a long life. The numbers of plants has always been very variable. SEE

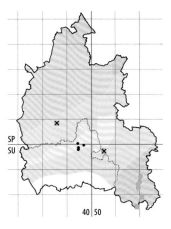

22	V	Dry Sandford Pit	SSSI, BBOWT	SU4699	2010	HJK	2
22	V	Confidential		SU49P	2009	HJK	
22	V	Confidential	SSSI	SU49P	2009	SEE	
23	S	Clifton Heath		SU552971	2007	HJK	1995 site not re-found
22	V	Tubney Woods	LWS	SP445001	2005	AWM+	
23	S	Kingwood Common	LWS	SU696825	1995	RdA	
23	S	Nettlebed Common	LWS	SU705871	1995	RdA	
23	W	Witney Lake and Meadows	Other	SP358083	1986	JHC	Abs. RPG 2009
23	S	Nuneham Park		SU549975	1985	Sev+	

⬇ *Potentilla anglica*   **Trailing Cinquefoil**
Native   **Scarce in Oxon and vc23**

(Peter Creed)

Potentilla anglica can be confused with *P.* × *mixta* (*P. anglica* × *P. reptans*). It is much less common than the hybrid. In *P. anglica* the petioles of the upper stem leaves are much shorter than those of the lower stem (1–2 cm). Both species have four, occasionally five petals, but the hybrid is infertile. *P. anglica* is a trailing perennial found on sandy/acidic soils, frequenting woodland edges and rides. It is commonest in W and SW England and Ireland, where it is increasing, but losses have occurred in the S and E, including Oxon, probably due to habitat destruction. In FlOx it is listed as uncommon, probably as this type of soil is uncommon; it is scarce and declining. SEE

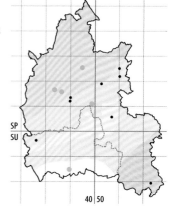

23	C	Weston on the Green		SP527190	2010	HJK	Few
23	C	Stratton Audley Quarry	SSSI, LWS	SP601251	2009	RWHS	
23	W	Eynsham Park		SP398121	2008	HJK	
23	S	Brasenose Wood and Shotover Hill	SSSI, LGS	SP570058	2008	HJK	
23	W	North Leigh Common	LWS	SP400135	2007	WOR	
23	S	Crowsley Park	LWS	SU731794	2007	JHW	
22	V	Badbury Forest – Eaton Wood	LWS	SU262964	2006	SEE	Several on main E–W ride
23	C	Gavray Drive Meadows	LWS	SP602219	2002	CRL	
23	W	Ramsden Hill		SP343303	1995	HJK	
23	C	Loop Farm Flood Meadows	LWS	SP487110	1987	GH	
23	W	Wychwood	NNR, SSSI	SP335165	1986	HJMB	

➡ *Comarum palustre* (*Potentilla palustris*)   **Marsh Cinquefoil**
This attractive plant of marshes is often grown as an ornamental. It is mostly found in the N and W and is not native in our area. It grows in the pond at Nuneham Courtenay Arboretum SU553986, introduced from the Lake District by K J Burras. CRL

⬇ *Geum rivale*   **Water avens**
Native   **Scarce in Oxon and vc23**

(Peter Creed)

A rhizomatous perennial found in a wide variety of damp habitats: marshes, meadows and open woodland. It is most frequent in Scotland, Wales, N England, East Anglia and the New Forest. There has been a big decline nationally, but notably in SE England. It has a few localities in vc23. It was most recently found at Worcester Hill, where there were seven good plants. Despite many recent visits it has not been seen since the 1990s at Sydlings copse, a former stronghold, or at the Wootton Millennium wood meadow since 1998. SEE

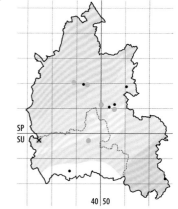

22	V	Letcombe Cressbeds	LWS	SU372851	2011	EL	Planted
23	S	River and Rowing Museum		SU766820	2010	SR	
23	W	Worcester Hill Bank and Marshes	LWS	SP428196	2009	CRL	7
23	C	Ambrosden		SP605187	2003	JMC	
23	S	Long Wood	LWS	SP535106	2001	CRL	
23	C	Noke Wood & Sling Copse	LWS	SP557116	2001	CRL+	
23	W	Wootton Jubilee Fields	LWS	SP443194	1998	JMC	
22	V	Taylor's Hill		SU248971	1998	SEE	Not re-found 2007
22	V	Marcham Park		SU449971	1995	HJK	Error
23	W	Ditchley Estate		SP387203	1990	AJD	
23	C	Cherwell Meadows		SP502114	1990	GH	
23	S	Sydlings Copse	SSSI, BBOWT	SP555096	1990	RL	

⬇ *Alchemilla filicaulis* ssp. *vestita*
Native

Hairy Lady's-mantle
Scarce in Oxon and vc23

Alchemilla filicaulis is our most frequent wild species. The densely hairy upper part of the stem, whole of the inflorescence and upper side of leaves distinguish it from other wild species. It is a short-lived perennial found in rough pasture and woodland borders throughout GB, but mainly in the N and W, where the numbers are stable. It is in the lowland areas of the S and E where the greatest decline has been experienced. There are still a few colonies scattered in Oxon especially in the woodland rides of large estates. At Ashdown House a change in the mowing regime of the broad ride resulted in an increase in area and number of plants recorded. In vc23 there were 40 sites in FlOx but only four sites have been recorded 2000–11; it may still be found at other sites. SEE

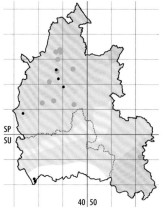

23	W	Leys Farm		SP372258	2010	HJK	2 sites
23	W	Kings and Wootton Woods	LWS	SP403190	2009	WOR	
22	V	Middle and Hailey Woods	LWS	SU280825	2008	SEE	Increasing on main ride
23	W	Cotswold Wildlife Park		SP237084	2007	SJH	New
23	W	Ditchley Estate Laurel Wood ride		SP382222	2007	AJD	8 sites
22	V	Upper Wood	LWS	SU286813	2006	SEE	Scattered over rides
23	W	Standridge & Wisdon's Copses		SP316126	1988	PJ	
23	S	Greenfield & College Wood		SU719910	1988	VP	
23	C	Cradle & Grounds Farm Banks	LWS	SP372230	1987	GH	
23	C	Ribbon Marsh	LWS	SP393330	1987	GH	
23	W	Middle Barton Fen	SSSI	SP442261	1987	GH	
23	W			SP446119	1987	HJMB	

⬇ *Aphanes australis*
Native

Slender Parsley-piert
Scarce in Oxon, Rare in vc23

This is a small sprawling annual species which differs from the much commoner *A. arvensis* in having weak, slender stems with long internodes and cuneate leaves. The sepals are curved inwards. It is found growing in acidic soils and rarely in arable conditions. Nationally this is widespread and appears to have a stable population. In Oxon the number of records has declined since publication of FlOx, maybe because of identification problems, or it is overlooked. SEE

23	S	Sydlings Copse	SSSI, BBOWT	SP555096	2011	HJK	>100 new
23	C	Tadmarton Golf Course		SP391354	2008	HJK	
22	V	Confidential	SSSI	SU49P	2007	SEE	Few plants
23	S	Crowsley Park	LWS	SU729795	2007	HJK	New
23	W	Cogges Wood	LWS	SP380110	1985	JMC	
23	S	Brasenose Wood and Shotover Hill	SSSI	SP565062	1981	DTS	
23	C	Broughton Park		SP416384	1977	PS	
23	O	Southfields Golf Course		SP5505	1977	RCP	

Rosa

Roses

The treatment in FlOx of native microspecies and hybrids of *Rosa* (here listed alphabetically) had benefited from confirmations by A L Primavesi. FlBe (p. 590) has identification and ecological notes. Our only 2000–11 records (only *R. obtusifolia* with expert confirmation) were:

Rosa rubiginosa

Sweet-briar

This small, apple-scented shrub grows in calcareous, low-nutrient grassland and is also planted. Druce had 34 sites, FlOx 40 tetrads, FlBe c. 11 records, and we recorded >40 in 2000–2004, so it is not Scarce.

Rosa obtusifolia

Round-leaved Dog-rose

23	W	Radcot Bridge	SU288996	2001	SEE	1

Rosa sherardii

Sherard's Downy-rose

23	S	Model Farm, Shirburn	SU6896	2001	DB	Introduced

Rosa tomentosa

Harsh Downy-rose

23	W	Ditchley, Kiddington side	SP390208	2007	AJD	1 small new

Frangula alnus
Native

Alder Buckthorn
Probably Scarce in Oxon and vc23

This small tree was planted for charcoal production and so its native distribution is blurred, but it seems to have declined nationally since 1962. It naturally grows in wet, peaty woods, which is a rare habitat that has suffered from drainage schemes. In several of its 2000–11 sightings it is thought to have been planted. It has never been common in Oxon, Druce 1927 described it as rare. FlOx also mentioned that it was rare, mainly in the N and W of the county, but there are only tetrad grid references for nine of its sites there. SEE

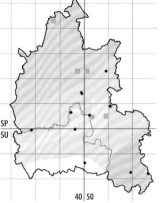

22	V	Chilton disused railway line	LWS	SU503864	2008	SP	
23	S	Henley		SU765821	2008	SR	
23	W	Radcot Bridge Farm		SU284995	2007	SEE	1 tree, planted?
23	C	Hampton Gay		SP4917	2005	HJK	Planted?
23	C	Kidlington Meadows Community Woodland		SP493153	2005	CRL	Planted?
22	V	Farmoor Reservoir	LWS	SP445065	2004	HJK	
23	S	Kingwood Common	LWS	SU693825	2004	VR	
23	C	Bicester		SP5923	2003	HJK	Planted?
22	V	Cothill Fen	SAC, SSSI	SU462998	2002	JMC	
23	O	Long Meadow	LWS	SP522054	2000	IC	
22	S	Little Wittenham		SU567935	1998	RCP	
23	O	Boundary Brook Nature Reserve	SLINC	SP533047	1991	OUWG	
23	S	Waterperry Wood	SSSI	SP607090	1980	HJK	Present 2008

Ulmus plotii
Native endemic microspecies

Plot's Elm
Last record in Oxon and vc23 1974

This distinctive slender tree has small, narrow leaves, and was first described at Hanwell near Banbury by Robert Plot in 1677. The narrow trees formerly lent a characteristic appearance to the landscape of N central England where it was most abundant, but it has declined. It is usually found in hedgerows on neutral to base-rich, deep soils along river valleys. At Hanwell it was both planted and "wild" but seems to have been lost, most likely to Dutch Elm disease, to which it is very susceptible. Palmer recorded it in 1974 on the E side of the Ray in hedge at bottom of first field below bridge SE of Astley Bridge Farm, Merton. DNA studies indicate that only material from one clone has all the characteristic features of the species, while morphologically similar plants are genetically dispersed in the *U. minor* group (Coleman *et al.* 2000). CRL

Parnassia palustris
Native

Grass-of-Parnassus
Vulnerable ■ Rare in Oxon and vc23

(Peter Sheasby)

This small perennial is widespread in the N and W. Oxon has an outlier at the S of its UK range, where populations differ in being diploid rather than tetraploid (Wentworth and Gornall, 1996). It is restricted to calcareous valley-head fens of the Corallian Ridge, where it requires short, unshaded sward. While "plentiful around Oxford" in the 17th Century, Druce listed 24 sites, but only two tetrads were recorded in FlOx. Parsonage Moor has the biggest population; flowering varies annually but the increase from 30 flowers in 2006 to 732 in 2010 may reflect the grazing introduced by BBOWT along with scrub control, reed cutting and new peat cutting. Eutrophication is however a threat – when maize was grown on adjacent land Water-cress flourished along the water-course; though spring-fed sites are often resilient due to phosphate being adsorbed by the tufa (Wheeler 2002). The other extant sites (where seedlings have been numerous) are mown. Spartum, Weston and Barrow Farm Fens are now ungrazed and often dry, dense and very shaded. CRL, JAW

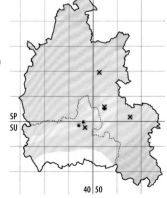

23	O	Lye Valley	SSSI	SP547052	2007	JAW	70 fls 4 m patch in SSSI, 6 fls outside
22	V	Confidential	SSSI	SU49P	2007	JAW	12 fl 4 m across 27 Aug
22	V	Parsonage Moor	SAC, SSSI, BBOWT	SU460999	2006	HJK	>30 fl or fr
23	O	Lye Valley	SSSI	SP547057	1990	EN	2007 JAW Not seen
23	S	Spartum Fen	SSSI	SP655017	1988	EN	2007 JAW Not seen
22	V	Barrow Farm Fen	SSSI	SU466975	1986	AIS	2009 NE Not seen
23	C	Weston Fen	SSSI	SP526194	1983	HJMB+	2007 JAW Not seen

Euphorbia platyphyllos
Archaeophyte

Broad-leaved Spurge
Last record in Oxon ?1990, in vc23 1979

This annual spurge of lime-rich soils, notably arable field margins, is known from a few places in vc23 from 1883; Druce cited Tackley and his garden in Oxford (**OXF**, probably with seed from Madeira); Westcott Barton in 1931. It was between Witney by-pass and green lane N of Grove Farm, Brize Norton (SP2909, 1978 Loukes **OXF**), SP4313, SP5017 (1979 Killick, arable field entrance). Erskine and Killick doubt a 1990 record in Marcham Churchyard. It was newly at City Farm SP4311 2013 Watkins, conf. T. Walker. In GB it is mostly southern, with Oxon near its N limit; it is declining owing to farming. HJK

Euphorbia exigua
Archaeophyte

Dwarf Spurge
Vulnerable ■ Not Scarce in Oxon and vc23

(Phil Cutt)

This is an annual of dry, calcareous soils which is locally frequent on field margins, but also on open, dry grassland and disturbed habitats. It can be diminutive or quite robust and is found with *E. helioscopia, Viola arvensis, Kickxia spuria* and *K. elatine*. Dwarf Spurge is widespread in England, mostly in central and eastern areas, but declined dramatically due to agricultural intensification, especially the use of herbicides. It tolerates raised nutrient levels. The Northmoor Trust (now the Earth Trust) survey showed that in 1999 it was still abundant in the Chilterns and on the Corallian Ridge. FlOx p. 180 had 319 tetrads, we had 63 sites in 2000–11, and large populations occur locally. JHW, CRL

Salix aurita
Native

Eared Willow
Rare in Oxon and vc23

This much-branched shrub has, like *S. cinerea*, ridges under the bark but differs in having slender divergent twigs, small rugged leaves with wavy margins and tips often twisted. It grows on acid soils, heathland and moorland, in woods, scrub and by watercourses. Druce 1927 described it as not uncommon and widespread. FlOx had it in 53 tetrads; Killick doubted many of these as few Oxon habitats are now suitable, but it was re-found at Lye Valley, and in 1995 in the Chilterns. There are reliable records (1968–81) of *S. × multinervis*, the hybrid with *S. cinerea*. FlBe cites Frilford and Barrow Farm Fen, undated. In GB, widespread, especially in the N and W, but there have been losses in SE England due to modern farming and drainage. HJK

Salix myrsinifolia
Native

Dark-leaved Willow
Last Oxon record 1960s, re-found 2013; last vc23 record 1886

(Juddy Webb)

This shrub or small tree mostly grows N of Lancashire along river banks, favouring neutral soils and moderate nitrates. It appears to have increased, probably through better recording. In vc22 Webb found one in 2013 at Cothill Fen SAC. SU460996. Seemingly not introduced, it was there in the 1960s (as *S. phylicifolia* in Atlas 1962) though not in the Floras of Berkshire by Druce, Bowen or Crawley. The nearest native sites are in East Anglia, where it is in a similar condition in Chippenham Fen. CRL, JAW

⮕ *Salix repens*
Native
Creeping Willow
Near Threatened ■ **Rare in Oxon, last vc23 record 1995**

This small shrub grows in a variety of habitats; in Oxon it was in damp heaths. Druce knew it from Peppard Common and Menmarsh Farm; at Otmoor in 1946 and in three FlOx tetrads, not re-found. It was newly at Lodge Hill SP508003, vc22 (Oxon), probably introduced. In GB it is widespread especially in the N and uplands but Oxon lies in a wide and increasing gap in inland England. HJK

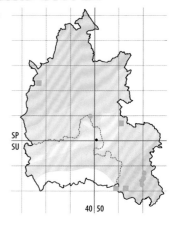

23	S	Witheridge Hill		SU695840	1995	RdA
23	S	Kingwood Common	LWS	SU696825	1995	RdA
23	S	Highmoor and Lower Common Wood	LWS	SU702850	1995	RdA
23	S	Nettlebed Common	LWS	SU705871	1995	RdA
23	C	Pixey and Yarnton Meads	SAC, SSSI	SP482098	1981	HJMB

40 | 50

⬇ *Viola canina*
Native
Heath Dog-violet
Vulnerable ■ **Scarce in Oxon and vc23**

(Phil Cutt)

This is similar to *V. riviniana* but it has no basal rosette, the leaves have rounded bases but are not cordate and the spur is yellowish. It is a small perennial with erect flowers, found in acid heathland and fens. FlOx had 40 tetrads, but Killick felt some of these were errors. Nationally a decline has been noted especially since 1950, probably due to increased drainage and fertilisation. Nutrient-poor acid grassland and fens are a scarce habitat in Oxon and it has been lost from several of its former sites but Otmoor remains a stronghold for the species. SEE

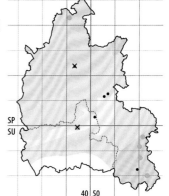

23	S	Otmoor	SSSI	SP575128	2008	SEE
23	S	Kingwood Common	LWS	SU693825	2004	VR
23	*W*	*Glympton Heath*		*SP433237*	*2002*	*UF*	*Not re-found HJK 2010*
22	V	Kennington Pool	LWS	SP518034	2002	AWM+
23	C	Noke Wood & Sling Copse	LWS	SP557116	2001	CRL+
22	*V*	*Confidential*	*SSSI*	*SU49P*	*1996*	*AB*	*Not re-found SEE 2007/8*
23	S	Nettlebed Common	LWS	SU705871	1995	RdA
23	S	Shirburn Hill	SSSI	SU715955	1991	NCCV

40 | 50

⬇ *Viola persicifolia* (*V. stagnina*)
Native **Schedule 8, s. 41, Critically Endangered, Nationally Rare** ■ **Rare in Oxon and vc23**
Fen Violet

(Phil Cutt)

This is a short-lived, low-growing perennial of fens and wet meadows. Always rare in the UK, it is now only found sporadically at two Cambs fens, though it flourishes in the turloughs (lakes) of Eire and by big rivers in Eastern Europe. Found in Otmoor in 1964 (FlOx), it was then ploughed. It appeared in a hay meadow 500 m to the SE in 1996 following removal of scrub. Monitoring by the Rare Plants Group shows it increased and then declined. It suffers in wet springs, and in 2009 formed only a few shoots and no open flowers. Management is carried out by the tenant who did further willow clearance in 2009/10 followed by extensive germination, flowering and seedset. After commissioning a review (M Palmer 2006), Natural England has been funding hydrological and soil chemistry studies as well as an experimental introduction to the adjacent RSPB reserve. Searching at Druce's other site, Menmarsh, which survived till 1956, was negative. CRL

Viola palustris
Native

Marsh Violet

Last confirmed record in Oxon uncertain, last vc23 record 1927

This is a small perennial, which has long runners. The leaves are kidney shaped on long stalks. It grows in acid bogs and marshes and has declined nationally, with a big decrease in SE England, due to habitat loss. Druce 1886 considered it almost extinct, only being found in the Ray catchment area. Druce 1927 recorded it from Stow Wood but it was not seen there or anywhere else during the survey for the FlOx. FIBe quotes it as being at Cothill, Chilswell Copse and Hen Wood, with records noted in Atlas 2002, but there are no TVERC records for these localities. SEE

Viola tricolor
Native

Wild Pansy

Near Threatened ■ Scarce in Oxon and vc23

(Peter Creed)

This annual or perennial is widespread throughout the UK, but has suffered a severe decline. On light, sandy soils with moderate nutrients, it was formerly common in arable fields, but with the loss of this habitat is now a plant of disturbed ground. Large-flowered *V. arvensis* and garden escapes have sometimes been identified as this. In FlOx it had 78 tetrads, and in FIBe seven sites. Of five sites found in 2000–11, two were new. CRL

23	C	Johnsons Buildbase Corner		SP561200	2009	RH-B	New
23	O	Blackbird Leys		SP558034	2008		
23	S	Wells Farm	BBOWT	SP622005	2008	RdA	
23	C	Kidlington		SP476148	2006	JE	New
22	*V*	*Old Cemetery, Abingdon*		*SU487973*	*2000*	*HJK*	*2010*
23	W	Radcot Farm, Faringdon		SU283993	1997	SEE	
22	*V*	*Confidential*		*SU49P*	*1997*	*HJK*	*Tip, ex garden*
23	W	Wheat field N of Tackley		SP474215	1996	AWM	
23	W	Downs Road Settlement Field		SP386047	1993	JMC	
23	W	Signet Road Verge		SP248101	1991	RVNR	
22	V	Wixen Bush	LWS	SU333858	1991	RV	
23	C	Finmere Railway		SP625322	1989	RK	
23	W	Charlbury Meadow		SP363191	1987	LP+	
23	W	Rabbits Piece Copse (Brize Norton)		SP314084	1986	GH+	
22	V	Ridgeway Path		SU396843	1986	DJNH	
23	S	Oakley Hill	LWS, BBOWT	SU758995	1986	RSRF	
23	W	West of Abel Wood	LWS	SP404147	1985	BBONT	
22	V	Whitley Copse		SP440046	1985	HS	
23	Be	Hemdean Bottom Public Path		SU708763	1985	LC	
23	C	Banbury to Bicester Railway		SP576237	1984	FlOx	
23	*O*	*Port Meadow Tip*		*SP40Z*	*1979*	*HJMB*	
23	C	Hook Norton Cutting & Banks	SSSI, BBOWT	SP359321	1977	HJMB	
23	W	Weavley crossroads		SP467185	1975	BJC	
23	W	Great Tew South Park		SP401290	1969	RWHS	
23	S	Withy Copse		SU682803	1968		
23	S	Aston Rowant	SAC, NNR, SSSI	SU727973	1968	FlOx	

Radiola linoides
Native

Allseed

Vulnerable ■ Last Oxon and vc23 record 1881

This slender annual is scattered in S and W coastal areas but has had a big decline. It favours acidic and very low-nutrient damp soil. Druce had Binfield in 1881 **OXF**, FlOx two tetrads both (improbably) on limestone and FIBe none in our area. CRL

Hypericum androsaemum
Tutsan

With 16 2000–11 records in vc23 and one in vc22, this is not scarce in Oxon. Most of the records are from the S district. Some locations may be introduced, but it is well established and spreading. SEE

Hypericum maculatum
Imperforate St John's-wort

H. maculatum had been in 49 FlOx tetrads (p. 125), many in the N; we recorded it 17 times in vc23 by 2007 so it is Not Scarce. HJK

⬇ *Hypericum montanum*
Native   GB Red List Near Threatened ■ **Rare in Oxon and vc23**

Pale St John's-wort

(Peter Sheasby)

This perennial herb is widespread in England and Wales, and has declined. It grows in dry calcareous grassland or scrub, with very low-nutrient status. It appears to have had a calamitous decline in Oxon, Druce had 19 sites including Nuffield, Henley and Lambridge Wood, and FlOx p. 125 had 33 tetrads, mostly Chiltern; those on Oolite and Killick's near Hanborough station (SP4214, 1991) have not been re-found. FlBe had three sites, including Bagley Wood, but none recent; a few plants were newly found on Boars Hill (SP485036) Lambrick, 2014. CRL

23	S	Bottom Wood	LWS	SU656782	2010	JK+	Rare, new
23	S	Straw Hill	LWS	SU662777	2009	JHW	Rare
23	S	Warren Bank	SSSI, BBOWT	SU653858	2008	JHW	1
23	S	Lambridge Wood	SSSI	SU737843	1988	HJMB	
23	W	South Leigh Railway Line West		SP392080	1987	Eco	
23	S	Huntley Wood	pLWS	SU674773	1987	JHW	
23	S	Wood, Turners Court		SU643885	1986	GB	
23	S	Warburg	SSSI, BBOWT	SU720880	1986	NP	
23	S	Nuffield Common	LWS	SU670880	1981	OCMR	
23	S	Henley Golf Course		SU755806	1981	OCMR	

⬇ *Geranium columbinum*

Long-stalked Crane's-bill

We recorded this small annual of dry, especially lime-rich grassland and stony places because most records in GB are SW of a line London–Chester, with many losses NE of this. With 12 2000–11 records in vc23 it is not Scarce, but they compare with 52 tetrads (FlOx p. 185). The only recent records outside the Chilterns were at Hook Norton railway cutting (SP357315), Swere bank (SP354310), Stratton Audley quarry (SP601251), Linch Hill (SP411042), and in vc22 (Oxon) at Wytham (SP463000). The many losses are due to habitat destruction, grassland management and scrub growth. HJK

⬆ *Lythrum hyssopifolium*
Archaeophyte   Schedule 8, s. 41, Endangered, Nationally Rare ■ **Rare in Oxon, Last vc23 record 1948**

Grass-poly

This little annual requires seasonally flooded open ground. It was not seen in the county from 1948 until Souster found the current population near Cholsey in 1968. This is one site among seven that Druce mentioned. It is carefully managed by appropriate ploughing in a low intensity cereal field margin prone to flooding. Numbers have been monitored by the RPG and fluctuate with the weather from zero to c. 100,000 in 2008 when the large numbers enabled seed to be sent to the Millennium Seed Bank. A sighting on a trackway at Piddington, 2008 by A Helliwell, could not be re-found the following year. It was at five sites in GB (Wigginton 1999) but now more, including Slimbridge Wetland Centre and around reservoirs. CRL

⬇ *Lythrum* (*Peplis*) *portula*
Native

Water-purslane
Scarce in Oxon and vc23

Water-purslane has tiny flowers and distinctive obovate leaves. This low-growing annual is limited in Oxon to damp or seasonally wet places (pond edges, woodland rides) on rather acid soils where shade, trampling or clearance deters competitors. It is easily overlooked, which could explain why the distributions now and in FlOx (10 tetrads 1962–93) differ. It was in vc22 (Oxon) in Bagley in 1833, and a post-1986 Atlas 2002 record in SP40. In GB it is widespread, but scarcer in the Midlands and E England where it has decreased since 1950 with drainage, path improvement and over-growth. HJK

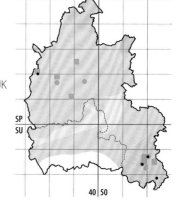

23	S	Nettlebed Common	LWS	SU703871	2010	JHW	10; 3 other sites
23	W	Foxholes	SSSI, BBOWT	SP251201	2009	HJK	2
23	S	Well Pond, Stoke Row Pond		SU680841	2009	RdA	E and W basins
23	S	Binfield Heath, The Common		SU739786	2009	JHW	New; along 20 m
23	S	Kingwood Common	LWS	SU696825	1995	RdA	
23	W	Wychwood	NNR, SSSI	SP330165	1984	PS+	

Epilobium lanceolatum
Native

Spear-leaved Willowherb
Last certain Oxon record 1987, in vc23 1986

This perennial willowherb resembles *E. montanum* but the leaf shape and margin are distinctive. In dry habitats, waste places and gardens; nearly all Killick's records in S England and S Wales were by railway tracks. Palmer reported it in Oxon in 1958 in a Fringford garden (SP6028), and in 1964 at Milton (SP4434) and Cropredy (railway, SP4646). Subsequently seen in 22 other FlOx tetrads (p. 177) it seemed to have spread, but some were errors, and none are recent. In GB it is largely stable and mainly in the SW. HJK

22	V	Railway W of Didcot		SU509913	1987	HJK	
23	S	CS Lewis	BBOWT	SP562065	1986	HJMB	
22	V	Sutton Courtenay Gravel Pits		SU518930	1985	HJMB+	
22	V	Ferry Lane, Moulsford		SU5882	1985	FlBe	Wall, conf. Pennington

Epilobium roseum
Native

Pale Willowherb
Rare in Oxon and vc23

This perennial willowherb resembles *E. montanum* but has flowers whitish when young, the stigma not four-lobed and leaves with 4–15 mm stalks. It is often casual and sparse, in damp disturbed places, sometimes shaded. FlBe calls it "rare" and some records could have been *E. ciliatum*. Druce had only three sites outside Oxford, and Brenan (1946) deemed two colonies worthy of report, Palmer had seen it only three times, Bowen none, so Killick (first find 1997) doubted many of the 59 tetrads (FlOx p. 177). In GB it is widespread but less common than in 1962 despite better recording. HJK

22	V	**Bath Street, Abingdon**		SU496972	2008	HJK	New 1, garden
23	S	**Sydlings Copse**	SSSI, BBOWT	SP556095	2006	HJK	New
23	S	**Kingwood Common**	LWS	SU694830	2004	VR+	New
23	S	Spartum Fen	SSSI	SP655017	1997	HJK	**OXF**
23	O	Walton St, Oxford		SP5006	1988	RCP	Garden

Epilobium palustre
Native

Marsh Willowherb
Rare in Oxon and vc23

(Phil Cutt)

This delicate stoloniferous perennial is easily overlooked or misidentified. It is common throughout the UK except in central England where is has declined through agricultural improvement. It grows in damp, slightly acid and low-nutrient conditions. Druce had 13 sites and FlOx 39 tetrads. The few 2000–11 records may reflect a combination of former over-recording, real decline, and lack of recording. It was formerly also at Tubney, Radley and Wytham (FlBe). CRL

23	S	**Greenmoor, Woodcote**		SU645870	2010	RdA	New
22	V	**Parsonage Moor**	SAC, SSSI, BBOWT	SU460997	2009	JAW	26, 30 in Ruskin
22	V	**Abbey Fishponds**	LNR, LWS	SU513979	2009	RdA	Rare, new
23	S	Withy Copse	Other	SU682803	1991	GH+	
22	V	Raleigh Park	LWS	SP493053	1989	HS	
23	S	Spartum Fen	SSSI	SP655017	1988	NCC	Not seen JAW
22	V	Confidential	SSSI	SU49P	1986	SW	Not seen SEE
23	S	Brasenose Wood and Shotover Hill	SSSI, LGS	SP568058	1985	RH-B	
22	V	Sutton Courtenay Gravel Pits		SU518930	1985	HJMB	
22	V	Barrow Farm Fen	SSSI	SU466975	1983	HJMB	Not re-found
23	W	Foxholes	SSSI, BBOWT	SP250205	1981	HJMB	
22	V	Hitchcopse Pit	SSSI, BBOWT	SU452996	1981	HJMB	Not re-found
22	V	Sheepstead Folly Meadow		SU455982	1981	JY	
22	V	Dry Sandford Pit	LGS, BBOWT	SU467995	1980	HJMB+	Abs. JAW
23	W	North Leigh Common	LWS	SP401136	1975	HJMB	Not re-found

Tilia cordata

Small-leaved Lime

Pollen analysis suggests that *Tilia cordata* became the dominant tree at Wytham after the last ice-age. There are numerous records for this attractive tree in Oxon. It has been planted widely in parks, gardens and towns so that its natural distribution is obscured. Watlington Park has some fine specimens. SEE

➡ *Daphne mezereum*   Mezereon
Native   Vulnerable, Nationally Scarce ■ Scarce in Oxon and vc23

(Peter Creed)

This low-growing deciduous shrub grows in ancient and secondary woodlands and mature scrub on calcareous, and sometimes quite nitrogen-rich, soils. It has bright pink flowers early in the season and red berries but is easily overlooked for much of the year. Its populations have declined due to habitat loss and uprooting, and the current distribution is somewhat confused by natural bird dispersal from gardens. In GB its main centres of distribution are in Lancs, the S Pennines and south-central counties. In Oxon Druce had 14 sites and FlOx 10 tetrads, it is known in six sites in the Chilterns in chalky scrub with reasonable light levels, and well established woodland. Protection from deer has been necessary in some sites. JHW, CRL

23	S	Bottom Wood	LWS	SU664784	2009	JHW	New, 4
23	S	Almshill Larch		SU738885	2007	JHW	25
23	S	Warburg	SSSI, BBOWT	SU720882	2006	RdA	New, 3
22	V	Hurst Hill	SSSI	SP476042	2002	JW	New
23	S	Pishill Woods	SSSI	SU713905	2000	JHW	
23	S	Lucy's Copse		SU753807	1997	JHW	
23	S	Greenfield & College Woods		SU719910	1988	VNP+	
23	S	Aston Rowant	SAC, NNR, SSSI	SU730970	1969	HJMB	

⬇ *Turritis glabra* (*Arabis glabra*)   Tower Mustard
Native   s. 41, Endangered, Nationally Scarce ■ Last Oxon and vc23 record 1981

This small crucifer is a biennial or short-lived perennial. Nationally it has strongholds in the Breckland, Worcs and Hants, but has declined hugely. It is usually found on disturbed or open grassy, dry, slightly calcareous banks with raised nutrients. Seeds can survive for long periods in the soil. Druce had four sites, FlOx three tetrads and FlBe none. CRL

23	W	Reed Hill	SSSI	SP382175	1978	JMC	
23	S	Sydlings Copse	SSSI, BBOWT	SP556096	1974	HJMB	
23	W	Upton Down, Burford		SP222119	1972	HJMB	Doom 1981

➡ *Cardamine amara*   Large Bitter-cress
This native early-flowering, winter-green perennial has a distinctive oily taste. It is widespread in England and S Scotland but absent from much of Wales and the SW; mostly stable, it is spreading in Ireland. Usually in winter-flooded woodland or wet meadows; it may be transported by vegetative parts which break off. It tolerates slight acidity and high nitrates (Grime *et al.* 1988). Druce listed 27 sites and FlOx (p. 137) had 48 tetrads, and we found 19 in Oxon, 11 of which were in vc23 and seven were new. Not Scarce. CRL

Cardamine impatiens   Narrow-leaved Bitter-cress
Native   Nationally Scarce ■ Unconfirmed in Oxon and vc23

This small biennial is easily overlooked, but distinguished by the acute, clasping auricles of the stem leaves. It grows mainly in wet woods on limestone in W and SE England. It tolerates raised nutrients and has declined slightly. It has been recorded in Oxon only since 1970 at The Warren, Sarsgrove SP3024, Hardwick, Banbury, Steeple Aston and Culham SU5094; as FlOx (p. 137) says "confirmation… is desirable". Our area of vc22 lacks it. CRL

⬇ *Lepidium heterophyllum*   Smith's Pepperwort
Native   Last Oxon and vc23 record 1983

This small biennial or perennial is widespread in the BI though mostly in Scotland, Wales and the SW. It prefers dry heaths and tolerates some nutrients, but has suffered a huge decline. Druce had Leafield and Bullingdon Green, FlOx p. 142 eight tetrads and FlBe none in our area. CRL

Lepidium ruderale
Archaeophyte

Narrow-leaved Pepperwort
Rare in Oxon, Last vc23 record 1978

This annual is a casual coloniser of walls and rubbish tips, but especially bare ground by the sea. It is found mainly in southern GB. As a casual this has declined nationally and locally, it was in five FlOx tetrads especially near Idbury SP 2220–22. As a halophyte it has spread along salted roads. It is probably this which accounts for its appearance at Tubney. The only site recorded is on the edge of a lay-by at Tubney on the A420; by 2015 it has spread along both sides of the A420 for at least 100 metres. It could well be found on other regularly salted roadsides. SEE

22	V	Tubney Lay-by		SU439996	2009	SEE	2014 on both sides of A420

Lepidium latifolium
Native but ?alien in Oxon

Dittander
Last Oxon record 1997, one post-1967 record in vc23

Dittander, a tall rhizomatous perennial, was formerly grown for flavouring. In vc23 not known to Druce, and found after 1967 only at Brize Norton (SP3008) but not since. Killick found it on the W bank of the Thames N of Sandford Lock SP531017 (vc22 (Oxon)) from 1991 until lost in 1998. In GB it is native in maritime grassland, saltmarshes and on sea walls. Elsewhere, scattered and probably introduced, and has increased since 1962. HJK

Descurainia sophia
Archaeophyte

Flixweed
Rare in Oxon and vc23

This is an annual, arable flower which grows to 70 cm. It is found in light soils in fields and waste places. It is widespread throughout GB and although it declined there has been little change since 1962. In FlOx it was cited in eight tetrads mainly and FlBe cites 10 records in our area. Although still broadly speaking in both these general locations, it is not commonly found in either in 2000–11. SEE

22	V	Pead's Farm Frilford		SU443972	2011	HJK	24 on 2 sites, new
22	V	Confidential		SU49U	2009	HJK	3 plants
23	S	Culham, edge arable field E of Thames		SU5195	2005	HJK	
22	V	Tubney Lodge, arable field		SU438994	1998	SEE+	
23	S	Wells Farm	BBOWT	SP620008	1997	RM	
22	V	Tubney Manor Farm		SU440994	1997	LH	
22	V	Collins Farm, field 1		SU437975	1996	LH	

Arabis hirsuta
Native

Hairy Rock-cress
Near Threatened ■ Scarce in Oxon and vc23

(Peter Creed)

This is a perennial of calcareous pastures, which has declined, probably due to a decline in habitat with 'improved' agricultural techniques; this decline is noted in Atlas 2002 as being especially pronounced in the SE of GB. Even in Druce 1927 it was described as local and rare, FlOx suggested scarce, though it was found in 35 tetrads. Of the 23 tetrads north of Oxford only four were revisited, two of the others were on the railway embankment, which rarely gets visited. With only five 2000–11 records in vc23 it is now probably scarce. The 2000–11 sites were all mentioned in previous floras. SEE

23	C	Stratton Audley Quarry	SSSI, LWS	SP601251	2009	BC	
23	W	Reed Hill	SSSI	SP379174	2008	WOC	10 plants
23	W	Bigger Stone Hollow		SP328195	2007	CMJ-H	
23	W	Ashford Bridge to Combe Cutting (Cotswold Line)	LWS	SP409152	2006	SEE	
23	W	Ashford Bridge to Combe Cutting (Cotswold Line)	LWS	SP390157	2005	FHW	
23	W	Wychwood	NNR, SSSI	SP330165	1984	PS	
23	C	Verge Middleton Stoney		SP537253	1984	HJMB	
23	S	Warburg	SSSI, BBOWT	SU716879	1979	VP	
23	S	Aston Rowant	SAC, NNR, SSSI	SU730970	1979	OCMR	

Draba muralis
Archaeophyte

Wall Whitlowgrass
Nationally Scarce ■ Last Oxon record 1999, in vc23 1991

This tiny winter annual is only native on the northern and western limestones. It has declined nationally. It favours dry open sites with neutral pH but tolerates high nutrients. Druce had it as a probable alien at North Aston and Wytham. It was in seven FlOx tetrads (p. 139), and FlBe had it at Youlbury, Boars Hill (1949–99). Both known Oxon sites (North Aston and Drayton Churchyard) have been searched; newly re-found on Drayton Churchyard wall SP428415 2015 J Shanklin. CRL

Diplotaxis tenuifolia
Archaeophyte

Perennial Wall-rocket
Scarce in Oxon, Rare in vc23

This perennial of dry banks is still centred on ports and industrial areas, preferring slightly alkaline and high nitrate conditions. It has declined nationally, but as a salad plant it is increasing as a casual. With us it appeared on roadsides and disturbed ground. Druce had it near Oxford at Botley and Wolvercote. FlOx (p. 143) had eight tetrads. CRL

22	S	Didcot Power Station road		SU513910	2009	HJK	
23	W	Newbridge Mill, field A		SP403019	2007	AH+	
22	V	A420/A417		SU299952	2004	SEE	
22	0	Botley, Oxford		SP4902	2002	FlBe	Allotment
23	C	Yarnton Churchyard		SP476117	1975	FlOx	

Teesdalia nudicaulis
Native

Shepherd's Cress
Near Threatened ■ Rare in Oxon, last vc23 record 1882

(Peter Creed)

This small winter annual is found in well-drained sandy soils, preferring bare or disturbed ground. It used to be common locally throughout GB, but has declined, especially in central England. It has a short-lived seed bank and this may have contributed to its decline along with scrub invasion and afforestation. It has not been seen in vc23 since 1882 and is presumed extinct. It was also presumed extinct in N Berks (Bowen 1968, now in Administrative Oxon), but has been recorded from parts of the Coralllian Ridge since the 1980s and on Boars Hill more recently. The plant has been in decline but now with better management seems to be holding its own. SEE

22	V	Confidential	SSSI	SU49P	2009	SEE	Declining
22	V	Birch Copse set-aside	pLWS	SU488032	2004	CRL	100s

Microthlaspi perfoliatum
Native

Perfoliate Penny-cress, Cotswold Penny-cress
s. 41, Schedule 8, Vulnerable ■ Scarce in Oxon and vc23

(Peter Creed)

This is a small arable annual; nationally the native population is confined to the Cotswold area of Glos and Oxon and had greatly declined prior to Plantlife's intervention. Changes in agricultural practices mean there are few arable sites, but it has spread into quarries, where soil heaps provide suitable germination conditions. FlOx cited five tetrads In Oxon; the population is fairly stable now, here it is managed by the ANHSO Rare Plants Group, initially for Plantlife's 'Back from the Brink' programme. Palmer's Bank is a more traditional arable site, where Palmer first found the species in 1996. It has been found at Bridgefield Bridge since 1930 and Network Rail has granted the site 'conservation status'. It has spread from the Stanton Harcourt gravel pit along the verges at Linch Hill, where it has been recorded since 1996. The OFG continue to monitor the plant yearly at these three sites. The Wychwood Flora Group monitors the site at Temple Mill quarry where it was found in 2001, a subsequent landslip has provided more suitable habitat. The Oxford Conservation Volunteers have removed scrub and there are now hundreds of plants. SEE

23	W	Palmers Bank	LWS	SP3717	2009	SEE	
23	W	Ashford Bridge to Combe Cutting (Cotswold Line)	LWS	SP385160	2009	SEE	
23	W	Linch Hill, verges		SP414044	2009	AWM+	Plants confined to South end of site
23	C	Temple Mills Quarries	LWS	SP343362	2008	PS	

⬇ *Iberis amara*
Native

Wild Candytuft

(Rod d'Ayala)

This is an annual, a calcicole which favours bare open ground. The species is considered to be native in the Chiltern and Wessex Downs, elsewhere in GB it is regarded as an alien. It was in 28 FlOx tetrads, some sites have been lost in Oxon, perhaps due to changes in agricultural practice and also since the outbreak of myxomatosis, as the plant may have been dependent on rabbits to provide suitable areas for germination. It has a long-lived seed bank and it regenerates in old sites after disturbance. Further searching is always worthwhile. SEE

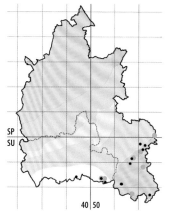

23	S	Holly Hill (Elmore Park Grassland)	LWS	SU631813	2011	HJK	
23	S	Swyncombe		SU665895	2010	JHW	100's
23	S	Watlington & Pyrton Hills	SSSI	SU707943	2010	HJK	
23	S	Shirburn Hill	SSSI	SU718951	2010	HJK	
23	S	Aston Rowant	SAC, NNR, SSSI	SU727968	2008	CRL	30 plants
22	S	Aston Upthorpe Downs	SSSI	SU545835	2007	SR	Abundant
23	S	Swyncombe Downs	SSSI	SU670914	2007	SR	Abundant
23	S	Span Hill Chalk Pit	pLWS, LGS	SU747770	2007	SR	400+ until 2011
22	S	Unhill and Ham Woods	LWS	SU562820	2002	CRL	
22	V	Ilsley Bottom	LWS	SU441841	2001	CRL	
23	S	Mrs Baxter's Farm		SU680917	1999	SK	
23	S	Watlington and Pyrton Hills	SSSI	SU710942	1991	NCC	
23	S	Huntley Wood	pLWS	SU674773	1987	JW	
23	S	Warburg	SSSI, BBOWT	SU720880	1987	NP	
23	S	Chinnor Hill	SSSI, BBOWT	SP766007	1971	RSRF	

⬇ *Thesium humifusum*
Native

Bastard-toadflax

(Phil Cutt)

This woody, semi-parasite on grasses, is a perennial of chalk grassland. It is found mainly on heavily grazed grassland in central southern England. It has suffered a decline with the decline of sheep grazing and ploughing of downland especially in East Anglia. Short turf seems to be more important than aspect. It has always been described as rare in Oxon. Found in five tetrads in FlOx and is now confined to Taynton and a few sites on the Wessex Downs and Chilterns. It is easily overlooked so possibly diligent searching of old sites, may yet produce results. SEE

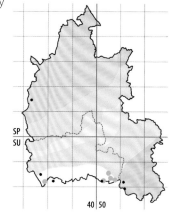

23	S	Hartslock	SSSI, BBOWT	SU619793	2008	HJK+	Several localities
23	W	Taynton Quarries	SSSI	SP234147	2007	HJK	Frequent on humps of limestone
22	V	Crog Hill and Scary Hill	LWS	SU323835	2007	SEE+	20+ plants
23	S	Fiddle Hill	LWS	SU614819	2004	JMC	
22	V	Kingstone Coombes	LWS	SU271849	2003	CRL	
22	V	Blewbury Hill		SU523823	2002	CRL	
22	V	Kingston Down	LWS	SU288820	1998	CRL+	
22	V	Moulsford Downs	SSSI	SU578827	1991	NNC	
22	V	Blewbury Hill	LWS	SU530824	1990	HJMB	
22	S	Fairmile to Kingstanding		SU560834	1986	HJMB	

⬇ *Persicaria bistorta*
Native, doubtfully so in Oxon

Common Bistort
Rare in Oxon and vc23

This showy perennial is widespread in Scotland, England and Wales but declining especially in the S and E. It grows in neutral waterside and marshy places, tolerating high nutrients. Druce had 19 sites and FlOx (p. 119) had 14 tetrads, but records need confirmation and FlBe says it may be mostly a garden escape. CRL

23	S	Stoke Row		SU684844	2007	JHW	>20 garden escape?
23	W	Eynsham Abbey Fishponds		SP430090	2004	CRPG	New
23	S	Peppard Common	LWS	SU704814	2004	VR+	New
23	W	Burford Tannery Loop		SP257119	1996	SJW	
22	V	Church Copse		SU436993	1993	OCMR	

⬇ *Persicaria mitis* (*P. laxiflora*)
Native

Tasteless Water-pepper
Vulnerable, Nationally Scarce ■ Scarce in Oxon and vc23

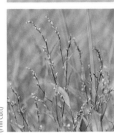

(Phil Cutt)

This annual is scattered in central, S and E England, requiring open drying water-side mud. It favours neutral pH, and flourishes with high nutrients but has declined. Druce had 11 sites and FlOx (p. 120) 25 tetrads (perhaps over-recorded). FlBe had seven sites, many now lost. CRL

23	O	New Marston Meadows	SSSI	SP518075	2010	JAW	Many, new
23	O	Port Meadow with Wolvercote Common and Green	SAC, SSSI	SP499077	2009	CRL+	Occasional
23	O	Binsey Green	LWS	SP493077	2008	SEE	4
22	V	Willow Walk Meadow	LWS	SP496056	2008	SEE	10
23	W	Glympton Valley	LWS	SP427197	2003	CRL	New
23	O	Lye Valley and Cowley Marsh	LWS	SP544049	1991	EN	
22	V	Hinksey Stream Complex		SP494055	1989	NRA	

⬇ *Persicaria minor*
Native

Small Water-pepper
GB Red List Vulnerable ■ Last record in Oxon and vc23 pre-1990

This species is distinguished from *P. mitis* by its leaves to 15 mm across and >5 times as long as wide, and having five petals, rather than four. It is a slender annual, scattered in England and Wales, but has declined. It favours slightly acid, nutrient-rich, muddy water margins. Druce had seven sites but FlOx only one (Dorchester, SU5894, pre-1990), and FlBe none since 1940. CRL

Polygonum rurivagum
Archaeophyte

Cornfield Knotgrass
Scarce in Oxon and vc23

This erect annual differs from *P. aviculare* by its narrow leaves (<4 mm) and its gaping tepals, which reveal the achene. It is found in calcareous arable fields, and described in Atlas 2002 as possibly spreading or possibly better identified, whereas Stace 2010 states it is rare and decreasing. In Oxon it would appear to be the latter, but identification problems could have led to its being missed. In Druce 1927 it was described as local in many dry cornfields. Its decline is probably due to changes in agricultural practices. FlOx cites 43 tetrads and records that it grows on ant hills at Aston Rowant. There are tetrad records in TVERC as well as those listed below. It would probably reward further searching. SEE

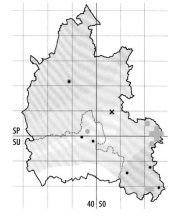

22	V	Confidential		SU49U	2011	HJK	Conf. Mountford
23	S	Ipsden Farm		SU628853	2010	JHW	Conf. J Akeroyd
23	S	Warburg	SSSI, BBOWT	SU723876	2010	JHW	
23	S	Harpsden, edge of maize field		SU759795	2010	JHW	
23	S	Stanton St John		SP565095	2009	HJK	Absent
22	V	Tubney lay-by on A420		SU439996	2009	SEE	6
23	W	Broad Assarts, Ditchley Estate		SP387217	1997	AJD	
22	V	Bradley Farm		SP463018	1996	LH	
23	S	Rectory Farm		SP565095	1996	LH	
23	S	Aston Rowant	SAC, NNR, SSSI	SU730970	1979	OCMR	

Fallopia dumetorum
Native   s. 41, Vulnerable, Nationally Scarce ■ Rare in Oxon, Last vc23 record 1981

Copse-bindweed

(Camilla Lambrick)

This is a climbing annual which is self-pollinated and has a long-lived seed-bank. It is a local plant of central S England, but has declined perhaps due to reduced woodland management. It prefers hedges and woodland edges on well-drained neutral soils, and tolerates high-nutrient levels. Druce had no vc23 records, but cited Tubney as did FlBe; FlOx (p. 122) had 12 tetrads but noted that confusion with *F. convolvulus* var. *subalatum* is possible. At Tubney it had c. 50 stems in five clumps among brambles and bracken, and it is setting seed. CRL

22	V	Tubney A420, NW verge	SP444000	2009	RH-B	2 sites
23	W	Alvescot	SP290042	1981	HJMB	

Rumex pulcher
Fiddle Dock

Fiddle dock was in 31 FlOx tetrads but recorded in our survey because it is near to the northern limit of its native area which lies S of the line from the Severn to the Wash. It was seen nine times in Oxon (seven in vc23) in 2000–10 and in 1999 15 and 13 respectively, so is Not Scarce. HJK

Rumex palustris
Native   Last Oxon and vc23 record <1987, new in 2014

Marsh Dock

This annual to short-lived perennial dock grows in wet, nutrient-rich mud exposed in summer and autumn. It differs from *R. maritimus* in the fruit's spines <2 mm and slightly stiff, about as long as the width of the valve, not 2–3 times as long. Previously reported by Druce from Otmoor in 1881 (lost by 1884), and Atlas 2002 has dots for SP21 and SP61 for 1970–86, not known to FlOx authors. Found in Port Meadow (SP501078) by Webb in 2014 and confirmed by J R Akeroyd. In GB it is mostly in E England, with a stable distribution since 1930. HJK

⬇ *Rumex maritimus*   Golden Dock
Native   Last Oxon and vc23 record 1993

This small annual, or short-lived biennial, does turn golden in fruit. As well as being coastal in the E, it is distributed widely in central England in damp alkaline places with raised nutrient levels. Nationally it has increased in frequency since 1962. It is very similar to *R. palustris* (q.v.) but with different chromosome numbers (40 and 60), moreover they often grow together. Druce had eight sites including Port Meadow, Binsey and Otmoor. FlOx had four tetrads and FlBe none. CRL

23	C	Oddington		SP5414	1993	PMG	By road
23	O	Binsey Wetlands		SP490077	1986	SC	
23	W	Pinkhill Fm, Farmoor		SP4206	1973	RCP	**OXF**
23	W	Chimney		SP3600	1970	AJR	**OXF**

⬇ *Drosera rotundifolia*   Round-leaved Sundew
Native   Near Threatened ■ Rare in Oxon, last vc23 record 1830

This Sundew typically grows in low-nutrient bogs and heathy ground. At Parsonage Moor (22 V; SU460997) Erskine found four plants in 1994 on tussocks; it was also reported after a trial peat cutting in 2005 (K. Porter pers. comm.) but perhaps then damaged. FlBe had undated records at Frilford Heaths and Chilswell Hills. In GB, widespread in the N and W but has declined in SE England owing to habitat destruction. HJK

⬇ *Minuartia hybrida*   Fine-leaved Sandwort
Native   s. 41, Endangered, Nationally Scarce ■ Last record in Oxon 1995, in vc23 1981

This annual needs dry places on light alkaline infertile soils (mainly chalk and limestone) in grass, tracks, arable margins and artificial habitats free of competitors. It was in 20 tetrads (FlOx p. 114) but few records are detailed or recent. It was in FlBe from Buckland, Pusey (SU3596), Cothill, Dog House (SU4498), Cholsey Fair Mile, Radley Station and Moulsford, all undated. Scattered in England but surviving best on chalk and by railways, but much decreased by modern farming. HJK

22	V	Marcham Park		SU449971	1995	HJK	Rough grass
23	*S*	*Cart Gap*		*SU6286*	*1981*	*HJK*	*Not re-found 2008*
23	S	Chinnor Chalk Pit	SSSI	SP757000	1980	RSRF	Also tetrad SP7400 in 1994

⬆ *Stellaria pallida*   Lesser Chickweed
Native   Scarce in Oxon, Rare in vc23

(Phil Cutt)

This small inconspicuous annual is confined to dry sandy soils. It differs from *S. media* being a much less robust plant, it frequently has no, or extremely small, petals and purple anthers, the seed is usually <0.9 mm. Seed and sepal sizes overlap with those of *S. media* so identification can be very difficult. Nationally and locally there has been an apparent increase in the number of locations, possibly due to better recording. Both Bowen and FlBe cast doubts on old records (*S. apetala*) and in some cases these sites no longer have suitable conditions. At Yew Tree Farm, a new site, it was found over a wide area during a search for *Veronica praecox*. SEE

22	V	Confidential	SSSI	SU49P	2008/9	SEE+	
22	V	Confidential		SU49P	2011	HJK	Sparse, new
22	V	Thornhill Walk, Abingdon		SU493981	2011	HJK	Few new
22	V	Hitchcopse Pit	SSSI, BBOWT	SU452996	2007	SEE+	Frequent
22	V	Confidential		SU49U	2007	HJK	
23	W	Yew Tree Farm, Standlake		SP384047	2006	SEE	Several clumps
23	W	Ashford Bridge to Combe Cutting (Cotswold Line)	LWS	SP386159	1998	JMC	

Stellaria palustris
Native
s. 41, Vulnerable ■ **Probably Not Scarce in Oxon, Scarce in vc23**

Marsh Stitchwort

(Judy Webb)

This is a bluish-green perennial, its slender stems, as Druce says "preferring the company of other herbage". It is scattered in England with a concentration in the east. Nationally it has suffered a big decline. It grows in marshy vegetation and wet MG4, favouring neutral and moderately enriched soils. Druce had 25 sites and FlOx 36 tetrads, and FlBe 11. CRL

23	C	Loop Farm Flood Meadows	LWS	SP487109	2010	JK	Meadow
23	C	Meadow NE of Icworth, Yarnton		SP488119	2010	JK	
23	0	New Marston Meadows	SSSI	SP522071	2010	JAW	1000s
23	S	Otmoor	SSSI	SP573128	2008	SEE+	
23	W	Minster Lovell Marsh	LWS	SP314118	2007	WOR	
23	0	Port Meadow with Wolvercote Common & Green	SAC, SSSI	SP4808	2004	JE	
23	C	Otmoor	SSSI	SP572145	2004	JE	
23	C	Muswell Hill North	pLWS	SP639153	2003	CRL	New
23	C	Lamb's Pool	BBOWT	SP352361	2002	RHa	New
23	0	West Cowleys (Meadow next to Wolvercote SSSI)	LWS, OPT	SP483094	2001	AWM	
23	C	Enslow Marsh	LWS	SP485188	1993	JMC	
23	W	Minster Lovell Marsh	LWS	SP314118	1991	AJD+	
23	0	Cherwell Bridge, Hall Farm		SP517098	1991	EN	

Cerastium diffusum
Native ?introduced in Oxon
Last Oxon record 1995, in vc23 1975

Sea Mouse-ear

Sea Mouse-ear, a small annual in light soils mainly by the sea, has four petals and stamens and bracts lacking papery tips. FlOx cites records in tetrads SP4808 (1939), SP6434 (1964), and Chipping Norton (SP3226, 1975, Sandels). It was in vc22 (Oxon), at Didcot station (SU 5290, 1993–95, Palmer). HJK

Cerastium pumilum
Native
Nationally Scarce ■ Rare in Oxon and vc23

Dwarf Mouse-ear

C. pumilum is a small, easily overlooked winter annual of lime-rich substrates – short grass, banks and quarries. It resembles C. semidecandrum but has petals as long as (not ¾ as long as) the sepals, and the papery tip to the bracts is <¼ of their length. The Taynton record and two in 1954 by Palmer at Stonesfield and Fawler are in FlOx. Two new records need confirmation. The latest in FlBe is Wytham pit in 1967. It is mainly in SW England, and has been decreasing to the E of this. HJK

23	W	Whitehill Quarry	LGS	SP268107	2011	BB+	New
23	W	Wychwood	NNR, SSSI	SP332167	2007	WOR	New
23	W	Ironstone Quarry, near Fawler		SP372173	1987	HJMB+	
23	W	Taynton Quarries	SSSI	SP236151	1986	HJMB+	
22	V	Wytham Woods	SSSI	SP457082	1986	RH-B	

Cerastium semidecandrum
Little Mouse-ear

Little Mouse-ear, an annual of sandy soils, is relatively infrequent, but by 2010 it was seen in 26 sites in Oxon (14 in vc23) so is Not Scarce. HJK

➡ *Moenchia erecta*
Native

Upright Chickweed
Vulnerable ■ **Rare in Oxon, last vc23 record 1886**

The small annual Upright Chickweed is seen in April–May on poor dry sandy acid soils free of competitors. In vc23 noted in 1794, in Druce (1886) from Ramsden Heath and in Druce (1927) from South Leigh Heath but probably extinct. No Bowen (1968) or FlBe records in Oxon, but found in set-aside near Frilford between 1996 and 2005 in small fluctuating numbers. In GB, scattered in S England and Wales but much decreased in the Midlands and N. HJK

22	V	Confidential		SU49N	2005	HJK	100; 2 sites, new

⬇ *Sagina nodosa*
Native

Knotted Pearlwort
Vulnerable ■ **Last record in Oxon and vc23 1985**

This is a small perennial, which grows in damp, base-rich locations with low nutrients. Also found in calcareous grasslands. It is widespread throughout the British Isles, but has suffered a big decline since the 1950s, especially in S England. This decline is presumably due to agricultural improvements. There are no recent records from FlOx or TVERC and it is presumed lost from its former strongholds e.g. Wychwood Forest, N. Leigh heath. SEE

23	W	Cogges Wood	LWS	SP380110	1985	JMC	
23	W	Wychwood	NNR, SSSI	SP338170	1984	PS	
23	W	Coombe Fen	LWS	SP408150	1983	HJMB	WOR 2008
23	C	Weston Fen	SSSI	SP526194	1983	HJMB	

Sagina subulata

Heath Pearlwort

This small annual, reported in FlBe at Boars Hill (SP4802) in 1918, is probably long extinct. HJK

➡ *Sagina apetala* (*S. apetala* ssp. *apetala*)
Native

Annual Pearlwort
Seemingly scarce in Oxon, Rare in vc23

In Stace 2010 edition this is now a separate species and differs from *S. filicaulis* (formerly *S. apetala* ssp. *erecta*) in that the sepals are erecto-patent in fruit with the outer sepals sub-acute to acuminate, not with sepals patent in fruit with the outer sepals sub-obtuse to obtuse. It is an over wintering annual, which is probably under recorded. It is scattered throughout the British Isles and is found in dry sandy or gravel heaths as well as man-made habitats, e.g. base of walls, pavement cracks. It was recorded from 29 FlOx tetrads. The lack of precision of previous records make it difficult to assess distribution change. SEE

22	V	Peads Farm Frilford		SU443972	2011	HJK
23	S	Sydlings Copse	SSSI	SP557097	2007	HJK
22	V	Private		SU 449983	2007	HJK
23	C	Tadmarton Heath Golf Club		SP 390397	2007	HJK

⬇ *Scleranthus annuus*
Native

Annual Knawel
s. 41, Endangered ■ **Rare in Oxon and vc23**

A deep-rooted annual which stands out in dry conditions. There has been a huge decline both nationally and locally, which may be due to increased fertilisation. There has been only one 2000–11 recorded site in vc22 (Oxon) and one in vc23. Druce 1927 describes it as 'locally common on arable land with dry sandy soils;' but by the time FlOx was published there were only 23 records in vc23 and many of these were at tetrad level only. Several of those were in the S, which have not been re-found recently, despite extensive searches in the late 1990s (Sutcliffe & Kay 2000). In 2012 Larkman newly found it in abundance at City Farm, Eynsham. SEE

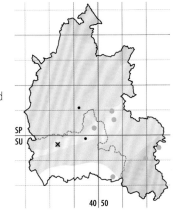

22	V	Confidential	SSSI	SU49P	2010	SEE	50+ plants, new
23	S	Mr Miller's farm		SU696907	1999	SJG+	
22	V	Buckland Warren	SSSI	SU333963	1996	SEE	Not seen since
23	Bu			SU750950	1987		
22	S			SU560834	1986	HJMB	
22	V	Youlbury		SP483029	1984	RH-B	
23	S	Shotover House	pLWS	SP586062	1981	DTS	
23	S	Sydlings Copse	SSSI, BBOWT	SP556096	1974	HJMB	

Spergula arvensis
Archaeophyte

(Peter Creed)

This is an annual of open, disturbed, light, neutral to acid soils. Nationally, it has suffered a decline due to agricultural intensification. The number of locations in Oxon has also declined steeply from no fewer than 95 FlOx tetrads, though it does not qualify as scarce. The Arable flowers project in the 1990s produced many records, notably in the S. Surprisingly many old records from the Nettlebed and Kingwood areas were not re-found. SEE.

22	V	Confidential		SU49U	2010	HJK	Rare
23	S	Hardwick Farm		SU654787	2010	JHW	7 fields >200
23	S	Caversham Heath Golf Course		SU693762	2010	JHW	24
23	S	Crowsley Park Farm		SU724787	2010	JHW	
23	S	Elsfield		SP542104	2009	HJK	>1000
22	V	Gorse Farm		SU289930	2009	SEE	25+
23	C	Tadmarton Camp		SP387357	2008	HJK	>100
23	W	Eynsham		SP402118	2008	HJK	1
22	V	Folly Park		SU296950	2007	SEE	7
23	S	Collins Farm		SU657788	2007	HJK	
23	W	Shilton Bradwell Grove Airfield	LWS	SP246068	2003	JMC	
22	V	Tubney Woods	LWS	SU445995	2003	JMC	
22	V	Confidential		SU49T	2003	JMC	
23	S	Model Farm		SU6896	2001	DB	
23	S	Coombe End Farm		SU626798	2000	SG	
23	S	Path Hill Farm		SU661790	2000	SG+	
23	S	Manor Farm		SU706822	2000	OS+	
23	S	Blackmore Farm		SU716805	2000	SG+	
23	S	Greysgreen Farm		SU724823	2000	SG+	
23	S	Rotherfield Greys		SU739829	2000	SG+	

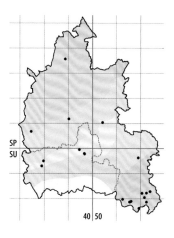

SP
SU

40 | 50

Spergularia rubra
Native

S. rubra has leaves which are linear and flattened, as opposed to linear and cylindrical in *S. marina*. The latter has become increasingly common on salted road verges. *S. rubra* is an annual of dry sandy soils, with a partly coastal distribution in Britain. It was in nine FlOx tetrads but is now only found in three locations in vc23, six others having been lost. Low nutrients and open ground are required for it to thrive. SEE

23	S	Caversham Heath Golf Course		SU688769	2010	JHW	
23	S	Caversham Heath Golf Course		SU694756	2010	JHW	Abundant over 6 locations
22	V	*Jespers Hill*		*SU299952*	*2009*	*SEE*	*Since lost due to development*
23	S	Brasenose Wood and Shotover Hill	SSSI, LGS	SP565057	2006	SHW	
23	S	Witheridge Hill		SU695840	1995	RdA	
23	S	Kingwood Common	LWS	SU696825	1995	RdA	
23	S	Nettlebed Common	LWS	SU705871	1995	RdA	
23	S	Binfield Heath		SU741780	1986	HJMB	

➡ *Agrostemma githago*
Archaeophyte

Corncockle
Last wild record in Oxon 1992, in vc23 1991

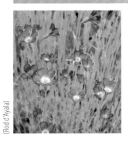
(Rod d'Ayala)

The handsome annual Corncockle was formerly a common weed in cereal crops, also in waste ground. Its survival depended on seed production but after its control by seed cleaning it became rare. It was seen between 1967 and 1996 in only seven FlOx tetrads and two sites in vc22 (Oxon). Many of its seeds are short-lived but Mabey (2010) cites one case of seed longevity and the A420 colony may have been another. FlBe has 13 undated records. Its survival, after a big decline, has depended since 1993 on wildflower sowings and stewardship schemes. The map excludes some garden records. In GB it was widespread in England, mainly SE of a line Exeter–York, but now most often in East Anglia and the Thames Valley. HJK

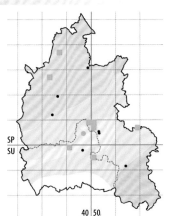

⬇ *Silene noctiflora*
Archaeophyte

Night-flowering Catchfly
Vulnerable ■ Scarce in Oxon and vc23

(Peter Sheasby)

This annual Catchfly of cultivated land, germinating in spring, grows mainly on dry sandy or lime-rich soils. Before 2000 it was seen twice in 1997, six times in FlBe (1977–90) and in 87 tetrads (FlOx p. 118, 1968–91). We could not re-visit many tetrads and half were N of Northings SP20, but we hardly ever found *S. noctiflora* where we did re-record *Euphorbia exigua* which can grow with it. In an arable strip in a set-aside field it appeared in good numbers in 2007, falling to few in 2009, then 40 in 2010 and 100 in 2011, mostly in the part ploughed in autumn where it adjoined the part ploughed in spring. In GB it has hugely declined – 60% between 1987 and 2004 (Braithwaite *et al.*, 2006) as herbicides and fertilisers increased and crops were sown in autumn rather than spring; it is now least rare in lowland England. HJK

23	W	Spelsburydown farm		SP352236	2010	RH-B	7
22	V	Confidential		SU49T	2010	HJK	Ploughed, 23 >100 in 2011
23	W	Salt Way, Ditchley	SSSI, LNR	SP386194	2009	BL	1
23	W	Field's edge nr Spelsbury		SP366225	2007	PS	
23	W	Ditchley Estate		SP387217	2007	AJD	<1997s
23	W	Stonesfield		SP396188	2004	JE	Frequent
23	W	Glyme Farm, Chipping Norton		SP330263	2002	PS	
23	W	Filkins		SP243037	1997	HJK	
23	W	Cassington		SP446119	1987	HJMB	

⬇ *Silene gallica*
Archaeophyte

Small-flowered Catchfly
Endangered, Nationally Scarce ■ Last Oxon and vc23 record before 1990

This winter annual of S England and Wales prefers dry sandy arable, grassland and wasteland with slightly acidic soil and tolerates raised nutrients. It has declined hugely and is now largely restricted to coastal sites. Druce recorded it as an alien at Harpsden; FlOx had it at Gallowstree, Sonning (SU6880) before 1990. FlBe cited Buckland Warren in 1966. CRL

→ *Silene conica*   **Sand Catchfly**
?Native   **Endangered, Nationally Scarce ■ Rare in Oxon, last vc23 record pre-1927**

(Phil Cutt)

Sand Catchfly, a small annual of poor acid sandy soils, grows among very short grass, sand-loving annuals and bare patches, best seen in June and (if wet) July. Numbers vary, and are best after previous hot summers. Before 1927, it was in vc23 at Botley, Goring and Headington. In vc22 (Oxon) Bowen recorded it in 1981 at Hitchcopse Pit, and in 1980 at Dry Sandford Pit. It was at Frilford Heath from 1913 but Druce doubted if it was native; FlBe gives data from W of A338 (1974–81), and Killick's from 2001–4 from the mown edge of set-aside E of it, where numbers ranged from 100 in 1997 and 300 in 2000 to three in 2010. It is scattered in S England and S Wales, especially sandy heaths in East Anglia and coasts, but lost from many inland sites. HJK

22	V	Confidential		SU49P	2010	HJK	3, bare with *Plantago lanceolata, Aira caryophyllea*
22	V	Frilford Heath, Ponds and Fens	SSSI	SU442974	2002	FlBe	
22	V	Confidential		SU49N	2000	HJK	300 with various small annuals
22	V	Hitchcopse Pit	SSSI, BBOWT	SU452996	1981	HJMB	Hitchcopse Pit

↓ *Dianthus armeria*   **Deptford Pink**
Native   **Sched 8, s. 41, Endangered, Nationally Scarce ■ Last wild record in Oxon and vc23 1981**

This delicate small annual or biennial has suffered a huge decline though widespread in England. It prefers neutral and low nitrate conditions. Short sward is also important, and lack of grazing may have contributed to its demise; Druce had six sites and FlOx four – Deddington Hill near Mollington by BBOWT 1981, Chinnor, and Balscote where it is no longer found (Sheasby). CRL

→ *Dianthus deltoides*   **Maiden Pink**
Native   **Vulnerable, Nationally Scarce ■ Rare in Oxon, absent in vc23**

(Phil Cutt)

This is a perennial with erect flowering stems up to 45 cm high. It is found in scattered localities throughout GB, mainly, though not exclusively, on base-rich soils, overlying limestone or chalk. There has been a decline nationally before 1930, from either, overgrazing and nutrient enrichment or undergrazing and scrub encroachment. The only site for this in Oxon is on private land, where it was first recorded in 1930. It now survives in one patch about one metre square. The site is now managed for the species and it still survived in 2015. Fitter's 1982 site, the latest in FlOx, and any recent sites in vc23 are believed to be garden escapes and have not survived. SEE

| 22 | V | Confidential | SSSI | SU49P | 2009 | SEE | Approx. 24 flowering spikes |
| 23 | 0 | Boundary Brook | | SP533047 | 1991 | OUWG | Introduced |

Chenopodium   Goosefoots

Problems can be experienced in the identification of this group and few of the records in FlOx or since have been confirmed by experts. Only a selection is therefore given here; FlOx (pp. 111–2) gives past tetrad records. Goosefoots typically grow in waste places with high nutrient status. CRL

⬇ *Chenopodium bonus-henricus*   Good-King-Henry
Archaeophyte   Vulnerable ■ Scarce in Oxon and vc23

This perennial was cultivated as a green vegetable. It is still widespread in GB despite a steep decline, even steeper here. Braithwaite *et al.* (2006) found a significant decrease between 1987–8 and 2003–4; it was often on roadsides by farms, which are now too disturbed. Druce listed 35 sites, FlOx included 106 tetrads (perhaps not all correct) while FlBe had five recent sites – Faringdon, Little Coxwell, West Challow, Pucketty Farm and Grove. CRL

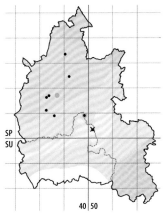

23	0	Godstow Nunnery		SP484091	2009	RH-B	1
23	W	Wychwood	NNR, SSSI	SP328163	2005	PS	Five Ash Bottom ride
23	C	South Newington Valley	LWS	SP404336	2003	CRL	
23	W	Whiteways Quarry	LWS, LGS	SP420246	2002	AW+	
22	*V*	*Kennington Pool*	*LWS*	*SP518034*	*2002*	*AWM+*	*2004*
23	W	Minster Lovell Bank	LWS	SP327112	2001	CRL	
23	W	Witney Lake & Meadows	Other	SP360090	2001	GH	
23	C	37 Acre Field	LWS	SP577136	2001	CRL	
23	W	Wychwood	NNR, SSSI	SP338170	2000	JMC	
23	C	Barford St John		SP437330	1999	HJK	By N–S road
23	W	Fawler		SP371171	1982	RH-B	

⬇ *Chenopodium hybridum*   Maple-leaved Goosefoot
Archaeophyte   Rare in Oxon and vc23

This annual is usually a casual of deep, humus-rich, cultivated soil. It occurs in SE England, but has declined. Druce recorded 13 sites, and FlOx 23 tetrads. In 2000–11 it was in gardens (also vc22 (Oxon) Park Cres, Abingdon, HJK, 2012) and waste areas; The Kidneys is a former tip. CRL

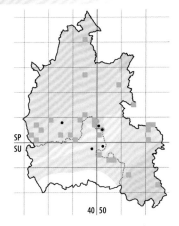

23	0	Oxford, Worcester College		SP508066	2007	RH-B	
23	W	Ducklington, Witney Rd		SP356079	2006	HJK	Garden
23	0	Aston's Eyot and The Kidneys	SLINC	SP523051	1986	RH-B	& 2011
23	W	Broadwell, wet scrub and pond		SP252036	1985	RJ	

⬇ *Chenopodium murale*   Nettle-leaved Goosefoot
Archaeophyte   Endangered ■ Last record in Oxon and vc23 <1990

This annual, mostly of S England, has declined markedly since 1962. It prefers nutrient-rich rubbish tips. Druce had nine sites e.g. Iffley Rd rubbish heaps 1911, FlOx had 20 records pre-1990, all tetrads and unconfirmed; FlBe gave Sutton Courtenay 1978 and Didcot 1980. CRL

| 22 | V | Sutton Courtenay Gravel Pits | | SU518930 | 1985 | HJMB+ | |

⬆ *Chenopodium ficifolium*   Fig-leaved Goosefoot
Archaeophyte   Not Scarce in Oxon, Scarce in vc23

This annual of S and central England has increased in recent years both nationally and in Oxon. It is found in cultivated and waste ground and meadows, and tolerates high nutrients. Druce had eight sites, six in Oxford and one in Didcot. FlOx had 30 tetrads; most of the 15 records (nine in vc23) in 2000–11 are close to Oxford and at new sites, possibly suggesting a spreading population. Bowen (1968) had three sites, FlBe had Didcot in 1969. CRL

Montia fontana
Native

Blinks
Scarce in Oxon and vc23

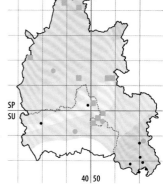

Blinks is small, annual to perennial, in bare ground, short grass or arable; mostly on seasonally wet acid or neutral sand or gravel. It is easily overlooked, which could explain why the distributions now and in Druce (1927) and FlOx (11 tetrads, p. 113) all differ. FlOx suggested a decline due to drainage. FlOx did not distinguish the subspecies; the few records in FlBe were ssp. *chondrosperma*. In GB it is widespread, including wider colonies and bigger plants in streams and flushes. HJK

22	V	Jarn Field	OPT	SP488022	2010	CRL	100s, new
23	S	Hardwick, opposite King Charles Head		SU662788	2010	JHW	Many, new
23	Be	Mapledurham Playing Fields		SU699756	2010	JHW	11 patches, in >1 sq.m, new
23	S	Peppard Cricket Ground		SU703815	2010	JHW	Several patches in 2 × 2 sq.m, new
23	S	Kennylands Field, Sonning Common		SU713794	2010	JHW	Many in 1 × 0.6 m, new
23	S	Nettlebed Common	LWS	SU700871	2006	JHW	Many, new
22	V	Folly Hill, Faringdon		SU294948	2004	SEE	In FlBe, once only, new
23	Be	Caversham Park		SU727768	2004	JHW	Recreation ground, new
22	V	Arable margin west of Hutchins Copse		SU435916	1992	HJK	Few
23	S	Clifton Hampden manor		SU549957	1980	HJK	Sparse in damp lawn
23	S	Warburg	SSSI, BBOWT	SU716879	1968	VP	Freedom wood

Hottonia palustris
Native and introduced

Water-violet
Vulnerable ■ Not Scarce in Oxon and vc23

This decorative perennial of still, shallow base-rich water, is often planted. It is unable to set seed from flowers of the same clone, requiring the different flower type (thrum or pin). It is widespread in central and S England but does not tolerate much disturbance or high eutrophication, and has declined, mostly pre-1930. Druce had 29 sites and FlOx (p. 147) 22. It has appeared at some new sites, but disappeared in others, sometimes due to shading. In 2000–11: 15 sites in Oxon and 13 in vc23. CRL

Lysimachia vulgaris
Yellow Loosestrife
We studied this plant of river banks and ditches; with 38 2000–10 records in Oxon (30 in vc23) it is Not Scarce. HJK

Anagallis tenella
Native

Bog Pimpernel
Scarce in Oxon and vc23

(Phil Cutt)

This is a creeping, evergreen perennial, which has procumbent stems from which the pale pink flowers rise on short stalks. It needs wet open sites to survive and has always been commoner in the damper western parts of the country where its numbers are stable. It has declined in most of E England, and Oxon, probably due to drainage schemes and eutrophication. In Oxon It was recorded in 15 tetrads. It is found mainly in fens. At the private site it dominates some stream banks and short mown turf. At Parsonage Moor, Lye Valley, and Sydlings Copse, it can still be found in reasonable numbers in taller vegetation. SEE

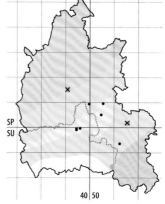

23	O	Lye Valley	SSSI	SP547051	2010	JAW	
22	V	Confidential	SSSI	SU49P	2010	SEE	Plentiful in several sites
22	V	Parsonage Moor	SAC, SSSI	SU460997	2010	JAW	In several locations
23	S	Rokemarsh		SU624936	2009	JAW	New, unfavourable conditions
23	S	Sydlings Copse	SSSI, BBOWT	SP556096	2008	HJK	
23	O	Wolvercote		SP497094	2005	CWDG	
22	V	Tubney Woods	LWS	SU445995	2004	JMC	
23	S	*Spartum Fen*	*SSSI*	*SP655017*	*1990*	*EN*	*Not re-found by HJK in1998*
23	S	*South Stoke Marsh (north)*	*LWS*	*SU594844*	*1986*	*GH*	
23	W	*Coombe Fen*	*LWS*	*SP408150*	*1983*	*HJMB*	*Not re-found by WOR in 2008*

→ *Anagallis foemina*
Archaeophyte

(Phil Cutt)

Recording methods make it difficult to assess the stability of the population as the Blue Pimpernel is often confused with the blue version of *A. arvensis*, which has numerous minute hairs on the edge of the petals. *A. foemina* has few small hairs four cells long. In Atlas 2002 this annual is shown as being scattered over central and S England and East Anglia. It seems to be usually in arable land unlike *A. arvensis,* which can occur in semi-natural habitats too. In Oxon blue forms have been recorded since Druce 1886, when it was described as rare, but widespread, which is a description that probably applies equally well today. There were five records in 2000–11. FlOx had 17 tetrads for *A. foemina* and eight for the blue *A. arvensis*. There are no specific records at TVERC pre-2000. SEE

22	V	Wytham Woods	SSSI	SP462080	2010	AWM	Regular since 2002
23	W	Bridle track from Stonesfield		SP377179	2009	SEE+	3 plants
23	W	Shilton Bradwell Grove Airfield	LWS	SP247075	2008	BB	3 sites
23	W	Stonesfield, Astall Leigh garden		SP298115	2008	BB	Abundant
23	W	Arable field SE of Stonesfield		SP300115	2007	BB	Scattered

⬇ *Centunculus minimus* (*Anagallis minima*)
Native

Chaffweed
Endangered, GB Near Threatened ■ Last record in Oxon and vc23 1983

This tiny annual is largely coastal and hugely declining. It grows in open, damp, sandy, acidic, and low-nutrient soils. It is easily missed on account of its inconspicuous and early flowering. Druce had it at Binfield **OXF** in 1884 and JPM Brenan at Bladon Heath **OXF** in 1946; FlOx p. 148 gave no records; FlBe cited Frilford (1947 EW Jones). Last seen at Nettlebed (1983 Bowen). CRL

23	S	Nettlebed Common	LWS	SU705871	1983	HJMB
23	S	Brasenose Wood and Shotover Hill	SSSI, LGS	SP567057	1981	DTS
23	S	Sydlings Copse	SSSI, BBOWT	SP556096	1974	AJJ

→ *Samolus valerandi*
Native

Brookweed
Not Scarce in Oxon, Scarce in vc23

This is a short-lived perennial, surviving in permanently wet conditions, limited to calcareous and sometimes saline soils. Although this species is regarded as declining (Atlas 2002), especially in inland locations, it seems quite stable in Oxfordshire. Given that Druce thought it rare and decreasing in 1927, 11 FlOx tetrads and 12 sites in Oxon now, indicate a good survival rate. The plant needs open conditions, so is transient and several old sites have gone, but they are replaced. In the confidential location it is doing particularly well with four sites containing hundreds of plants altogether. SEE

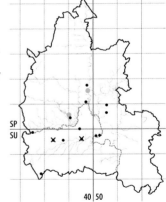

22	V	Confidential	SSSI	SU49P	2010	SEE+	4 sites
22	V	Pond by Barton Lane		SU512973	2009	DG	
22	V	Radley Gravel Pits	LWS	SU527975	2009	HJK	c.30
23	W	Dix Pit Extension	pLWS	SP406045	2008	SG	
22	W	N. bank Thames, Kelmscot		SU252987	2008	SEE	1 large plant
23	C	Cassington to Yarnton Gravel Pits	LWS	SP471109	2006	CRL	
23	S	Sydlings Copse	SSSI, BBOWT	SP556096	2006	SEE+	Last seen 2008
22	V	Tubney Woods	LWS	SP445005	2005	FHW	
23	O	Stansfeld Field Study Centre	pLWS	SP555065	2005	RdA	
22	V	Lovells Court rushy field		SU377956	2003	JMC	
23	C	Bunkers Hill Quarry	LWS	SP475175	2001	CRL	
22	V	*Bushey Barn*		*SU336956*	*2000*	*SEE*	*2006, site overgrown*
23	W	Vicarage Pit		SP401056	1999	JAW	
23	C	Langford Meadows	LWS	SP479153	1987	GH	

Calluna vulgaris
Heather
Native   Near Threatened ■ Not Scarce in Oxon and vc23

Heather was in 40 tetrads in FlOx (p. 146) of which 26 were on Clay-with-Flints and high up in the Chilterns, but it was thought to be decreasing. The decrease has probably continued but we found it by 2010 in 28 sites in Oxon, (20 in vc23 and six outside the Chilterns), so here it is Not Scarce. In England much has been lost since 1950 to forestry, farming, mineral workings and scrub. HJK

Erica tetralix
Cross-leaved Heath
Native   Near Threatened ■ Rare in Oxon and vc23

This low-growing dwarf shrub of damp, open heathland, is frequent except in S central England where it has suffered a big decline. At Binfield small non-flowering plants survive heavy grazing and trampling by deer when protected by logs and brash. Over-shading and grazing are severe threats to this small colony, and remedial action may be difficult. Druce had Tadmarton and Binfield, FlOx two tetrads and FlBe none. JHW, CRL

| 23 | S | Binfield Heath, The Common | | SU738786 | 2010 | JHW | 8 |
| 23 | S | Kingwood Common | LWS | SU696826 | 2004 | VR+ | |

Erica cinerea
Bell Heather
Native   Near Threatened ■ Scarce in Oxon and vc23

(Rod d'Ayala)

This dwarf shrub occurs on well-drained acid soils throughout GB except S central England where is has declined, especially over chalk. In Oxon it occurs sparingly on dry woodland margins on the acid gravels of the Chilterns plateau, but could be lost from the NW. It commonly occurs with ling and is vulnerable to shade particularly where it grows under beech on woodland edges. Some colonies on Kingwood Common have benefited from exposure of mineral soil to promote germination, scrub control and some planting of seedlings. Druce had eight sites and FlOx six tetrads. FlBe gives Buckland Warren SU344956 which has now been coniferised. JHW, CRL

22	V	Memorial Garden	LWS	SP482025	2009	HJK	Introduced
23	S	Nettlebed Common	LWS	SU699872	2009	SR	
23	S	Burnt Platt, Stoke Row		SU692832	2008	JHW	2
23	S	Parklane Shaw	LWS	SU674807	2007	JHW	11 at 2 sites
23	S	Kingwood Common	LWS	SU696828	2007	JHW	38 in 3 sites
23	S	Peppard Common	LWS	SU704815	2006	JHW	6 at 2 sites
23	S	Witheridge Hill		SU695840	1995	RdA	
23	C	Tadmarton Heath Golf Course		SP390356	1993	HJK	Abs. 2008 HJK
23	S	Withy Copse		SU682803	1991	GH	
23	S	Pishill Woods	SSSI	SU715902	1981	GP	

Pyrola minor
Common Wintergreen
Native   Near Threatened ■ Last Oxon and vc23 record 1972

(Peter Creed)

This rhizomatous, evergreen herb is most abundant in Scotland and the NE. Having suffered a big decline it survives in E Berks and the New Forest. It likes deep leaf litter in boggy woodlands and plantations which are acidic and very low in nutrients. Druce had 20 records in the Chilterns, and FlOx (p. 146) 10 tetrads, including Witheridge Hill by Paul in 1972, and an unconfirmed record from Sarsgrove Wood. CRL

⬇ *Hypopitys monotropa*   Yellow Bird's-nest
Native   s. 41, Endangered ■ Scarce in Oxon and vc23

(Peter Creed)

This herb lacks chlorophyll and relies on *Tricholoma* fungi to extract nutrients from adjacent trees. It is widespread in GB, but mostly on very low-nutrient soils on the chalk of S England. The two subspecies are hard to distinguish and intermediates occur, as with Barber's 2011 find (confirmed by F Rumsey). Mostly in the Chilterns, though Killick saw it in a plantation S of Letcombe ?SU378830 c. 1980. Webb re-found it at Aston Rowant in 2013. Kirby found one in 2014 under beech in Brogden's Belt, Wytham where it was known to Druce, and "scores" had been seen by Elton in 1954. Druce had c. 20 sites, of which eight were on the Cotswolds; FlOx (p. 146) 25 tetrads and FlBe Buckland and Wytham. CRL

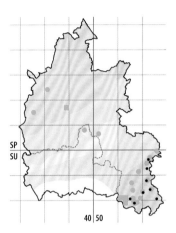

23	S	Christmas Common		SU718926	2011	RB	New
23	S	Long Toll Road, Woodcote		SU649806	2008	JHW	4, new
23	S	Gutteridge Wood	LWS	SU667789	2008	SP	10
23	S	Lambridge Wood	SSSI	SU731843	2008	JHW	81
23	S	Harpsden Wood	SSSI	SU758806	2008	JHW	2, new
23	S	Bear, Oveys & Great Bottom Woods	SSSI	SU702831	2004	JHW	2
23	S	Warburg	SSSI, BBOWT	SU716878	2001	MS	
23	S	Shirburn Wood		SU717947	1988	HJMB	
23	S	Common/College Wood		SU660808	1987	JHW	2 sites
23	S	Gutteridge Wood	LWS	SU668787	1986	SS	
23	S	Oakley Hill	LWS, BBOWT	SU758995	1986	RSRF	
23	O	Addison's Walk, Magdalen College, Oxford		SP522065	1985	RH-B	
23	S	Mongewell Woods Complex		SU655869	1979	GB	
23	S	Dean Wood and Westernend Shaw		SU683914	1979	PM	
23	S	Wyfold Wood/New Copse Complex		SU690809	1979	DJNH	
23	S	Walk Shaw	pLWS	SU677792	1978	JHW	

⬆ *Asperula cynanchica*   Squinancywort
This delicate perennial calcicole is widespread on chalk and more scattered on limestone grassland. FlOx had 35 tetrads while we found 30 sites in 2000–11, so Not Scarce. CRL

⬇ *Galium pumilum*   Slender Bedstraw
Native   s. 41, Endangered, Nationally Rare ■ Rare in Oxon and vc23

This small perennial of short turf in dry lime-rich grassland was first recorded in Oxon in 1901. It appeared in vc23 at four sites between 1938 and 1958, then in tetrads SP3818 and 4410 and SU6694, not repeated recently, and now at Hartslock. In vc22 (Oxon) it was at Wytham Hill in 1961, and at Hackpen Hill, regularly found widely scattered till 2015. It is limited to S England and has much declined with loss of chalk grassland and reduced grazing, and Oxon is now at the N end of its range. HJK

23	S	Hartslock	SAC, SSSI, BBOWT	SU617794	2010	RdA	Small area
22	V	Hackpen Downs		SU350856	2006	SEE	Frequent
22	V	Hackpen		SU383850	2006	SEE	100–200

⬇ *Galium tricornutum*   Corn Cleavers
Archaeophyte   s. 41, Critically Endangered, Nationally Rare ■ Last Oxon and vc23 record 1986
Re-introduced 2013

This small annual weed of arable fields was widespread in S England but has suffered a catastrophic decline and is now only at Rothamsted in arable. It requires calcareous and moderate nutrient conditions. Druce had 27 sites and FlOx (p. 228) recorded it in seven tetrads but noted "perhaps extinct". FlBe had it in the 1960s at Fairmile and Waylands Smithy. It was re-introduced in 2013 and 2014 at the Triangle, Upper Seeds, Wytham, an area known for other arable flowers. The OFG is working with Oxford University at the request of NEng and the BSBI. CRL

23	W	Ditchley Road Quarry		SP364198	1986	WDC	2 areas
22	V	*Wytham Woods*	*SSSI*	*SP462081*	*1985*	*CWDG*	*Re-introduced 2013*
22	V	*Whitehorse Hill*	*SSSI*	*SU302868*	*1981*	*HJMB*	

⬆ *Centaurium pulchellum*
Native

Lesser Centaury
Scarce in Oxon, Rare in vc23

(Peter Creed)

This annual species is differentiated from *C. erythraea* in that it does not have a basal rosette at flowering and the stem between the base of the calyx and the bract is more than one mm. It is found on calcareous soils in grassland and woodland rides scattered throughout England and in the Scottish borders. It is a good coloniser of disturbed ground and has increased nationally. It was described in past local floras as very local and rare. Palmer found the Flowing Spring colony in 1953 and FlOx cited five tetrads. Recent finds in Oxon have been near newly formed gravel pits and ponds, and fly ash deposits. It would seem to be increasing in the county. SEE

22	V	Sutton Courtenay Environmental Education Centre	BBOWT	SU501918	2009	RdA	Plentiful around pond, new
22	V	Radley Gravel Pits	LWS	SU528979	2009	HJK	Approx. 10 plants, new
23	S	Henley Road Gravel Pit	LWS	SU737747	2009	JHW	1 plant
22	V	Buscot reservoir		SU238966	2007	SEE	5 plants on east side
22	V	Badbury Forest – Eaton Wood	LWS	SU262964	2007	SEE	Plentiful on open ride
23	S	Span Hill Chalk Pit	pLWS, LGS	SU747770	2006	SEE+	Recorded annually to 2012
22	V	Wytham Woods	SSSI	SP445076	1985	RH-B	
23	W	Foxholes	SSSI, BBOWT	SP250205	1981	HJMB	

⬇ *Gentianella germanica*
Native

Chiltern Gentian
Vulnerable, Nationally Scarce ■ Scarce in Oxon and vc23

(Peter Creed)

This striking gentian is largely confined to the Chilterns, its curious absence from chalk further S may be because it was first established in the Chilterns, possibly as an introduction from its stronghold in E Europe. While Druce knew five sites FlOx had 24 tetrads and vc23 now has eight. It hybridises with *G. amarella*, and intermediates can be seen at Warburg and Oakley Hill, and formerly at Crowell and Chinnor Hills (FlOx) and Segsbury (FlBe). Oakley Hill may be a Druce locality of the hybrid, which he named *G. × pamplinii*. However at Watlington Hill both species occur close together without intermediates. At this site the Chiltern Gentian grows in slightly taller sward, perhaps on deeper soil. If sheep grazing declines, the sward usually becomes too dense for this species which then survives along footpaths. Populations vary with the spring weather. While it is normally biennial, individuals which are probably annual do occur, these are very small and slender with the long upper internode typical of *G. anglica*, but flower in late August with Chiltern Gentian. CRL

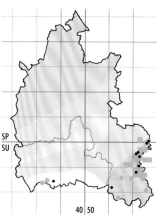

23	S	Warburg	SSSI, BBOWT	SU714881	2010	RdA	200–400
23	S	Aston Rowant	SAC, NNR, SSSI	SU722960	2009	RH-B	Frequent
23	S	Oakley Hill	LWS, BBOWT	SU758997	2008	JHW	1
23	S	Shirburn Hill	SSSI	SU714954	2007	JHW	16 in 3 lots
22	V	Hackpen, Warren & Gramp's Hill Downs	SSSI	SU370844	2006	SEE	>5000
23	S	Pishill Bank	LWS	SU725906	2006	CRL	17
23	S	Fiddle Hill	LWS	SU613819	2003	JMC	
23	S	Buckingham Bottom Meadow	LWS	SU728943	2002	RB	
23	S	Chinnor Hill	SSSI, BBOWT	SP766005	>2000	CRL+	c. 20
23	S	The Basin and Bazedown Park	LWS	SU641777	1992	NCC	Abs. SP
23	S	Middle Assenden Farm		SU741855	1992	NCC	
22	V	Segsbury/Letcombe/Castle		SU385845	1991	NCC	Abs. HJK 2009
23	S	Warren Bank	SSSI, BBOWT	SU653857	1989	GB	Abs. JHW 2007
23	S	Queen Wood, Christmas Common		SU717926	1988	DF+	
23	S	Hungrey Hill Wood/Cop Grove		SU735941	1987	SL+	
22	V	Crog Hill and Scary Hill	LWS	SU323837	1986	JMC	
23	S	Watlington and Pyrton Hills	SSSI	SU710942	1986	DF+	
23	S	Pishill Bank	LWS	SU725906	1986	DF+	
23	S	Swyncombe Downs	SSSI	SU673912	1981	JMC	Abs. JHW 2007
23	S	Swan Wood, Nott Wood and Devil's Hill		SU695855	1979	DJNH	
23	S	Henley Golf Course		SU755806	1973	VNP	

Oxfordshire's Threatened Plants **73**

⬇ *Gentianella anglica*   Early Gentian
Native, endemic   Sched 8, s. 41, Nationally Scarce ■ Scarce in Oxon, Rare in vc23

(Peter Creed)

Gentianella anglica is distinguished from the genetically similar *G. amarella* by the length of the upper internode and flower stalk. In *G. anglica* this is more than half the total length of the plant. The calyx lobes are equal and appressed; also it flowers earlier, May–June. (Plants with intermediate characteristics have been found, e.g. at The Hollies, Streatley, vc22). The flowers only open in the sun, making this small plant easy to miss. Early Gentian is an annual found on low-nutrient calcareous soils in grassland or fixed dunes. Nationally it is confined to S and central England and has declined, due largely to a reduction in grazing. In Oxon it is now found on a few sites on the Wessex Downs. Thin soils and an open sward appear more important than aspect for successful germination. The strongholds are on Hackpen Hill, in the vicinity of the White Horse and the road verges near Dragon Hill. The most recent site in vc23 was at Holly Hill, but that is unconfirmed; that at Taynton, the only one in FlOx, is now over grown by Tor grass. The OFG monitor the sites regularly and find the population numbers vary greatly at all of them. There are declining site numbers nationally as well as locally. Druce 1897 noted *Gentianella amarella* var *praecox* in more sites along the Wessex downs, but his description of this plant differs from Stace 2010 for *Gentianella anglica*. FlBe gives extensive notes (p. 748) on this species. SEE, HJK.

22	V	Kingston Down	LWS	SU285823	2010	SEE	31 in 2 sites
22	V	Whitehorse Hill	SSSI	SU292866	2010	SEE	17
22	V	Whitehorse Hill	SSSI	SU301867	2010	SEE	113, 4 sites
22	V	Hackpen Hill	SAC, SSSI	SU351850	2006	SEE+	17
23	*W*	*Taynton Quarries*	*SSSI*	*SP236151*	*1997*	*HJK+*	*11; abs. 2007*

⬇ *Lithospermum arvense*   Field Gromwell
Archaeophyte   Endangered ■ Rare in Oxon and vc23

This annual grew on arable fields, open grass and waste ground, on light, dry, especially lime-rich soils. Its seeds are short-lived. In FlOx (p. 198) it was in 58 tetrads (only five after 1987), most often over Oolite and Lower Chalk. In FlBe it was rare; among undated records was Odstone Down (SU287830). In GB it was common in lowland England but has almost disappeared owing to increasingly intensive farming and herbicides from 1950 onwards. HJK

22	V	Woodlands Farm track		SU338955	2011	SEE+	1, new
23	*C*	*Broughton Park*		*SP416384*	*<1990*	*FlOx*	*abs. 2010 HJK*
22	V	Path Lambourne Rd to Crog Hill		SU324833	2007	SEE	12, arable verge
22	*V*	*Wytham Woods*	*SSSI*	*SP463080*	*2004*	*AWM*	*Not seen since*
23	*W*	*Worton Wood*	*LWS*	*SP434278*	*2003*	*DP*	
22	*V*	*Shippon, field to W*		*SU472977*	*2000*	*HJK*	*Few, dying, herbicide*
23	S	Swyncombe, Lower Farm		SU666912	1999	SJG	
22	V	Hackpen, Warren & Gramp's Hill Downs	SSSI	SU353845	1997	SEE	
22	V	Tubney Manor Farm		SU436992	1997	OS	
23	S	Elsfield, Hill Farm		SP541094	1996	LH	
22	V	Buildings Farm, Gozzards Ford		SU459983	1996	HJK	

➡ *Echium vulgare*   Viper's-bugloss
We studied this species because of the decline of heathy habitats but with 31 2000–11 records in Oxon (18 in vc23) it is Not Scarce. HJK

Myosotis secunda   Creeping Forget-me-not
This hairy annual to perennial plant with an almost stalkless stigma is abundant in the N and W. It can be confused with both of the commoner aquatic *Myosotis* species. It requires acidic, wet places with low nutrients. Druce and FlBe had no records. As it is rare in central England the five FlOx records and an unconfirmed one from Taston Brook (SP35542157, 2006) are surprising. CRL, HJK

⬇ *Cynoglossum officinale*   Hound's-tongue
Native   Near Threatened ■ Not Scarce in Oxon and vc23

This downy, grey, unpalatable biennial is widespread in England and Wales but has declined substantially. It prefers calcareous or sandy, open ground and tolerates raised nutrients; often associated with rabbit warrens. In vc23 there were 33 FlOx (p. 202) tetrads, and about 25 sites in 2000–11, so has only declined a little. FlBe says it is on the verge of extinction in W Berks, but we found seven sites in vc22 (Oxon) and it has spread into set-aside fields. CRL

Cynoglossum germanicum

Native   Sched 8, s. 41, Critically Endangered, Nationally Rare ■ Rare in Oxon and vc23

Green Hound's-tongue

(Peter Creed)

This is an inconspicuous, greenish biennial or short-lived perennial. It has always been restricted in S England and is now also found only between Kent and Glos. It grows on moist but well-drained calcareous soils in woods and woodland edges. It appeared in abundance in Surrey after the 1987 storms, indicating long survival of seed in the soil. It has hooked seeds and tolerates high nitrogen, explaining its presence along old drove roads. The RPG, under NEng, has been monitoring and managing two sites for several years, and has found that the fluctuating populations respond well to reduction of shading, and removal of ivy, ground elder and cleavers. Garden experiments show that it is self-fertile and germinates and establishes readily, but is easily shaded out. Druce had six sites, including Pyrton, and FlOx three tetrads. CRL

23	S	Clare Hill, Pyrton		SU675977	2008	JHW	47 fl, 91 nfl
23	S	Knightsbridge Lane	SSSI	SU683968	2008	RdA	197 fl
23	S	Warburg	SSSI, BBOWT	SU715882	2008	RdA	>300 intr
23	W	Stratford Bridge		SP445186	2005	RPG	1
23	W	Bladon Quarry		SP453152	1970	RCP	Abs. RCP 1994

Cuscuta europaea

Native

Greater Dodder

Nationally Scarce ■ Rare in Oxon and vc23

(John Killick)

The flower heads are larger than in *C. epithymum*, 10–15 mm across, and flower later, from August onwards. It is an annual, rarely perennial, rootless parasite of nitrogen enriched, damp places by rivers and ditches, germinating primarily on common nettle, and spreading onto hop and other species, scrambling through scrub. Mainly in SE England; there have been some new sites in recent years though not outweighing the losses. It is present in some profusion in a damp meadow by Dorchester Bridge, previously cattle grazed and recently open access. Druce had 20 sites, FlOx (p. 197) 10 tetrads and FlBe had it at Cholsey, Streatley and Wallingford. JHW, CRL

23	S	Dorchester Bridge Meadow		SU580937	2010	JHW	Locally abundant, new
23	S	Shillingford		SU588934	2007	HJK	2 sq.m; since 1987
23	S	Dorchester Gravel Pits (Drayton Road Pit)	LWS	SU582952	2003	CRL	
22	S	Ferry Cot. Preston Crowmarsh		SU613910	1996	JMC	
23	S	By Thame		SU606970	1989	JMC	
22	S	Little Wittenham	SAC, SSSI	SU573929	1984	JB	
23	S	Warren Wood	LWS	SU763777	1980	AJJ	
23	W	Wychwood	NNR, SSSI	SP338170	1972	HJMB	

Cuscuta epithymum

Native

Dodder

Vulnerable ■ Scarce in Oxon and vc23

(Phil Cutt)

This rootless annual (rarely perennial) is parasitic on the stems of small shrubs and herbs. Its balls of pink flowers appear in mid summer on red stems which scramble through low vegetation. Its appearance can be erratic, sometimes absent, in other years prolific. It requires high light and low fertility. Druce had it at seven sites in heathland on gorse and heathers and it was found near Charlbury till 1935, but FlOx recorded eight tetrads only from chalk grassland in the Chilterns on *Lotus, Genista, Knautia, Euphrasia* and *Pimpinella*. It now seems to be mainly associated with *Origanum* and *Thymus,* on and around anthills. In GB it has declined substantially from central and N England and it is now chiefly in the S. JHW, CRL

23	S	Straw Hill	LWS	SU661777	2010	SP+	New
23	S	Kents Hill	LWS	SU725808	2010	JHW	54 sq.m
23	S	Holly Hill (Elmore Park Grassland)	LWS	SU629813	2009	JHW	
23	S	Hartslock	SSSI, BBOWT	SU621793	2008	HJK	Frequent
22	S	North Unhill Bank	LWS	SU564834	1991	NCC	

→ *Hyoscyamus niger*
Archaeophyte

Henbane

Vulnerable ■ Scarce in Oxon and vc23

(Rod d'Ayala)

Henbane, a striking biennial, inhabits rough and waste ground, especially of dry lime-rich and sandy soils, manured land and chicken-runs. Druce thought that plants in newly disturbed ground could be from dormant seeds and FlBe refers to seed longevity, but only records from Wychwood, Crawley, Hackpen and Oxford repeated older ones, and FlBe reports loss from many former sites. Other records appear casual. In FlOx (p. 195) it was in 25 tetrads. Except at Sutton, reported numbers are small. The map shows different distributions before and after 2000. In GB it has steadily declined, especially NW of a line Cardiff–Hull, owing mostly to herbicides. HJK

23	W	Sutton, Cricket Pitch Field		SP421062	2010	BP	500 plants
23	W	Blenheim Park, Combe		SP420169	2009	WC	7 on spoil heap by track
23	W	Manor Farm Meadow, Crawley	LWS	SP338119	2008	HJK	1 good plant
23	C	Barford St John Airfield		SP436338	2008	SG	3, edge of arable field
22	V	Hackpen Hill	SAC, SSSI	SU350849	2008	SEE	3 dead flowering shoots
23	W	Holly Court Farm, Finstock		SP387150	2007	HJK	NE corner of arable field above bank, >40
22	V	Hackpen Downs		SU350856	2006	SEE	6 large clumps nr rabbit warren
23	W	Blenheim Park – New Park pLWS and part of Great Park		SP435165	2001	PS	
23	W	Quarry Bank Crossroads		SP475184	2001	JMC	
23	W	Spoil heap Blenheim		SP420169	1998	JA	
22	V	Henwood by track		SP468026	1997	HJK	
22	V	Hackpen Hill	SAC, SSSI	SU353848	1997	SEE	
23	S	Kents Hill	LWS	SU727808	1997	JHW	
22	V	Haremoor Farm		SU303964	1996	SEE	
23	W	Radford Farm		SP408238	1991	AJD	

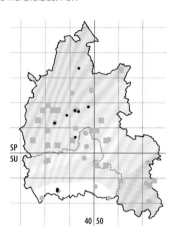

SP
SU

40 | 50

⬇ *Datura stramonium*

Thorn-apple

We have only 10 records of this coarse annual of rich soil, waste and disturbed ground, tips and cultivated land, but as an alien it does not qualify for the Register. It could have come with soya, wool or bird seed. It was in 22 tetrads (FlOx p. 196). It is often casual and/ or in small numbers so the data are mapped, not tabulated. In GB it is widespread but most frequent in S and central England, and may have decreased. HJK

(Peter Creed)

SP
SU

40 | 50

⬇ *Veronica scutellata*
Native

Marsh Speedwell

Near Threatened ■ Not Scarce in Oxon and vc23

This slender perennial of wet places prefers low nitrogen and slightly acidic conditions. It is widespread in the BI, especially in the N and W, but has declined in central England. In Oxon it is now mainly along the Thames and Cherwell, but also on the Chiltern plateau and in valleys in the Cotswolds. While Druce had 20 sites, FlOx (p. 220) had 33 tetrads, FlBe five, and we found 17 sites 2000–11, 14 of them in vc23. CRL

Veronica praecox
Neophyte

Breckland Speedwell
Last record in Oxon and vc23 2008

(Camilla Lambrick)

This small annual is native in S Europe and has a foothold in the Breckland, requiring dry open calcareous ground and extremely low nutrients. It was observed near Standlake (SP385048, HJMB, **OXF**, FlOx p. 220) from 1964 till 2008, on an open S facing slope at the edge of a former gravel pit (latterly rabbit fenced). Its decline, monitored by RPG, remains unexplained (Watkins 2011). CRL

Misopates orontium
Archaeophyte

Weasel's-snout
Vulnerable ■ **Rare in Oxon and vc23**

(Rod d'Ayala)

This spring-germinating annual used to be widespread in S England and Wales, but had a big decline. It was formerly in light, neutral to slightly acidic nutrient-rich arable fields; perhaps it is susceptible to herbicides. It was recently found in old quarries and gardens, Druce had seven sites and FlOx (p. 218) had 18 tetrads, largely to the SE of the Chilterns. FlBe gives Hitchcopse, Harwell, Didcot and Radley. It is in cultivation at 70, Newlands Ave, Didcot. CRL

23	C	Beney's Quarries, Alkerton		SP385430	2000	JMC	
23	O	20 Old Oxford Rd, Old Marston		SP5208	2000	HJK	OXF
23	S	Farm in Watlington		SU695926	1999	SJG	
22	V	Hitchcopse South Sandpit	LWS	SU456988	1979	PJK	
23	W	Ditchley Road Quarry		SP364198	1974	WDC	

Plantago coronopus

Stag's Horn Plantain

This was a candidate for the Register because in FlOx it was only in six tetrads and had declined. It is more frequently found on coastal sites but is found inland on sandy soils, in Oxon along the Corallian Ridge in farmland, and increasingly and elsewhere on road verges. Its spread in Oxon, 15 2000–11 records from vc23 and 10 from vc22, is associated with salting of roads; it is no longer Scarce. SEE

Hippuris vulgaris

Mare's-tail

Mare's-tail was in 41 FlOx tetrads including the Evenlode, Cherwell and Windrush. With 19 2000–11 records in Oxon (16 in vc23), it is Not Scarce but only two recent records (below) are from rivers. HJK

23	W	Heythrop Park	SP371267	2009	WOR	F
23	C	Cherwell Valley Somerton to Nell Bridge, comp 10	SP492339	2005	CRL	

Callitriche — Water-starworts

Callitriche is a difficult genus because leaf shapes can vary greatly and some species have terrestrial forms. It can be under-recorded, often being awkward to collect. Ripe fruits, not always present, can be needed for identification. Most records lack confirmation by experts. HJK

? ⬇ *Callitriche obtusangula* — Blunt-fruited Water-starwort
Native — **Rare in Oxon and vc23**

Its unwinged fruits should reliably reveal this perennial herb in mesotrophic to eutrophic rivers, ponds, ditches, streams, and also on wet mud as water levels drop. David (1958) associated it with alkaline waters in Hants and Derbys. The 28 FlOx records, mapped with two recent records, were distributed in the clay vales, differently from those of Druce who had found it locally common in 20 widely separated sites. In GB it is mainly in the SE, but many of the records in central England are pre-1987. HJK

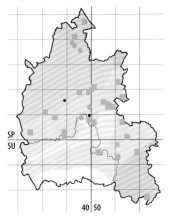

23	W	Ashford Bridge to Combe Cutting (Cotswold Line)	LWS	SP390157	2004	FHW	New
23	O	Port Meadow with Wolvercote Common & Green	SAC, SSSI	SP492097	2004	JE	
23	C	Studley, pond		SP593121	1981	HJK	**OXF**, conf. BM
23	S	Warborough		SU607932	1981	HJK	**OXF**, conf. BM

⬇ *Callitriche brutia* ssp. *hamulata* (*C. hamulata*) — Intermediate Water-starwort
Native — **Probably Scarce in Oxon and vc23**

This Water-starwort has narrow leaves with tips shaped like a bicycle spanner, but in deep or fast-flowing water the leaves of *C. obtusangula* can appear rather similar (N T H Holmes, pers. comm.). Its styles are persistent and reflexed. A perennial herb of acid (FlBe and Atlas 2002) and oligotrophic waters, which are uncommon in Oxon, so Killick doubted many of FlOx's (p. 214) 25 tetrad records outside Otmoor and North Leigh Heath. FlBe has none. The recent records from Otmoor etc. are plausible but unconfirmed. In GB it is widespread but many of the records in central England are pre-1987. HJK

23	W	Ramsden Heath		SP344158	2006	CRL	Rare
22	V	Radley Gravel Pits	LWS	SU504973	2006	DG	
23	C	RSPB Otmoor	pLWS, RSPB	SP556132	2004	RSPB	
23	C	RSPB Otmoor	pLWS, RSPB	SP564146	2004	RSPB	
23	C	RSPB Otmoor	pLWS, RSPB	SP565134	2004	RSPB	
23	C	Otmoor	SSSI	SP572130	2004	JE	
23	C	RSPB Otmoor	pLWS, RSPB	SP585147	2004	RSPB	
23	W	North Leigh Common	LWS	SP401136	1969	ARP	

⬇ *Limosella aquatica* — Mudwort
Native — **Rare in Oxon and vc23**

This inconspicuous annual needs mud left exposed by falling water levels, and flourishes with raised nutrient levels. An uncommon and erratic plant that is widely distributed in the BI and expanding in Scotland. It sometimes becomes abundant on reservoir margins. Druce had four sites around Oxford, FlOx (p. 217) three tetrads and recounted its fluctuations in the same area; long known by the slow-moving Castle Mill Stream. Following the high water levels of 2007–9 it disappeared there, but re-appeared on Port Meadow where the same summer floods had created extensive mud. CRL

22	O	Port Meadow with Wolvercote Common & Green	SAC, SSSI	SP4806	2010	CRL+	Few
23	O	Castle Mill Stream, Oxford		SP500071	2006	JE	20
23	O	Binsey Wetlands		SP490077	1986	SC	
23	O	Port Meadow with Wolvercote Common & Green	SAC, SSSI	SP493095	1981	HJMB	

Stachys germanica
Native Schedule 8, s. 41, Endangered, Nationally Rare ■ **Rare in Oxon and vc23**

Downy Woundwort

(Phil Cutt)

This handsome biennial was first recorded in GB in 1632 near Witney. It used to be "quite common" on calcareous soil from Lincs to Hants and Kent, but has been restricted to the Oolite of Oxon for about 50 years, along tracks and hedgerows and in game-crops. It is often associated with Roman settlement and its native status has been doubted. The seed survives long periods in the soil and the plant typically appears after disturbance and then declines – disturbed in 2006 at Freebord, 350 plants in 2007, dwindled to three with five seedlings in 2012. However disturbance at the Saltway in 2011 was not followed by seedlings but that in 2013 was. Germination can be 25–50% in the first year, occurring between late spring and early autumn. Long studied by Dunn (1997), the management of two sites is now co-ordinated by a partnership of landowners, statutory authorities and volunteer groups. A third site is flourishing. FlBe reported a failed planting at Wytham Hill in 1965. Druce had c. 11 sites, as did FlOx. In 2010 plants from Reed Hill grew as an introduction in gardens at Burford and Didcot. CRL

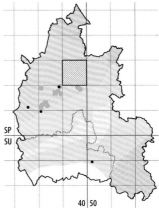

23	W	Salt Way, Ditchley Confidential	SSSI	SP385194	2005 2000	WC AJD	Abs. 2006-09 New in 1991, 44 in 2000
		Confidential			*1992*	*AJD*	*Last seen 1993*
23	W	Worsham Lane	SSSI	SP308096	1990	JMC	
23	W	*Asthall Leigh Valley*	*LWS*	*SP306115*	*1987*	*JMC*	*Last seen 1989*
23	W	Ironstone Quarry, near Fawler		SP372173	1987	HJMB+	
23	W	Sheers Copse/Ash Copse, Ditchley		SP391195	1985	RSRF	
23	W	Conifer pltn, S of Bangry Bottom		SP316122	1981	JY+	
23	W	Minster Lovell		SP317119	1980	Stewart	
23	W	Manor Farm Meadow, Crawley	LWS	SP337119	1979	JMC	1 plant seen once
23	W	Reed Hill	SSSI	SP383176	1979	JM	1978 JMC
23	W	*Sturdys Castle*		*SP474184*	*1968*	*HJMB*	*Not re-found AJD*

Stachys arvensis
Archaeophyte Near Threatened ■ **Rare in Oxon and vc23**

Field Woundwort

(Peter Creed)

This is an annual species of arable fields, allotments and road verges. It is generally found on calcareous soils and mainly in lowland areas of GB. It has suffered a big decline in recent years due to increased use of herbicides. There are 82 tetrad records in FlOx, but only three 2000–11 records. It was felt that many of the records in FlOx were out of date by publication. However at City Farm, Eynsham it was found in abundance in 2012. SEE

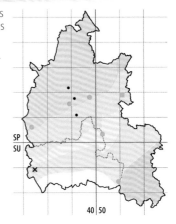

23	W	Combe, arable field		SP412176	2009	HJK	1 plant
23	W	Ditchley		SP387218	2007	AJD	3 plants
22	V	*Bushy Heath Buscot*		*SU234961*	*1992*	*SEE*	*2 plants*
23	0	*Iffley*		*SP528033*	*1989*	*HJMB*	
23	C	*Quarry Bank*		*SP476180*	*1987*	*AL*	
23	W	*East End*		*SP392154*	*1986*	*RH-B*	
23	S	*South Stoke Marsh (north)*	*LWS*	*SU594844*	*1986*	*GH*	

Galeopsis angustifolia

Red Hemp-nettle

Archaeophyte   Schedule 8, s. 41, Critically Endangered, Nationally Scarce ■ Scarce in Oxon, Rare in vc23

(Peter Creed)

This charming annual, naturally a plant of screes, used to be common in cornfields of SE England. It had a massive decline, perhaps partly because being late-flowering it fails to set seed in winter-sown crops. It grows on calcareous soils in moderate nutrient conditions. In Oxon it is now mostly in quarries, gravel pits and on conservation headlands. Always in small numbers, CRPG found 46 at Lidstone Piece in 2012, but the headland had not been ploughed and the vegetation was quite tall. Druce described it as "common", FlOx (p. 206) had 57 tetrads, but some may have been *G. tetrahit*. FlBe had nine sites. CRL

23	S	Warburg	BBOWT	SU720878	2010	RdA	2 introduced
22	V	Radley Gravel Pits	LWS	SU532984	2008	DG	New
23	W	field edge near Spelsbury		SP366225	2007	PS	New
23	W	Whiteways Quarry	LWS, LGS	SP420246	2002	AW	New
22	V	Radley Gravel Pits	LWS	SU523974	2001	HJK	New
23	S	Farm at Watlington		SU680917	1999	SJG	
23	W	Lidstone Piece, Spelsburydown		SP355235	1998	AJD	
22	V	Chilton disused railway		SU497855	1991	NCC	
23	W	Stonesfield Common, Bottoms & Banks	SSSI	SP392168	1987	HJK	Abs. 2007
22	V	Cherbury Camp	LWS	SU374963	1986	EC	
22	V	Lockinge, Mead Platt		SU427839	1986	EC	
22	V	Sutton Courtenay Gravel Pits		SU518930	1985	HJMB+	
23	S	Nuneham Park & Clifton Heath		SU549975	1985	SJE	
23	C	Banbury to Bicester Railway		SP576237	1984	FlOx	
23	S	Lime Corner		SU647782	1981	SS	
23	S	Nettlebed Common	LWS	SU703876	1981	SS	
22	V	Yew Down, Lockinge		SU422838	1979	LR	
22	V	Abbots Heath		SU461844	1979	LR	
23	W	Ditchley Road Quarry		SP364198	1974	JMC	
23	S	Woodeaton Quarry	SSSI, LGS	SP533123	1973	HJMB	
23	W	Church Enstone Quarry		SP384250	1971	RCP	
23	W	nr Sturdy's Castle		SP469189	1970	BRC	

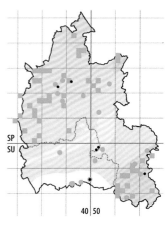

Galeopsis speciosa

Large-flowered Hemp-nettle

Archaeophyte   Vulnerable ■ Last Oxon record 1984, in vc23 1976

This showy annual was once common especially in N England, Wales and the fenlands where it was a weed of root crops. It suffered a huge decline and is now mostly in quarries. Braithwaite *et al.* (2006) found it had decreased significantly between 1987–8 and 2003–4, especially on non-peaty soils. It prefers neutral pH and tolerates high nutrients. Druce had seven localities, FlOx (p. 207) only three tetrads and FlBe one from "Wytham" in 1984. CRL, HJK

Galeopsis bifida

Bifid Hemp-nettle

Native   Scarce in Oxon and vc23

This annual is only distinguished from the closely related common *G. tetrahit*, with which it often grows, by the more divided lower petal with wider dark markings, so it may be often overlooked. It is widely distributed in England and S Scotland, as an arable weed on calcareous, nutrient-rich soil; with us now more often in waysides and woodland, perhaps reflecting loss of arable examples. At Burnt Mill it may become overgrown. Druce had it as an arable weed commonly in all districts. FlOx had 10 tetrads 'possibly more in arable fields', the latest at Warmington, 1992, J W Partridge. FlBe cited Cumnor, Frilford, Boars Hill, Wallingford. CRL

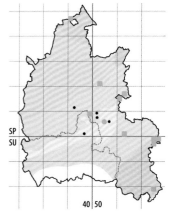

23	W	South Freeland Meadows	pLWS	SP426115	2013	ALa	Big clump in shade
23	S	Brasenose Wood and Shotover Hill	SSSI, LGS	SP568059	2012	HJK	Few in shade
22	V	Lashford Lane Fen	SAC, SSSI, BBOWT	SP467011	2011	HJK	Few by path
23	O	Almonds Farm and Burnt Mill Fields	LWS	SP518093	2010	JAW	Field to North, 51
23	O	New Marston Meadows	SSSI	SP519075	2010	JAW	1
23	O	Lye Valley	SSSI	SP548058	1969	HJMB	

⬇ *Marrubium vulgare*   White Horehound
Probably not native   Nationally Scarce ■ Last Oxon and vc23 record 1992

This plant is native only in calcareous rocky areas, especially coastal cliffs of England and Wales. It is widely naturalised from being grown as an ornamental and medicinal plant, but has suffered a huge decline. It flourishes with very high nutrients, notably on rabbit and stock latrines. It requires open conditions and is not susceptible to grazing, but often lost when grazing is discontinued. Druce had 15 sites. It has gone from the Old Reading Rd in Newnham Murren where Palmer saw it in 1992. FlOx (p. 207) had two tetrads. FlBe: extinct. CRL

⬇ *Nepeta cataria*   Cat-mint
Archaeophyte   Vulnerable ■ Not Scarce in Oxon, Scarce in vc23

This perennial of waysides, hedges and arable field margins is usually on dry calcareous soils. It is mostly in small numbers; re-found in hardly any of the 30 FlOx tetrads (p. 207), but many recent records appear new. FlBe gave only undated records. It has decreased since 1927. In GB its range has declined steeply especially NW of a line Glos-Northants-Cambs owing to intensive farming, scrub growth and in Northants, hedge removal (Gent *et al.* 1995); it is increasingly limited to the SE. HJK

22	V	Confidential		SU49P	2012	HJK	3 good plants by barn
23	W	Oxfordshire Way		SP376179	2010	JHW	New
22	V	Near Shippon		SU471977	2010	HJK	Verge cut at 40 cm, new
22	S	Aston Upthorpe Downs	SSSI	SU543832	2010	RH-B	2 new
22	S	Hill Barn Farm		SU553845	2010	RH-B	6 new
23	S	Goring nr Grove Farmhouse		SU612828	2010	JHW	Under hedge, new
23	S	Crowmarsh nr Cart Gap		SU627877	2010	JHW	126 plants, 100 m of field edge
23	S	Bix Valley		SU732865	2010	JHW	Disturbed path sides, new
23	S	Playhatch field to W of road		SU739763	2010	JHW	16, crop verge, new
22	V	Gozzards Ford		SU464987	2009	HJK	1, N verge 200 m W of T-jct, new
23	S	Culham, Thame Lane		SU522958	2006	HJK	3, grass verge, new
23	S	Span Hill Chalk Pit	pLWS, LWS	SU747769	2006	JHW	1 flg, abs. 2007
22	S	Unhill and Ham Woods	LWS	SU565827	2004	ShW	New
23	W	Standlake		SP392035	1999	HJK	1, hedge W of lake
23	W	3-road junction		SP382147	1998	AJD	2 clumps on E side
23	S	Icknield way nr Hill Farm		SU721969	1995	Marcan B	
22	S	West Hagbourne Moor		SU535872	1992	HJMB+	
23	W	Salt Way, Ditchley	SSSI, LNR	SP388192	1987	AJD	

(SP / SU) 40 | 50

(Peter Sheasby)

⬇ *Clinopodium ascendens*   Common Calamint

There are 17 2000–11 records for *C. ascendens* in vc23; although this has declined from the 39 records in FlOx it is Not Scarce. Its stronghold remains in the S with some locations not having been found in C and W. SEE

(Peter Creed)

⬇ *Clinopodium calamintha*   Lesser Calamint
Native   GB Red List Vulnerable, Nationally Scarce ■ Rare in Oxon, last vc23 record 1994

This species is similar to *C. ascendens* but it has short, 1–2 mm calyx teeth and short 0.1 mm, hairs. It is a short-lived perennial of dry, calcareous sandy or gravelly soils. It has probably declined due to changes in cutting regimes of pastures and is now confined to road verges, railway embankments and waste ground. There are no 2000–11 records for vc23, nor has it been re-found in nine of Druce 1927 sites. Palmer saw it at Talbot Inn, SP4408, in 1970. There have been records since 1963 from Abbey fish ponds. SEE

22	V	Abbey Fishponds	LNR, LWS	SU512979	2006	HJK	Still present 2015
23	W	Spelsbury verge, Saltway		SP356232	1994	CRL	
23	W	Abbey Farm, Eynsham		SP4208	1991	RCP	

⬇ *Clinopodium acinos*   Basil Thyme
Native   **s. 41, Vulnerable ■ Not Scarce in Oxon and vc23**

This small creeping annual favours nutrient-poor, well-drained calcareous sands or gravels, when open or well grazed. Nationally and locally there has been a huge decline in this species. 75 localities were recorded in FlOx but only 14 2000–11 records have been received for vc23. Increased fertilisation and better weed control probably account for its decline, but recording in Oxon especially in the N of the county has been less comprehensive than for FlOx. SEE

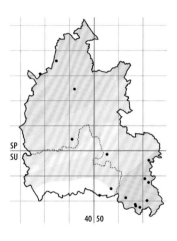

23	S	Warburg	SSSI, BBOWT	SU723874	2010	JHW	3 plants
23	W	Whiteways Quarry	LWS, LGS	SP420246	2009	AW	
23	S	Chazey Heath		SU688775	2009	JHW	14 plants
23	S	Confidential		SU78E	2009	JHW	Private, new
23	S	Sonning Common		SU717802	2009	JHW	8 plants
23	C	Temple Mills Quarries	LWS, LGS	SP347359	2007	PS	Quarry
23	S	Nuney Green Chalk Pit		SU669787	2007	JHW	2 plants
23	S	Mapledurham, near Bottom Shaw		SU671780	2007	JHW	A few
23	S	Russell's Water, Gt Cookley Hill		SU708889	2007	JHW	4 plants
23	S	Aston Rowant	SAC, NNR, SSSI	SU724962	2007	HJK	A few
23	W	Devils Quoits	LGS	SP411047	2005	HJK	2 sites
22	V	Blewbury, Lower Chance Farm		SU523823	2002	CRL	
22	S	Lollingdon Hill	LWS	SU570849	2002	CRL	2 sites
23	W	Rollright Flick Quarry	LGS	SP281307	2001	CRL	
23	S	Holly Hill (Elmore Park Grassland)	LWS	SU630813	2001	CRL	
23	C	Upper Heyford Airfield	LWS	SP525269	2000	CRL	

⬇ *Thymus pulegiodes*   Large Thyme
This perennial of calcareous grassland in S and E England (also on heaths in vc22 (Oxon)) has declined near the edge of its range, which is close to Oxon. However, with 22 2000–11 records in Oxon (16 in vc23) it is Not Scarce. HJK

➡ *Mentha pulegium*   Pennyroyal
?Native   **Sched 8, s. 41, Critically Endangered, Nationally Rare ■ Rare in Oxon and vc23**

This is a short-lived perennial of seasonally inundated grassland. It is found on heavily grazed land especially commons and heathy pastures. Destruction of habitat and change of land use seem to be the probable reasons for a big decline nationally. It has never been common in Oxon and there are only three FlOx tetrads records and one vc23 record in 2000–11. At Shellingford part of the old quarry has been used for land fill and part is an SSSI for its geological interest; the species may have been brought in with top soil in this area. It was first found in 2000 but it has now spread throughout the SSSI. Previously found on Port Meadow and Otmoor, but Druce 1927 reported it was nearly extinct. In 2011 in Cornbury Park, vc23, two patches were found by Webb near the house. SEE

23	W	Cornbury Park	pLWS	SP35081822	2011	JAW	New, 2 patches, lawn
22	V	Sutton Courtenay Environmental Education Centre	BBOWT	SU499918	2010	RdA	New ? Introduced
22	V	Shellingford Crossroads Quarry	SSSI	SU326941	2009	SEE	Introduced?

Salvia pratensis

(Peter Creed)

Native

Meadow Clary

Sched 8, Near Threatened, Nationally Scarce ■ **Not Scarce in Oxon or in vc23**

This iconic perennial was known to Elizabethan gardeners but not recorded in the wild until 1699, though its genetic gradation across the country suggests it is long established. It was used medicinally for eye complaints, and has a curious distribution with its stronghold at its northern limit in the UK, on the Oolite of west Oxon. Druce had c. 22 sites and it was in 20 FlOx tetrads and also six contemporaneous TVERC sites. It is also found in Glos, Kent and Sussex with small populations in Surrey and Wilts. It prefers waysides and ancient grasslands on chalk and limestone, and may need raised magnesium levels (Scott 1989). It was extensively monitored in the 1980s by Dunn and no new sites have been found since. Studies by Cornwallis at Glyme Farm show that it requires relaxation of grazing to allow seedset, and its seed germinates readily but does not establish in closed sward. Monitoring by the RPG for Plantlife found that at Ardley several large plants seen by Everett in 1985 had survived. Sadly most had died by 2008 and 12 seedlings could not be re-found; the vegetation nearby was rank with Hogweed and Cow Parsley, and the Meadow Clary leaves were often eaten by slugs. Since then the RPG has twice introduced plants raised from seed from the original plants into an area where the topsoil had been scraped off by the Highways Authority (arranged by the County Ecologist). Of four planted out in 2000 three were inadvertently weed-killed; the survivor has flowers and surviving offspring. Of 27 planted out in 2007 most were uprooted by rabbits. Additionally seed from the original plants was scattered into 2 m² in 2005 and another 2 m² in 2006; a few young plants grew at first but mostly then disappeared. Other sites are currently monitored and managed by the Cotswold RPG; some of their records in 2015 had bigger populations than previously. At Kitesbridge an inexplicable change has occurred from plants resembling *S pratensis* to resembling *S. verbenaca*. CRL

23	S	Warburg	BBOWT	SU720878	2010	RdA	2 sites, 7 intr
23	W	Glyme Valley	SSSI	SP327264	2008	LC	1000s
23	W	Road verge N of Crawley		SP340124	2008	RH	1
23	W	Holly Court Bank	SSSI	SP386150	2007	HJK	1000s
23	W	West of Abel Wood	LWS	SP403147	2007	HJK	1
23	W	Ashford Bridge to Combe Cutting (Cotswold Line)	LWS	SP409152	2007	WOR	49
23	C	Ardley lay-by		SP536250	2006	CRL	23, see text
23	W	Langland Farm, Finstock		SP364163	1999	AJD	122
23	W	*Kitesbridge Salvia Site*		*SP296116*	*1998*	*JMC*	*Now abs.*
22	S	North Unhill Bank	LWS	SU562833	1998	MHa	
23	W	*Stonesfield Common, Bottoms & Banks*	*SSSI*	*SP394165*	*1996*	*JMC*	*Abs.*
23	W	Wigwell	LWS	SP358201	1995	CMcN	23
23	W	Lower Farm Meadow, Taston		SP363216	1995	CPRG	108
23	W	*Charlbury roadside verge*		*SP367219*	*1995*	*CMcN*	*Abs. 1999 CRL*
23	W	Stonesfield Common, Bottoms & Banks	SSSI	SP390162	1995	RC	53
23	W	*Railway Whitehill Bridge*		*SP394157*	*1995*	*CMcN*	*Abs. 2007 HJK*
23	W	Ashford Bridge to Combe Cutting (Cotswold Line)	LWS	SP410152	1995	CMcN	
23	W	Salt Way, Spelsbury		SP355234	1994	CRL	63
23	W	*Charlbury roadside verge*		*SP367219*	*1994*	*CRL*	*Abs. 1999 CRL*
23	W	Cornbury Park		SP358175	1992	AS	3
23	W	Eynsham By-pass road verge		SP432088	1988	JMC	
23	C	Middleton Stoney Park		SP536236	1976	EWJ	
23	W	Spelsbury		SP360230	1968	Anon	

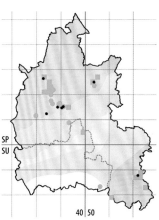

SP
SU

40 50

Salvia verbenaca

Native

Wild Clary

Near Threatened ■ **Not Scarce in Oxon or vc23**

This aromatic perennial was often planted on graves, and is usually on low-nutrient soils. It is widespread in S England, but has suffered a big decline. Druce had c. 30 sites and FlOx (p. 211) had only 19 tetrads; but it may have stabilised as of the 20 2000–11 sites (11 in vc23), seven are new. It is now mostly on road verges or in cemeteries. CRL, HJK

◉ *Melampyrum pratense* — Common Cow-wheat
Native — Near Threatened ■ Scarce in Oxon and vc23

This semi-parasitic annual grows in acidic woodlands with low nutrients. It has large seeds which are distributed by ants. It is widespread in the UK except for E central England where is has declined considerably, and here is almost confined to the Chilterns. While Druce had 20 localities, FlOx (p. 222) had 35 tetrads, and none recent in FlBe. JHW, CRL

23	S	Harpsden Wood	SSSI, WT	SU761807	2010	SR	
23	S	Holme Copse		SU663796	2009	JHW	15x7 m
23	S	Goring		SU627812	2007	JHW	2 patches
23	S	Lackmore Wood		SU660813	2007	JHW	2 patches
23	S	Valentine Wood		SU666805	2007	JHW	30
23	S	*Nuney Green*		*SU669788*	*2007*	*JHW*	*Abs.*
23	S	Brasenose Wood and Shotover Hill	SSSI	SP560052	2006	ShW	
23	C	Stoke Wood	LWS, WT	SP555277	1990	JMC	
23	S	*Warren Bank*	*SSSI, BBOWT*	*SU653857*	*1989*	*GB*	*Abs. JHW 2007*
23	S	Queen Wood		SU717926	1988	DF	
23	S	Common/College Wood		SU660808	1987	JHW	
23	S	Oaken Copse		SU640874	1986	GB	
23	W	Cogges Wood	LWS	SP380110	1985	JMC	
22	V	*Matthew Arnold Field*	*OPT*	*SP485024*	*1985*	*HJMB*	*Abs. CRL*
23	W	Rangers Lawn		SP333194	1984	AMS	
23	S	Stanton Great Wood	SSSI	SP588093	1982	JMC	
23	W	Foxholes	SSSI, BBOWT	SP250205	1981	HJMB	
23	W	Bruern Woods	LWS	SP265195	1981	JY	
23	W	Tar Wood	LWS	SP398075	1981	HJMB	
23	S	Pishill Woods	SSSI	SU715902	1981	GP	
23	S	Waterperry Wood	SSSI	SP607090	1980	HJMB	
23	W	Northbrook Marsh	LWS	SP484214	1969	EWJ	

Euphrasia — Eyebrights
Euphrasia anglica, E. arctica, E. tetraquetra, E. pseudokerneri and *E. confusa* were reported in FlOx (p. 222) but none of this difficult group have been confirmed since. CRL

➡ *Parentucellia viscosa* — Yellow Bartsia
This semi-parasite of damp open grassland has appeared as a casual in Oxon but not in vc23 since 1940. It was in a ditch by the new Didcot Link Road (SU5090, 1982 Killick), and in a field on the outskirts of Faringdon (SU298951, 2001 Erskine), which has since been developed as a skateboard park. Fifty grew in short grass on set-aside near Frilford in 1999 and 2000, decreasing to one in 2002 (SU4497, Killick). It has declined as a native, often near the sea, in SW GB. HJK, SEE, CRL.

◉ *Pedicularis palustris* — Marsh Lousewort
Native — Vulnerable ■ Rare in Oxon and vc23

(Peter Sheasby)

This is an annual or biennial semi-parasite, which grows in marshes. It is very similar to *P. sylvatica* but has two pairs of lateral teeth on the upper lip; the calyx has two short broad lobes. It can cope with enriched habitats and used to be plentiful in suitable areas in Druce's day. It has declined in central and S England due to drainage and agricultural improvements. It has suffered a big decline in vc23, where FlOx had seven tetrads and there are now only two locations, one with two sites. Similarly in vc22 there is only one 2000–11 location. The locations which remain are in protected sites, both of which have a long history of records and the numbers of plants appears healthy. SEE

23	O	Pixey and Yarnton Meads	SAC, SSSI	SP485098	2010	AWM	Approx 15 plants
23	O	Lye Valley	SSSI	SP547051	2010	JAW	2 sites
22	V	Parsonage Moor	SAC, SSSI, BBOWT	SU466997	2010	JAW	Scattered across the reserve
22	V	*Confidential*	*SSSI*	*SU49P*	*1975*	*SEE*	*Not re-found since 2000*

SP
SU

40 50

⬇️ *Pedicularis sylvatica*   Lousewort
Native   **Vulnerable** ■ **Rare in Oxon and in vc23**

(Peter Sheasby)

This is a perennial semi-parasite, found on damp heaths and moorland. It is similar to *P. palustris*, but has only one pair of lateral teeth on upper lip and the calyx has four lobes and is glabrous. This species has declined in central and S England, and in Oxon this decline is marked, due to loss of habitat. It was recorded in 11 FlOx tetrads and re-found in three. It appears lost from its remaining site in vc22 (Oxon) at Parsonage Moor. SEE

23	C	Cradle and Grounds Farm Banks	LWS	SP366328	2009	HJK	8 plants
23	C	Cradle and Grounds Farm Banks	LWS	SP371329	2008	PS	
23	C	Berryfields Farm	LWS	SP337327	2004	PS	
23	S	Nettlebed Common	LWS	SU705871	1995	RdA	
22	V	Parsonage Moor	SAC, SSSI	SU462998	1975	PGM	Abs. 2009 HJK

➡️ *Lathraea squamaria*   Toothwort
Toothwort, a parasite of trees, has declined in GB, but here, in 24 FlOx tetrads, and in 19 2000–11 sites in vc23, it is Not Scarce. HJK

➡️ *Orobanche elatior*   Knapweed Broomrape
This broomrape is a parasite on *Centaurea scabiosa*. It was found in 13 sites in vc23 and 11 in vc22 (Oxon), so is Not Scarce. SEE

➡️ *Orobanche hederae*   Ivy Broomrape
Native or ?introduced in Oxon   **Scarce in Oxon and Rare in vc23**

This annual or perennial parasite is restricted to ivy, especially *Hedera hibernica*, but we also have it on *H. helix*. It was in Oxon since 1973; in five FlOx tetrads (p. 224). The colony in Killick's Abingdon garden has persisted since 2002; it could perhaps have arrived when he took home for checking a specimen from Wolfson College. The native areas in Atlas 2002, in SW England, Wales and Ireland, mostly lie near the coast and where the February minimum for 1901–1930 was above 38 F, but the cold 2010 winter has not reduced it here. HJK

23	O	Oxford Botanic Garden	SP520060	2012	HJK	On *H. hel* and hib
22	V	Abingdon, garden	SU490975	2010	HJK	40 on *H. helix*
23	O	Magdalen College	SP521061	2009	HJK	40 on ?alien ivy
23	W	Lay-by, Bampton	SP303027	2002	SEE	SEE 2009
23	O	Wolfson College	SP512084	1996	HJK	Under Aesculus, 2008

⬇️ *Pinguicula vulgaris*   Common Butterwort
Native   **Vulnerable** ■ **Rare in Oxon, last vc23 record 1990**

(Peter Sheasby)

This is an insectivorous perennial herb which survives in open, nutrient-poor, calcareous communities. The species is stable and common in the uplands of Scotland, Wales and England. South of the Tees/Exe line it has declined severely, probably due to drainage and lack of grazing. Druce had 11 sites in scattered fens throughout Oxon. With only five mentions in FlOx, the species was already in serious decline. Parsonage Moor has a stable population. The vegetation is cropped by Exmoor ponies, 20 or more plants are found regularly. At the confidential site it has been in danger of being overshadowed by tall, coarse vegetation but new management may help it survive; two plants were found in 2015. The last record in vc23 was at Bullingdon Fen (Lye Valley) in 1990, but searches since 2000 have failed to find a single plant. SEE

22	V	Confidential	SSSI	SU49P	2009	SEE	7 flowers; 1 in 2013
22	V	Parsonage Moor	SAC, SSSI, BBOWT	SU460988	2009	HJK+	
23	W	Taston Brook and Springs	LWS	SP357217	1998	AJD	
23	O	Lye Valley	SSSI	SP547057	1990	EN	Searched 2006–2009 by J. Webb, SEE+, with no results
23	S	Spartum Fen	SSSI	SP655017	1988	BBOWT	Not seen since
23	W	Coombe Fen	LWS	SP408150	Pre 1983		Abs. 2008 WOR
23	C	Weston Fen	SSSI	SP526194	pre 1983	HMJB	

⬇ *Utricularia vulgaris* agg.
Native   **Scarce in Oxon**

We have two species of Greater Bladderwort, both insectivorous; leaves are modified to form bladders and both are free floating. They are found in calcareous, slow moving, nutrient-poor fens or ponds. Increased drainage and fertilisation reduced the number of records of Bladderworts in Oxon, before FlOx which cited six tetrads in vc23. Because some records are aggregates and identifying the two species can be unreliable, it is harder to assess trends in the individual species. CRL

Utricularia vulgaris   **Greater Bladderwort**
Native   **Scarce in Oxon and vc23**

This is found in calcareous, slow moving, nutrient-poor fens or ponds. It flowers more frequently in the S than the N, and identifying it accurately from *U. australis* is not reliable. *U. vulgaris* is distinguished by the lower lip of the corolla having reflexed margins; the pedicel is 8–15 mm, recurved but not elongating after flowering; glands are present inside only the abaxial side of spur (Stace 2010). Seventeen sites are cited in Druce; this reduced to four in FlOx. The old records for Otmoor and Wolvercote in vc23 are still extant, but those for the Thames and Cherwell are gone. At Parsonage Moor SU460999 in 2010 non-flowering plants, tentatively identified using Poland and Clement's vegetative key, were found in several pools, following extensive clearing of *Phragmites australis*. SEE

23	C	RSPB Otmoor	pLWS, RSPB	SP561129	2010	HJK	Uncountable
22	V	Parsonage Moor	SAC, SSSI, BBOWT	SU460999	2010	JAW
23	C	Otmoor	SSSI	SP572139	2006	FHW
23	C	Wolvercote pond at Dukes lock		SP487107	2005	JE	Abundant
23	C	RSPB Otmoor	pLWS, RSPB	SP565135	2003	JMC
23	W			SP270150	1979	ML

➡ *Utricularia australis*   **Bladderwort**
Native   **Rare in Oxon, last vc23 record 1993**

This segregate usually favours slightly less calcareous and less nutrient-rich water. One flower appeared in a *Chara*-filled new peat digging at Cothill (SU460996, 2012 Webb, confirmed by J J Day), where it was known to Druce and in 1970s to Morris and FlOx. Druce had two vc23 sites (Oxford and Russell's Water Common). The most recent record in FlOx was at Otmoor, FlBe had it at Barrow Farm Fen in 1971. CRL

23	C	Otmoor		SP5612	1993	NTHH
22	V	Cothill Fen	SAC, NNR, SSSI	SU459997	1978	HJMB
22	V	Cothill Fen	SAC, SSSI	SU462998	1975	PGM

⬇ *Campanula latifolia*   **Giant Bellflower**
Native   **Rare in Oxon and vc23**

(Peter Sheasby)

This large perennial thrives in damp woods, preferring slightly alkaline soil and tolerating raised nutrient levels. It grows mainly in the N and W of GB and has declined, though often planted and escaping. Druce had one native and three introduced sites, FlOx p. 225 had 16 tetrads, and FlBe two, one of which was introduced. CRL

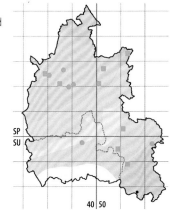

23	S	Confidential		SU67	2007	JHW	1 new
22	V	Fen South of Sherwood		SU442975	1990	WF
23	W	Ditchley Park Complex		SP387198	1985	JMC
23	W	Sarsgrove Wood	SSSI	SP307244	1979	
23	*W*	*Heythrop Park*		*SP365265*	*1979*	*HJMB*	*Not re-found*
23	S	Aston Rowant	SAC, NNR, SSSI	SU730970	1979	OCMR
23	W	Out Wood	SSSI	SP407207	1969	FlOx

Campanula rapunculus
Archaeophyte

Rampion Bellflower
Endangered ■ **Last Oxon and vc23 record 1985**

This is a tall perennial herb, formerly grown in gardens for ornamental, salad and vegetable (roots) use. Since 1700s, when it ceased to be used as a vegetable, it has steadily declined. It is now a relict of garden escapes found in rough grass on verges, railway embankments and waste ground. In FlOx there was one record by Fitter at Lewknor (SU 6896) in 1985 and it was considered 'rare'. SEE

Wahlenbergia hederacea
Native

Ivy-leaved Bellflower
Near Threatened ■ **Last Oxon record 1956, not in vc23**

This dainty creeping perennial herb of damp, wet or boggy places on acid soils grows in pastures, heaths or open woodland. It was only in vc22 (Oxon) – in Bagley Wood (vc22) between 1666 and 1956, and in Wootton Heath once in 1865. G Bloom and Killick searched part of Bagley Wood around SP510016 in c. 1995 but the area is now too dry and overgrown. In GB it is mostly in Wales and SW England having been lost from most former sites farther east. HJK

Jasione montana
Native

Sheep's-bit
Vulnerable ■ **Last Oxon and vc23 record 1995**

This is a sprawling biennial, commoner in the W than the E of GB, on acidic well-drained soils, both maritime and inland. With the loss of lowland heath there has been a big decline both regionally and locally. Heathland is now a very rare habitat in Oxon. Even in Druce 1927 it was recorded from only eight localities. In FlOx the last record was from Bayswater in 1940s, but it appeared in 1995. The species was thought to be extinct in vc22 (Oxon) since the last record was from Boars Hill in the 19th Century. SEE

Menyanthes trifoliata
Native and planted in Oxon

Bogbean
?Scarce in the wild in Oxon and vc23

(Peter Creed)

Bogbean, an emergent aquatic perennial in marshes, bogs, fens and lake margins in shallow often acid, nitrogen-poor water, is also planted in ponds. This account concentrates on big colonies and sites with near-typical habitats; 50 records by d'Ayala and others in garden ponds, educational centres and some nature reserves, believed planted, are omitted. In 17 tetrads (FlOx p. 197); nine records, some lost, in FlBe. In GB typically in the N and W; in SE England it has declined owing to drainage but increased as an ornamental. HJK

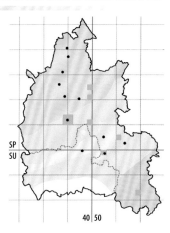

Nymphoides peltata
Native and introduced

Fringed Water-lily
Nationally Scarce ■ **Not Scarce in Oxon and vc23**

(John Killick)

This plant, formerly of slow-flowing rivers, has been lost from most of Druce's 12 stations on the Thames, and among 12 FlOx tetrads were some in the Thames and Cherwell, not re-found. However it has increased markedly in ponds, often introduced, and with 18 2000–11 records in Oxon (11 in vc23) it is Not Scarce. In GB as a native it has hugely declined. Both pin and thrum forms occur in the Thames Valley (FlBe), a fact used to argue that the plant is native here. HJK

⬆ *Carduus tenuiflorus*   Slender Thistle
Native on the coast, introduced inland   **Rare in Oxon and vc23**

This annual or biennial is common around the coast, but inland is usually scattered and introduced in well-drained waste places. It has been recorded in Oxon since 1794 but always rare, FlOx had three localities and FlBe only two recent ones. CRL

22	S	Offlands Farm		SU591847	2009	SO'L	50 dumped soil
23	W	Shifford Chimney Meadows	LWS, BBOWT	SP366012	2005	SP	
22	V	Turf Pits Covert	LWS	SU373963	1998	SEE	
22	V	Radley Gravel Pits	LWS	SU523975	1990	JMC	
22	V	Hitchcopse South Sandpit	LWS	SU456988	1979	AL+	

⬇ *Cirsium dissectum*   Meadow Thistle
Native   **Not Scarce in Oxon, Scarce in vc23**

(Phil Cutt)

This thistle is a perennial plant of damp, acidic pasture and hay meadows found on the flood plains of Oxon. Improved drainage and increased use of fertiliser have contributed to its decline nation-wide, but especially in the SE. In Oxon it was described by Druce 1886, as rare and very local, whereas in FlOx it was considered scarce with 36 tetrads, which was an increase on Druce 1927 who listed 18 sites. However the number of 2000–11 records is 12 in Oxon (seven in vc23), all of them in sites which now have some conservation protection, and the plant has spread where management has improved the habitat. SEE

23	W	Willow Meadows	LWS	SP273060	2011	SEE	>50
23	W	Alvescot Meadows	SSSI	SP273050	2010	SEE+	>50
22	V	Parsonage Moor	SAC, SSSI, BBOWT	SU460998	2010	HJK	20 flowers
23	C	Woodsides Meadow	SSSI, BBOWT	SP556178	2009	JAW	100+
23	S	Otmoor	SSSI	SP573129	2008	CRL	100+
22	S	Cholsey Marsh	LWS, BBOWT	SU595849	2008	SG	
22	V	Confidential	SSSI	SU49P	2007	SEE+	Spreading 2010
23	C	Pixey and Yarnton Meads	SAC, SSSI	SP484098	2006	AWM	Approx 200
23	C	RSPB Otmoor	pLWS, RSPB	SP564146	2006	HJK+	Frequent
22	V	Fernham Meadows	SSSI	SU293907	2006	SEE+	Frequent
23	W	Coldron Mill Complex	LWS	SP345211	2002	CRL	
22	O	Pasture by A34 Thames Bridge	LWS	SP482092	2001	AWM	
23	O	Warneford Hospital Meadow	Other	SP540059	1991	EN	
22	V	Iffley Meadows	SSSI, BBOWT	SP523032	1986	NCC	
23	S	Spartum Fen	SSSI	SP655017	1986	MP	

SP
SU

40 50

Serratula tinctoria
Native

Saw-wort
Not Scarce in Oxon, Scarce in vc23

This species is widespread in England and Wales, except East Anglia but has never been common in Oxon: described as 'local and rather rare' in Druce 1886 and 1927, and scarce in FlOx (23 sites). It is a plant of damp calcareous grassland, and changes in agricultural practices are probably the reason for the decline. It is scattered around the two vcs and never in large numbers, but frequently in conservation areas. SEE

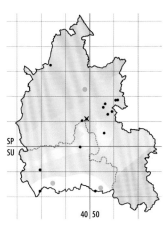

23	C	Asham Meads	SSSI, BBOWT	SP593140	2011	HJK	3 sites
23	C	Arncott Bridge Meadows	SSSI	SP608185	2011	JAW	
22	V	Parsonage Moor	SAC, SSSI, BBOWT	SU460998	2010	JAW	6
23	C	Woodsides Meadow	SSSI, BBOWT	SP556178	2008	HJK	Occasional
23	S	Brasenose Wood and Shotover Hill	SSSI	SP560054	2008	HJK	20
23	C	Wendlebury Meads and Mansmoor Closes	SSSI	SP564171	2008	HJK	Many
23	S	Otmoor	SSSI	SP575129	2008	SEE	
23	C	Field south of River Ray	LWS	SP617186	2008	RD	
22	V	Weathercock Down		SU294823	2008	SEE	
23	C	Pixey and Yarnton Meads	SAC, SSSI	SP468104	2006	AWM	Approx. 40
22	V	Fernham Meadows	SSSI	SU294907	2006	SEE+	Scattered
23	C	Berryfields Farm	LWS	SP337325	2004	PS	
22	V	Blewbury Hill	LWS	SU523823	2002	HJK+	
22	V	Ilsley Bottom	LWS	SU444835	2001	CRL	
23	C	*Loop Farm Flood Meadows*	LWS	*SP487110*	2000	CRL	*Abs. 2010 JK*
22	V	Pigtrough Bottom	LWS	SU346854	1991	NCC	
22	S	Aston Upthorpe Downs	SSSI	SU545835	1991		
23	W	Bank south of Cleveley	LWS	SP392234	1987	GH	

Centaurea cyanus
Archaeophyte

Cornflower
s. 41 ■ Not Scarce in Oxon and vc23

(Peter Creed)

Formerly a common arable annual flower, now mostly found scattered in wasteland, throughout GB, though less frequent in Scotland and Wales. There has been a steady decline due to a change in seed cleaning and use of herbicides, so of 27 FlOx tetrads only that at Chalgrove in 1969 was on arable land. Records have increased due to introductions from seed mixes, gardens and bird seed. This has been the case in Oxon. It can persist in the seed bank for several years, as at Radcot Bridge farm, where it was sown in the early 1990s as an experiment and was still to be found in 2007, though not in great numbers. No table as so many introductions, but records mapped. SEE

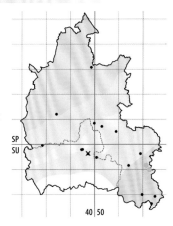

Hypochaeris glabra
Native

Smooth Cat's-ear
Vulnerable ■ Rare in Oxon, last vc23 record 1914

(Phil Cutt)

This is an annual which favours dry acidic soils. In GB its stronghold is in East Anglia and it is also found scattered around the coasts. It has been known at Frilford since Druce 1927 and Bowen 1968. There has been a huge decline nationally, but fortunately it is relatively safe and stable at its only Oxon site, where it has been recorded annually since 2008. It was last seen in vc23 in Stow wood, in 1914. SEE

22	V	Confidential	SSSI	SU49P	2009	SEE+	40–50 plants

➡ *Lactuca virosa*   **Prickly Lettuce**

L. virosa is usually in human-made habitats and often casual; with 12 2000–11 records in vc23 it is Not Scarce. It has greatly spread in GB. HJK

⬇ *Filago vulgaris*   **Common Cudweed**
Native   **Near Threatened ■ Not Scarce in Oxon, Scarce in vc23**

(Peter Creed)

This is a small annual up to 30 cm. It is covered in white woolly hairs and differs from *F. pyramidata*, in that the centre of the capitulum is also densely covered in hairs, whereas in *F. pyramidata*, the centre is much less hairy allowing the pyramid-like structure to be clearly seen. *F. vulgaris* also has acute (not apiculate) leaves which do not overtop the clusters of flower heads. It thrives in dry arable and sandy grasslands and heaths. There has been a big decline nationally especially in the S and W, due to increased cultivation of marginal land. In vc23 (12 tetrads) there is not much suitable habitat and it has declined here steadily. In vc22 (Oxon) it is still frequent, with 26 2000–11 records at TVERC, along the Corallian Ridge, from Faringdon to Frilford, Radley and Bagley Wood. SEE

23	C	Yarnton, pathway		SP476112	2009	RH-B
23	O	Port Meadow with Wolvercote Common and Green	SAC, SSSI	SP492097	2009	RH-B
23	W	Eynsham Park, N of N fork track		SP402118	2008	HJK West of back drive
23	C	Wendlebury Meads and Mansmoor Closes	SSSI	SP563175	2003	JMC
23	C	RSPB Otmoor	pLWS, RSPB	SP561134	2001	JMC
23	C	BOS Reserve Alkerton		SP392427	2000	JMC
23	C	Field by River Ray	LWS	SP618189	2000	CRL
23	S	Goring Heath Butler's Farm field 4		SU644788	2000	SK
23	S	Rotherfied Greys, Cowfields Farm field 8		SU729816	2000	SK
23	S	Furze Brake	LWS	SU538965	1997	JMC+
23	S	Henley Road Gravel Pit	LWS	SU735747	1996	JMC+
23	W			SP384045	1995	JMC

➡ *Filago pyramidata*   **Broad-leaved Cudweed**
Archaeophyte   **Sched 8, s. 41, Endangered, Nationally Scarce ■ Rare in Oxon and vc23**

F. pyramidata can be confused with *F. vulgaris*, with which it sometimes grows, by the sharply angled involucres (looking like small pyramids in the flower head). These are visible as there are fewer white woolly hairs obscuring the involucres of *F. pyramidata*. The obovate leaves overtopping the capitulum is not always a reliable feature for identification. This is a small annual, with a preference for dry arable sites. There have been no later records from the seven sites listed by Druce in 1894. FlOx cites the only vc23 site at Sonning and concludes that plants recorded there as *F. lutescens* were also *F. pyramidata*. It has declined similarly throughout its former strongholds in S GB. It is a poor competitor, and has suffered from nutrient enrichment. It was on Plantlife's 'Back from the Brink' programme, which had some success in stabilising extant populations. Populations at both Oxon sites have been monitored regularly since 1997. The attempted re-introduction at Dry Sandford Pit by seed in 2000 failed. SEE

22	V	Golf Course near Buckland Warren		SU334963	2009	SEE
23	S	Span Hill Chalk Pit	LGS, pLWS	SU747770	2009	SEE

➡ *Filago minima*   **Small Cudweed**
Native   **Near Threatened ■ Rare in Oxon and vc23**

Small Cudweed is a tiny annual of dry, open, infertile, heathy soils. There are pre-1978 FlOx tetrad records at Lew, Church Hanborough and Shotover, one at SU333963 (FlBe, undated) and two recent records. It is slowly declining in much of GB. HJK

23	C	Horsehay Quarry (West)	LWS	SP455274	2011	JK 1000s, new
22	V	Birch Copse set-aside	pLWS	SP488032	2003	CRL New

⬇ *Gnaphalium sylvaticum*
Native

Heath Cudweed
Endangered ■ **Rare in Oxon and vc23**

This short-lived perennial is widespread in Scotland and England but has suffered a huge decline. It requires open, heathy woods or grassland with acidic soil and low nutrients. Druce had 22 sites, mostly on the Chilterns and in FlOx 13 tetrads; in 2010 at Harpsden. FlBe had four, but in 2000–11 only at Birch Copse SP4802. CRL

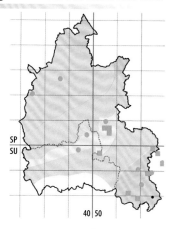

23	S	High Wood Harpsden		SU749796	2010	JHW	New
22	V	Birch Copse set-aside	pLWS	SP4802	2003	CRL	100s new
23	Bu	Cadmore End		SU790933	1992	HJK	Not since
23	S	Sydlings Copse	SSSI, BBOWT	SP555096	1990	RL	BBOWT
22	V	Confidential	SSSI	SU49P	1986	HJK	Not since
23	W	Foxholes	SSSI, BBOWT	SP250205	1983	JHC	BBOWT
23	S	Holly Grove	LWS	SU705845	1981	Doom	
23	W	Heythrop Park		SP365265	1979	HJMB	Abs. WER 2009
23	S	Coates Copse and Church Wood		SU690905	1979	Doom	
22	V	Hurst Hill	SSSI	SP476042	1978	GD	Not re-found
23	S	E end of Balham's Wood, Stonor		SU745893	1971	RCP	

⬇ *Inula helenium*
Archaeophyte

Elecampane
Near Threatened ■ **Rare in Oxon and vc23**

This persistent perennial was grown widely in the BI for its ornamental, medicinal and veterinary properties. It has suffered a big decline nationally as well as here. Druce had six sites, FlOx (p. 246) 11 tetrads and FlBe five sites. Seven of the FlOx tetrads were N of Oxford where our recording was low (see introduction); it was re-found in one (a single plant on a verge at Hook Norton, SP350337, Helm, 2015). CRL

22	V	Abingdon, Radley Lakes	LWS	SU520976	2010	HJK	c. 100 new
23	0	Oxford, Boundary Brook NR		SP532046	2007	PaM	New introduced
22	V	Badbury Forest – Eaton Wood	LWS	SU262964	2006	SEE	Frequent, new
22	V	West Hagbourne		SU509873	2006	HJK	>50
22	V	Buscot Park		SU239963	1997	SEE	
22	V	Buckland Estate		SU341988	1997	SEE	
22	V	Wytham Woods	SSSI	SP458077	1980	RH-B	

Pulicaria vulgaris

Small Fleabane

This Endangered RDB species is surely extinct in Oxon, the last record being in Otmoor, perhaps in 1834. HJK

⬇ *Solidago virgaurea*
Native

Goldenrod
Near Threatened ■ **Rare in Oxon and vc23**

This is a genetically variable perennial herb, formerly valued for medicinal purposes. It grows in a wide range of habitats preferring free-draining usually acidic and nutrient-poor soils which are infrequent in Oxon. It is widespread in the UK except the E Midlands. It declined mostly since 1950, perhaps reflecting eutrophication; Braithwaite *et al.* (2006) found a further significant decrease between 1987–8 and 2003–4. In Oxon it has also declined severely; FlOx had 34 tetrads giving an apparent spread since Druce's six sites, but Killick suspects many records were of ornamental species. The Wolvercote one is surprising. CRL

23	S	Deadman's Lane		SU666804	2007	JHW	3 flowering, 23 non-flowering, new
23	0	Wolvercote Paper Mill		SP487098	2001	RdA	Rare, new
23	S	Common/College Wood		SU660808	1987	JHW	
23	S	CS Lewis Reserve	BBOWT	SP562065	1986	HJMB	
22	V	Furze Wick Down (remains of)		SU395848	1986	HJMB	
23	S	Brasenose Wood and Shotover Hill	SSSI	SP560054	1981	DTS	
22	V	Hitchcopse Pit	SSSI, BBOWT	SU452996	1981	HJMB	Abs. FlBe 2005
22	V	Dry Sandford Pit	LGS, BBOWT	SU467995	1980	HJMB	Abs. FlBe 2005
23	C	Oxford Canal		SP492130	1979	RJC	
23	S	Nuneham Park & Clifton Heath		SU545985	1977	HJMB	

⬇ *Artemisia absinthium*
Archaeophyte

Wormwood
Rare in Oxon and vc23

This aromatic perennial was grown for medicinal and flavouring purposes. Now it is a casual of open anthropogenic sites, and flourishes in areas which are alkaline and have a high-nutrient level. It is frequent in central England but has declined. Druce cited six sites and it was present in 33 tetrads (FlOx p. 248). Of the 17 north of Oxford, none have been re-found. Ten sites were noted in FlBe. CRL

22	V	Chilton disused railway		SU508833	2002	CRL	New
23	W	Mouldens Wood and Davis Copse	LWS	SP340070	2001	CRL	New
23	S	Thames Island nr Streatley	LWS	SU599814	2001	CRL	New
23	O	Oxford Railway Station		SP504062	1992?	HJK	Now car park
23	O	Trap Grounds	LWS	SP504080	1988	CMJ-H	
23	S	Watlington and Pyrton Hills	SSSI	SU700941	1986	DF+	
22	V	Dry Sandford Pit	LGS, BBOWT	SU467995	1980	HJMB	
23	W	Port Meadow Tip		SP40Z	1979	HJMB	Now lost
23	O	Holywell Meadows, Oxford		SP524068	1978	JAW	
23	S	Dyke Hills	LWS	SU573937	1975	HJMB	Not re-found

⬇ *Chamaemelum nobile*
Native

Chamomile
s. 41, Vulnerable ■ Last record in Oxon and vc23 1983

This is a plant of the SW which has shown a big decline. It prefers slightly acid, quite nutrient-rich, sometimes water-logged commons, but cannot tolerate the dense sward that follows loss of grazing. It is on the northern edge of its range with us, Druce had seven sites, FlOx two and last record was at Nuney Green (SU6678). CRL

⬇ *Anthemis arvensis*
Archaeophyte

Corn Chamomile
Endangered ■ Scarce in Oxon, Rare in vc23

(Phil Cutt)

This is an aromatic annual flower of light calcareous or sandy soils, mainly on arable land. It was common in the Midlands and S England and scattered elsewhere. In 1897 Druce described it as local in the Frilford area. Like many arable flowers there has been a huge decline nationally and in Oxon, due to herbicides and improved seed cleaning. There was a further 63% decline between 1987 and 2003 (Braithwaite *et al.* 2006). After discussion with Q.O.N. Kay and Palmer, many records submitted for FlOx were omitted and only those for SP3818, 3820 and 5006 between 1970 and 1991 were accepted; two by Bowen were later added. The atypical plants at Clifton are dependent on the management regime. In vc22 it is still found at Carswell GC regularly, though in small numbers. At the confidential site (22 V, SU49N, 1996–2004) it probably came in grass seed and spread to a second site nearby in 2004. One appeared at Hitchcopse Pit (SU456989, 2014 Killick). SEE, HJK

23	C	Home Farm, Clifton		SP486308	2009	HJK	20
22	V	Carswell Golf Club		SU330962	2008	SEE	Few in rough
23	W	Ditchley, Broad Assarts		SP387218	2007	AJD	
22	V	By railway near Compton Beauchamp		SU276890	1998	SEE	Not since
23	S	Sydlings Copse	SSSI, BBOWT	SP555096	1990	PC	
23	S	Aston Rowant	SAC, NNR, SSSI	SU730970	1975	HJMB	

⬇ *Glebionis segetum* (*Chrysanthemum segetum*)
Archaeophyte

Corn Marigold
Vulnerable ■ **Not Scarce in Oxon and vc23**

(John Killick)

This is an annual arable flower, flourishing on light, often sandy soils. It has been recorded continuously from arable sites since the Iron Age. In Druce 1886 and 1927 it was described as locally common, and 186 tetrad records are in FlOx p. 249. But by the 1990s it was rapidly declining. This is probably due to improved seed cleaning and use of herbicides. It has been introduced in arable margins and stewardship sites not always successfully. Of 11 1990s sites at Elsfield four were lost by 2009. It is still widely found in Oxon on non-calcareous soils, 11 sites in vc23 and six in vc22, 2000–2011. SEE

➡ *Senecio sarracenius* (*S. fluviatilis*)
Neophyte

Broad-leaved Ragwort
Rare in Oxon and vc23

This striking stand-forming perennial of wet woodland had medicinal uses (known as Saracens Consound) before 1600. It was seen in Oxon by 1831 and known since 1872 on the site of medieval fishponds at Hanwell, and still thrives. Plants at Lodge Hill, Abingdon in 1980 (SU506999, Palmer, **OXF**) and 1983, at Goring (1957–61 and 1993, introduced, **RDG**) and at Heythrop Park (1979) were not re-found. It is scattered in GB, with many records in NW England. HJK

23	C	Fishponds Wood, Hanwell	LWS	SP437436	2009	HJK	400 shoots
23	O	New Marston Meadows	SSSI	SP519076	1990	EN	
22	V	*Lodge Hill*		*SU506999*	*1983*	*RH-B*	*Not re-found*
23	W	*Heythrop Park*		*SP365265*	*1979*	*HJMB*	*Not re-found 2008*

⬇ *Senecio sylvaticus*
Native

Heath Groundsel
Scarce in Oxon and vc23

This is an erect (to 70 cm) hairy annual which favours non-calcareous sandy soils. Although this species is 'stable' in Britain, it has not been re-found in many of its sites in S and W Oxon. In both Druce 1896 and 1927 it was described as local even in the right habitat. In FlOx (p. 251) it was recorded from 37 tetrads, the majority of which were in the S, where only one site was recorded in 2000–11. In FlBe it is described as very local. Further searching of old sites, especially along the Corallian Ridge may yet prove fruitful. SEE

23	S	Bottom Wood	LWS	SU665783	2010	SP	
22	V	Confidential	SSSI	SU49J	2009	SEE	
23	S	Waterperry Wood	SSSI	SP602090	2008	HJK	22, 2 sites new
23	C	Tadmarton Heath Golf Club		SP392395	2007	HJK	Several in copse by first tee
23	W	Watersley Copse		SP468226	2007	SD	New
22	V	Bagley Wood		SP511014	2007	LWS	Few SW corner main wood
23	W	Pinsley Wood	LWS	SP429135	2000	JAW	Re-found JK 2015
22	V	Hitchcopse Pit	SSSI, BBOWT	SU452997	2000	HJK	Also SP452001
22	V	*Buckland Warren Woods*	*LWS*	*SU338969*	*1997*	*SEE*	
23	S	*Witheridge Hill*		*SU695840*	*1995*	*RdA*	
23	S	*Kingwood Common*	*LWS*	*SU696825*	*1995*	*RdA*	
23	S	*Highmoor and Lower Common Wood*	*LWS*	*SU702850*	*1995*	*RdA*	
23	S	*Nettlebed Common*	*LWS*	*SU705871*	*1995*	*RdA*	
23	W	*Eynsham Park*		*SP3810*	*1993*	*HJK*	
23	W	*Cogges Wood*	*LWS*	*SP380110*	*1985*	*JMC*	
23	S	*Nuneham Park, Round Hill Wood*		*SU549975*	*1985*	*SEv*	
23	W	*Wychwood*	*NNR, SSSI*	*SP330165*	*1984*	*PS*	
23	C	*Horley*	*LWS*	*SP410430*	*1980*	*AN*	

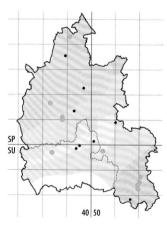

Tephroseris integrifolia
Native

Field Fleawort
s. 41, Vulnerable ■ Rare in Oxon, not in vc23

(Phil Cutt)

This short-lived perennial prefers tightly grazed sward overlying chalk. It is found on the chalk downlands of central S England. This habitat has declined along with the decline of sheep grazing, giving rise to a decline in the species both nationally and locally. Recently re-found at Aston Upthorpe this was the second 2000–11 record, the other being on the White Horse Hill. Pre 1960s it has been recorded from a range of sites along the Wessex Downs. SEE

| 22 | S | Aston Upthorpe Downs | SSSI | SU545835 | 2009 | MK-L | First since Bowen in 1979 |
| 22 | V | Whitehorse Hill | SSSI | SU297864 | 2005 | SEE | 50–100 found yearly |

Bidens cernua
Native

Nodding Bur-marigold
Rare in Oxon and vc23

This waterside annual is widespread in England, and had already declined pre-1930. Druce reported 15 sites and FlOx 21 tetrads (11 north of Oxford), and FlBe none. It prefers neutral to alkaline pH and tolerates high nutrients. CRL

23	C	Adderbury Lakes	LNR	SP477354	2008	RdA	New
23	O	Horseleas Meadow, Marston		SP518080	2008	RdA	New
23	W	Blenheim Park	SSSI	SP4216	1995	HJK	
23	C	Souldern		SP5030	1992	HJK	Pond
23	S	South Stoke Marsh (north)	LWS	SU594844	1986	GH+	
23	C	Otmoor N of Joseph's Stone		SP570147	1985	RM+	
23	W	Windrush		SP381061	1978	PG	
23	W	Cherwell		SP478248	1978	PG	
23	C	Cherwell		SP495154	1978	PG	
23	W	Blenheim Park	SSSI	SP430170	1971	MFVC	

SP
SU
40 50

Sambucus ebulus
Archaeophyte

Dwarf Elder
Scarce in Oxon and vc23

(Peter Creed)

Dwarf Elder forms robust perennial rhizomatous clumps in hedgerows, roadsides and rough ground. In 27 tetrads (FlOx p. 228); Woodell, surprised there were so many, had wondered if some *S. nigra* had been included. Nine sites N of Northings 20 were not re-visited. Records were added near Kencot (23 W) in 2013 (Carterton Rd SP256055 Killick). FlBe has records in 2004 from Woolstone, Coleshill and Kennington but no others since 1920. In GB it remains widespread despite a slight decline. HJK

23	W	Kencot		SP256050	2010	HJK	8 × 2 m
23	C	Weston-on-the-Green		SP522196	2010	HJK	40 × 6 m
22	V	The Avenue, Kennington		SP524015	2009	RH-B	30 along 30 m
23	S	Garsington, Denton Lane		SP584024	2008	HJK	35 × 2 m
22	V	Woolstone		SU295874	2007	HJK	120 m long
23	W	roadside nr Chipping Norton		SP297258	2000	PS	
23	C	Cradle House Reedbed		SP376328	1987	SA	
23	C	Weston Fen	SSSI	SP524198	1987	JMC	
23	S	Cottesmore Lane		SU636925	1985	EC	
23	W	Foxholes	SSSI, BBOWT	SP250205	1983	JHC	
23	W	Heythrop Park		SP365265	1979	HJMB	Abs. HJK 2008

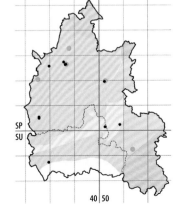
SP
SU
40 50

↑ *Valerianella carinata*
Archaeophyte

Keeled-fruited Cornsalad
No longer Scarce in Oxon, probably Not Scarce in vc23

(John Killick)

This Cornsalad is told from the common *V. locusta* by its fruits, shaped like an up-ended canoe rather than an egg, and is a winter annual of artificial habitats such as paths, paving, walls and gardens. In FlOx it was in only five tetrads (p. 230), but was seen in 2000–11 in 20 sites in Oxon (eight in vc23 plus one in 2012) and almost certainly under-recorded. Its numbers in an Abingdon garden since 2000 have fluctuated widely. In GB it is much increased since 1962 and is now solid in SW England and widespread elsewhere, especially SW of a line Cheshire–Essex. HJK

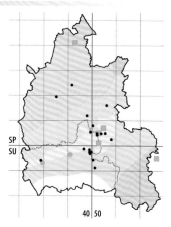

⬇ *Valerianella rimosa*
Archaeophyte   s. 41, Endangered, Nationally Rare ■ Rare in Oxon, Last vc23 record 1980

This winter annual of S England has suffered a huge decline. It grows in calcareous arable fields and quarries and does not flourish in raised nitrogen levels. It was recorded in five Druce sites and in seven FlOx tetrads. FlBe had three records, and the only 2000–11 record was short-lived. CRL

22	S	Hill Barn Farm, Aston Upthorpe	SU553845	2010	RH-B	2, abs. 2011

➡ *Valerianella dentata*
Archaeophyte

Narrow-fruited Cornsalad
Endangered ■ Scarce in Oxon and vc23

(Peter Creed)

The fruits of this small annual plant are needed to distinguish it from *V. rimosa*. In *V. dentata*, the fruits are narrower, 0.7–1.2 mm (not 1.5–2.5 mm); and the main tooth may have teeth. The plant is found on chalky arable soils and is scattered over GB as far N as the Cheviots, but has incurred huge losses. In FlOx (25 tetrads) it was described as 'mostly lost', but there are nine 2000–11 records. Their survival may be due to its relatively long seed-life and the increase in arable headlands. SEE

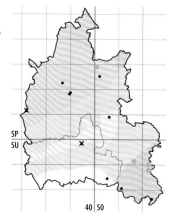

23	S	N of Oxford Crematorium	SP561090	2011	HJK	10 plants New
22	S	Hill Barn Farm	SU553845	2010	RH-B	
23	S	Playhatch	SU739763	2010	JHW	
23	W	Kings and Wootton Woods LWS	SP400187	2009	WOR	
23	S	Goring	SU613806	2009	JHW	
23	W	N. Westwell strip	SP2211	2007	HJK	Last seen 2003
23	W	Field edge, Spelsbury	SP336225	2007	PS	
23	W	Stonesfield	SP395181	2004	JE	
22	V	Confidential	SU49P	2003	JMC	Not since HJK
23	C	The Gorse and Heath	SP521252	2000	CRL	

⬇ *Valeriana dioica*
Native

Marsh Valerian
Near Threatened ■ Not Scarce in Oxon and vc23

This small perennial of marshes and fens is widespread in England but scarcer in the S and declining. Although reduced from 76 tetrads in FlOx to 13 records (2000–11) in vc23 and 11 in vc22 (Oxon) it is still far from Scarce in Oxon. It is fairly evenly spread in all districts. SEE, HJK

⬇ *Dipsacus pilosus*
Native

Small Teasel
Scarce in Oxon, Rare in vc23

(John Killick)

This is a bristly biennial found on disturbed ground on woodland rides and edges. In GB it is mostly found in the S Midlands, SE and Welsh borders, where the population is relatively stable. It requires damp conditions: ditches and stream banks. It appears to be decreasing in vc23 with only two recent records. It has been described as rare since Druce's flora of 1886, but in one of its sites Tubney Woods it has spread in recent years to the roadside verges and to Rockley Copse. This may be the same site as Druce's 'about Beslsleigh'. It requires ground disturbance to germinate and lack of woodland management may account for its decline. SEE.

23	S	Warburg	BBOWT	SU720878	2010	RdA	
22	V	Grove Wood		SU292968	2009	SEE+	100+ spreading
22	V	Tubney lay-by on A420		SU439996	2009	SEE	20+ on verge
23	C	Shelswell Park		SP601311	2007	GD	Pond
22	V	Rockley Copse		SP461019	2006	SEE	New
22	V	Coxwell Wood	LWS	SU258950	2000	SEE	small patch by arable
23	W	R Windrush		SP243126	1996	SJW	
23	W	Medley Brook channels		SP401037	1996	SJW	
23	S	Thame Park and New Park	pLWS	SP713035	1987	JMC	

⬇ *Hydrocotyle vulgaris*
Native

Marsh Pennywort
Near Threatened ■ Scarce in Oxon and vc23

(Phil Cutt)

This small perennial species favours fens, marshes and meadows, usually acidic. Nationally this species is declining, especially in the SE, due to drainage and increased fertilisation. These habitats have become increasingly scarce in Oxon and hence Marsh Pennywort is a scarce species. Druce 1886 stated it was local, listing 21 sites. In FlOx it was in 10 tetrads (Witney was the only Druce site to be re-found); and there are only six 2000–11 records in vc23. Some of these sites are very small, some e.g. Upper Windrush meadows are much larger, where several patches are recorded. The remaining sites all have some conservation status. SEE

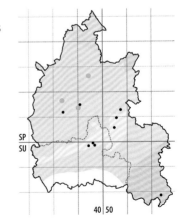

23	O	Lye Valley	SSSI	SP547058	2010	JAW	2 sites
22	V	Ruskin Reserve	SAC, NNR, SSSI	SU460996	2010	JAW	Abundant 2 sites
23	S	Binfield Heath		SU738786	2010	JHW	Abundant
23	W	Manor Farm Meadow, Crawley	LWS	SP339119	2009	SEE+	Frequent
23	W	Coombe Fen	LWS	SP408149	2008	WOR	Re-found 2015 JK
23	S	Otmoor	SSSI	SP573128	2008	SEE+	Widespread, P 2012
22	V	Confidential	SSSI	SU49P	2007	SEE	Present, 2012
23	S	Sydlings Copse	SSSI, BBOWT	SP556096	2006	HJK	
22	V	Gozzards Ford Fen	LWS, BBOWT	SU467987	2004	HJK	
23	W	Wychwood	NNR, SSSI	SP338165	1996	HJMB	
23	W	Middle Barton Fen	SSSI	SP443264	1991	EN	
23	W	North Leigh Common	LWS	SP401136	1975	HJMB	

SP
SU

40 | 50

Anthriscus caucalis
Native

(Peter Creed)

This is an annual plant of light sandy soils, with weak stems, which scrambles over adjoining vegetation. Nationally there has been a decline, which seems to have stabilised since 1962 and this is mirrored locally. Throughout Druce's time it was rare and very local in Oxon. It was recorded in six tetrads in FlOx and only four localities in vc23 were recorded in 2000–11; four have been added since. In vc22 it is found all along the Corallian Ridge, often in great numbers. SEE

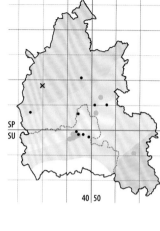

23	O	Eastern By-pass		SP513101	2010	JAW	Numerous
23	W	Lower Dornford Farm		SP457209	2009	WR	53
22	V	Confidential		SU49U	2009	HJK	
22	V	E of field N of Sheepstead Folly, Marcham 200 m S of road		SU458983	2008	HJK	Many
22	V	Albert Park (west end)		SU489973	2008	HJK	50
22	V	Confidential		SU49P	2007	HJK	11 sites, present 2011
22	V	A420, Tubney		SU438994	2006	SEE	
22	V	Frilford, vineyard near Dog House		SU453987	2006	HJK	
22	V	Confidential		SU49N	2005	HJK	
23	W	Shilton Bradwell Grove Airfield	LWS	SP250070	2004	HJK	2 sites
22	V	Farmoor Reservoir	LWS	SP445065	2004	HJK	
23	S	Barton bridle road		SP563102	2004	JMC	
22	V	Abingdon Boxhill Walk		SU497977	2000	HJK	
23	S	Lower Farm		SU676908	1999	SK	
23	C	Noke Manor Farm		SP537131	1997	OS	
23	O	Edge of St Cross playing field		SP518068	1986	RH-B	
23	W	Ascott under Wychwood		SP298175	1980	WOR	Abs. 2007

Scandix pecten-veneris
Archaeophyte

(Peter Creed)

This is a small distinctive annual arable weed. Its long pointed seedpod gives rise to its English name. It is found chiefly on calcareous clays in arable locations. It has suffered a serious decline both nationally and in Oxon. There were 24 tetrad records in FlOx, reduced to four 2000–11 records for vc23. FlBe had Aston Upthorpe (SU550844) in 2002. This decline is probably due to increased use of herbicides and to improved methods of seed cleaning. A later find at Hatford, 2012, was on a bund created in gravel extraction workings. Efforts are being made to introduce the seed to another part of the sand pit where it may survive. More recently it was found flowering in January along the Oxfordshire Way SP536132. SEE

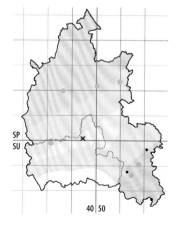

23	S	Crowmarsh		SU630876	2010	JHW	3 plants
23	S	Lewknor		SU710965	2010	TR	>100
22	V	Tubney Woods	LWS	SP445006	2007	SEE	Abs. last seen 1997
23	S	Sonning		SU732768	2004	JHW	<50
23	S	Hammond's Farm		SU646861	1999	SK	Widespread
23	S	Britwell Salome		SU677905	1999	SK	
23	C	Bicester		SP597234	1988	ML	
22	V	Pucketty Farm		SU314989	1979	MFVC	
23	W	Ditchley		SP364198	1974	WDC	

⬆ *Smyrnium olusatrum*
Archaeophyte

Alexanders
Scarce in Oxon, Rare in vc23

(Rod d'Ayala)

Alexanders is a stout perennial in hedgerows, waysides and waste places. In FlOx rare, only at Kelmscott (2298, 1972 Bowen); also in SU5880 in 1968 and SP5016 in 1995; FlBe cited only Didcot in 1976. All 2000–11 records are new; some could be introductions. In GB it is widespread especially near the coast and has increased in some inland areas. Milder winters may have helped its increase between 1987 and 2004 (Braithwaite *et al*. 2006). HJK

23	W	Between Little Minster turn and river bridge		SP316110	2009	HJK	50, new
22	V	Lashford Lane		SP470005	2008	HJK	Several sq.m, new
23	S	Kingwood Common	LWS	SU696831	2007	JHW	Planted?, new
23	S	Kidmore End Road		SU715774	2007	JHW	2, new
22	V	Rockley Copse		SP462022	2001	JMC	New

⬇ *Pimpinella major*
Native

Greater Burnet-saxifrage
Scarce in Oxon and vc23

This is a perennial, generally on basic soils. It grows by wood margins and grassy verges of roads or tracks, especially in or near ancient woods (Rackham, 1986.) It was in 50 tetrads (FlOx p. 188), many in Oxford or on clay NE of it, but also scattered elsewhere in vc23. In vc22 (Oxon) FlBe cited few recent colonies in oak woods and thickets. In GB it has recently declined slightly with the degradation of grassland (Braithwaite *et al*., 2006); while its distribution is hard to explain, our records are near the SW edge of its range and few are after 1990. A colony 10 x 1 m was by a road at Wytham SP471087 2012. HJK

23	S	RSPB Otmoor	pLWS, RSPB	SP567129	2010	HJK	2
23	S	Forest Hill		SP594084	2010	HJK	10
23	S	Warren Farm		SP598073	2010	RH-B	1
22	V	Wytham Woods	SSSI	SP456080	2009	FHW	200
23	O	Marston		SP532083	2002	HJK	Frequent
23	O	Brasenose Wood and Shotover Hill	SSSI	SP556050	1996	HJK	Few

⬇ *Sium latifolium*
Native

Greater Water-parsnip
s. 41, Endangered, Nationally Scarce ■ Rare in Oxon and vc23

(Alison McDonald)

This large perennial is widespread scattered in S and E England with a stronghold on the Somerset Levels. It has suffered a huge decline. It prefers neutral to calcareous conditions and tolerates raised nutrients. It is susceptible to grazing and shading. Druce had 19 sites and FlOx had 19 tetrads. FlBe had SP465098 in 2004. RPG has searched former sites and is monitoring the two populations. Seed has been collected, grown on by the OUBG and used to re-enforce the SSSI population. CRL

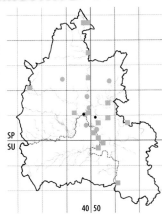

23	O	Almonds Farm and Burnt Mill Fields	LWS	SP519092	2010	JAW	22. Was in Druce
22	V	Wytham Ditches and Flushes	SSSI	SP465098	2009	AWM	54
23	V	Pixey and Yarnton Meads	SAC, SSSI	SP471101	2005	AWM	18
23	W	Woodford Br, *Eastern Meadow*		SP382244	1987	GO'D+	
23	C	Oxford Canal		SP492130	1979	RJC	
23	C	Pixey and Yarnton Meads	SAC, SSSI	SP473103	1977	JMC	

⮕ *Oenanthe fistulosa*
Native

Tubular Water-dropwort
s. 41, Vulnerable ■ Not Scarce in Oxon and vc23

(Judy Webb)

This distinctive perennial umbellifer is distinguished by its few (3–4) stout rays. It is characteristic of floodplain hay-meadows (MG4), but also found in pasture and water margins. It is widespread in England and Wales especially in the S and E, but declined severely after 1950 due to ploughing of hay-meadows for silage. It is usually on basic to neutral soils and tolerates quite high nitrogen. Druce listed 30 sites and it was recorded in 55 FlOx tetrads; it has been re-found whenever looked for in over 30, but in five the habitat has become unsuitable in a variety of ways. It has been lost when grazing lapsed. In 2000–11 we collected 36 records, FlBe gave 15 locations. The great majority of sites have some protection. Many lie in the Upper Thames Tributaries ESA, and appropriate management was eligible for payments under the HLS since meadows with this plant often qualify as S 41 habitat Lowland Meadows. CRL

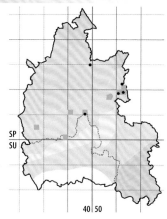

⬇ *Oenanthe silaifolia*
Native

Narrow-leaved Water-dropwort
GB Red List Near Threatened, Nationally Scarce ■ Scarce in Oxon and vc23

(Judy Webb)

This perennial umbellifer of floodplain hay meadows has a scattered distribution in S, central and E England. It has been lost from pre-1930 sites but new sites are being found perhaps reflecting lack of recording due to its early flowering and difficulty of vegetative identification. Druce had eight localities and FlOx p. 189 had 12 tetrads. At Bestmoor there are very large numbers in a hay meadow which has lost other components of MG4, probably through herbicides. At West Mead (table, line 4) it tends to grow with *Thalictrum flavum* along former channels, perhaps helped by its tolerance of moderate nitrate levels. The only recent record in vc22 (Oxon) is by Palmer at Newbridge in 1966. CRL

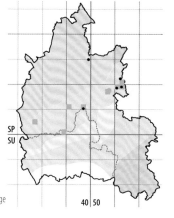

23	C	Meadow Farm Meadows	LWS, BBOWT	SP628190	2012	JAW+	Lots, new
23	C	Arncott Bridge Meadows	SSSI	SP608185	2011	JAW	147
23	C	Bestmoor	SSSI	SP491299	2010	Anon	abundant
23	C	Pixey and Yarnton Meads	SAC, SSSI	SP470103	2010	AWM+	524 in 2011
23	C	Field by Beacon Hill Ditch	pLWS	SP623223	2007	BBOWT	New Field
23	C	Essex Farm, Blackthorn		SP6220	1992	HJK	
23	C	SE of Astleybridge Fm, Merton		SP575174	1974	RCP	West side of Ray below bridge

⬇ *Oenanthe lachenalii*
Native

Parsley Water-dropwort
Near Threatened ■ Rare in Oxon and vc23

(Phil Cutt)

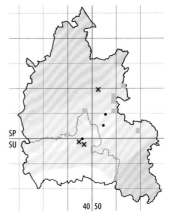

This perennial umbellifer differs from *O. fistulosa* in its bracts usually 1–5, and rays >3, slender, and from *O. silaifolia* in its stem with shallow ridges, 0.5 cm diameter. It grows around the coasts and inland on calcareous wetlands where it has suffered a big decline. In Oxon it is increasingly confined to base-rich fens on the Corallian Ridge and has been lost at three fens which had become overgrown. BBOWT has grazing at both its sites. Druce had seven localities and FlOx had 10 tetrads. CRL

23	O	Lye Valley	SSSI	SP547052	2010	JAW	>50
22	V	Parsonage Moor	SAC, SSSI, BBOWT	SU460999	2010	JAW	c. 170
23	S	Sydlings Copse	SSSI, BBOWT	SP556096	2006	HJK	Few
23	W	Newbridge Meadow		SP397016	1991	BBOWT	
22	V	Barrow Farm Fen	SSSI	SU467975	1991	JMC	Not re-found
22	V	Confidential	SSSI	SU49P	1986	SW	Not re-found
23	C	Weston Fen	SSSI	SP526194	1983	HJMB	Not re-found
23	O	Marston Ferry Link Meadows E		SP519089	1978	JAW	

SP
SU

40 | 50

⬆ *Oenanthe crocata*

Hemlock Water-dropwort

This very poisonous, robust water-side perennial of neutral pH tolerates raised nutrients. It is common in the south and west, and nationally was more or less stable (Atlas 2002), though with us, as in Cambs and Northants, it appears to be increasing. While Druce only had two extant sites, both in South Oxfordshire, FlOx (p. 189) had 23 tetrads, confined to the Thames and Ray. During the 1990s two were found on the Cherwell, two on the canal, while in 2000–11 we found 19 localities in Oxon, of which 15 were in vc23. CRL

⬇ *Oenanthe fluviatilis*
Native

River Water-dropwort
Rare in Oxon and vc23

(Peter Creed)

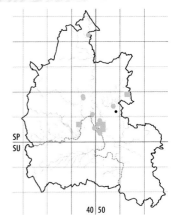

This aquatic perennial of clear, rather eutrophic rivers and streams is scattered and decreasing. Druce had it 'common in the shallower parts of all the larger streams', but in vc23 it was in only 10 FlOx tetrads. FlBe has only undated records. Oxon is near the NW edge of its range in England; in E and S England it is widespread but has declined owing to eutrophication, dredging and canalisation. HJK

23	S	Otmoor		SP584121	2004	JE	
23	O	R Cherwell		SP5107	1990	HJK	Leaves only, few
22	V	Hinksey Stream complex		SP494055	1989	NRA	
22	V	Kennington Pool	LWS	SP518034	1988	PA	
23	C	Loop Farm Flood Meadows	LWS	SP487110	1987	GH	
23	S	Shiplake		SU7676	1987	MN	
23	C	R Cherwell		SP469426	1970	RCP	North of Huscote Mill

SP
SU

40 | 50

Oenanthe aquatica
Native

Fine-leaved Water-dropwort
Scarce in Oxon and vc23

(Peter Creed)

This perennial umbellifer has a disjunct distribution being found in the E of England and in the Welsh marches. It prefers water-edge sites, especially ponds and ditches, which are slightly calcareous and high in nutrients. It has declined nationally. Druce had 14 sites, mostly on the Ray, but with four in South Oxon. FlOx p. 189 cited six tetrads. Braithwaite *et al.* (2006) found it decreased significantly between 1987–8 and 2003–4. CRL

23	C	RSPB Otmoor	pLWS, RSPB	SP553130	2011	HJK	4 new
23	C	Otmoor	SSSI	SP572139	2006	FHW	9
23	C	RSPB Otmoor	pLWS, RSPB	SP587150	2006	JE	
23	S	*Otmoor*	*SSSI*	*SP573130*	*2005*	*SEE*	*Abs. 2006*
23	C	Cutter's Brook Meadows	LWS	SP618218	2004	CRL	Re-found 2015 JK
23	C	Church Fields at Cutter's Bridge	LWS	SP634215	2004	HG	
23	O	New Marston Meadows	SSSI	SP517082	1991	NE	
22	V	*Kennington Pool*	*LWS*	*SP518034*	*1988*	*PA*	*Not re-found*
22	V	*Lockinge Park Lake*		*SU427875*	*1979*	*DJNH+*	

Bupleurum rotundifolium
Archaeophyte   s. 41, Critically Endangered ■ Last seen in Oxon in 1979, in vc23 1970

Thorow-wax

This annual was formerly a weed of lime-rich arable in southern England on soils with very high pH and moderate nitrogen levels. Druce had 25 sites, but it is now extinct in arable fields (Atlas 2002). The bird-seed alien *B. subovatum* has since been mistaken for it. Last records: in vc23 at Headington in 1970 and in Oxon at Lollingdon Hill in 1979. CRL, HJK

Apium graveolens
Native

Wild Celery
Rare in Oxon and vc23

(Phil Cutt)

This biennial herb is found mainly in coastal areas and in brackish conditions. There has been a decline, especially in inland sites. There are six old tetrad records in FlOx, none found during this survey, but a casual appeared by the Thames. In vc22 Wild Celery still flourishes at the Marcham salt spring site. Marcham is an old English place name associated with the presence of celery and there have been continuous records since 1853. The location is now sympathetically managed for Celery and it is hoped that the other saline species associated with this site will reappear. SEE

22	V	Manor Farm, Marcham	LWS	SU453960	2011	SEE	Approx 150 plants and seedlings
23	S	*S of River Thames opposite Abingdon*		*SU498961*	*2005*	*HJK*	*1 clump, not since*

⬇ *Apium repens*
Native

Creeping Marshwort
European Protected Species, IUCN Endangered, Sched 8, s. 41, Endangered,
Nationally Rare ■ Rare in Oxon and vc23

(Peter Creed)

This is a small, creeping perennial of heavily grazed wet pastures. Formerly it grew in Scotland (conf. Q. Cronk), Wales and Yorks, but for many years was only known in GB at Port Meadow, Oxford. It has since reappeared at Binsey and in Essex, but disappeared again. Monitoring since 1995 shows that it is eliminated by prolonged summer flooding which reduces soil oxygen, but reappears from the seed-bank. It requires long, warm summers for seed set, and tolerates raised nutrient levels. JNCC had DNA studies done (Grassly *et al.* 1996). English Nature's Species Recovery Programme supported monitoring, introductions, visiting Dutch sites and basic experiments by the RPG (McDonald & Lambrick 2006). NEng continues to support monitoring and further introductions and works with the City and the EA. Water levels on Port Meadow are a cause for concern for the species. Possible hybrids are being investigated at Leicester University. CRL

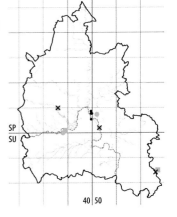

23	0	Port Meadow with Wolvercote Common & Green	SAC, SSSI	SP495086	2008	RPG	10 × 5 m veg
22	V	Willow Walk Meadow	LWS	SP496056	2008	AWM+	introduced 1996, 15 × 5 m
23	*0*	*Binsey Green*	*LWS*	*SP495077*	*2005*	*RPG*	*8; abs. AWM+ 2008*
23	*0*	*Port Meadow with Wolvercote Common & Green*	*SAC, SSSI*	*SP499077*	*2005*	*RPG*	*100s to 1000s*
23	*0*	*New Marston Meadows*	*SSSI*	*SP520073*	*1996*	*CRL+*	*48 intr, abs. 1998*
23	*W*	*Langel Common*	*Other*	*SP359098*	*1970*	*RCP*	*OXF, abs. CRL+ 2000*
23	*S*	*Henley-on-Thames*		*SU7684*	*1970*	*VP*	*Abs. VP 1980*
23	*S*	*Sandford-on-Thames*		*SP530018*		***OXF***	*Abs. CRL+ 2000*

⬇ *Apium inundatum*
Native

Lesser Marshwort
Vulnerable ■ Rare in Oxon and vc23

(Peter Creed)

This inconspicuous prostrate umbellifer grows submerged or on the edges of shallow water. It is widespread in the British Isles, requiring slightly acidic and low-nutrient conditions. It has suffered a big decline due to drainage, eutrophication and probably lack of grazing. Braithwaite *et al.* (2006) found a further significant decrease between 1987/8 and 2003/4. A few plants set seed on the edge of Fowls Pill during the exceptionally low water level in 2010, but became engulfed in *Glyceria maxima*. It has apparently failed to colonise the nearby New Pill. Druce had 16 sites including Otmoor and Nettlebed. FlOx (p. 191) had eight tetrads, FlBe had three old records from Oxon. CRL

23	C	Otmoor	SSSI	SP572140	2010	WC	6
23	C	Kirtlington Village Pond		SP500198	2005	RdA	Rare, new
23	*S*	*Kingwood Common*	*LWS*	*SU696825*	*1995*	*RdA*	
23	*S*	*Nettlebed Common*	*LWS*	*SU705871*	*1995*	*RdA*	

⬇ *Petroselinum segetum*

Corn Parsley

There are only 13 records in 2000–11 for this in vc23. In FlOx 36 sites are quoted, the majority being in C and W, whereas the S is now its stronghold. This would suggest that searching in C and W would be worthwhile. SEE

⬇ *Carum carvi*
Archaeophyte   s. 41, Critically Endangered, Nationally Scarce ■ Last Oxon and vc23 record 1988

Caraway

This perennial was naturalised or casual in arable land, meadows and waste ground. FlOx had it from N Oxford tip (SP4808, Bowen) and Sydlings Copse (SP5408), and FlBe only by the railway at Didcot in 1897. Our only recent record was >100 along the margin of an arable field at Kirtlington (23 C, SP509209, 1988, Killick, **OXF**) not seen in 2003. Introduced to GB by 1375, it is grown less than formerly, now scattered and lost from many places. HJK

🔻 *Torilis arvensis*
Archaeophyte   s. 41, Endangered, Nationally Scarce ■ **Spreading Hedge-parsley**

Rare in Oxon, Last vc23 record 1999

This undistinguished annual, or rarely biennial, was once frequent on heavy calcareous soils of SE England. It has had a huge decline, being vulnerable to herbicides and is a poor competitor. It grows in autumn-sown cereal crops especially on well-drained set-aside. At Cholsey it is carefully managed by the owner with agri-environment help, and monitored by RPG. Druce had 16 sites including Otmoor and Nettlebed, and FlOx p. 192 cited 17 tetrads. FlBe had Kingston Bagpuize (2002, Curtis). CRL

22	V	Chilswell Valley	LWS	SP503037	2008	RH-B	1
22	S	Cholsey Headland		SU602864	2008	CRL	c. 500
23	S	River Thames		SU505947	1999	JMC	
23	W	Wheat field N of Tackley		SP414215	1996	AWM	
22	V	Sutton Courtenay Gravel Pits		SU518930	1985	HJMB+	
23	W	Rangers Lawn		SP333194	1984	AMS	

➡️ *Torilis nodosa*
Knotted Hedge-parsley

This plant of thin grass and bare light soil has declined, especially in N England. It was in 22 FlOx tetrads; in 13 2000–11 sites in vc23, it is Not Scarce. In vc22 (Oxon) FlBe noted it in Didcot in 2004; since 2000 it was recorded widely in Abingdon and at five other places. HJK

➡️ *Arum italicum*
Italian Lord's-and-ladies

We recorded this species but our few recent records are ssp. *italicum* with white-veined leaves, presumed bird-sown, and do not qualify for the Register. HJK

🔻 *Spirodela polyrhiza*
Native   **Greater Duckweed**

Rare in Oxon and vc23

Our largest duckweed, a floating aquatic, was in 13 tetrads (FlOx p. 260) and in vc22 (Oxon) mostly in nutrient-rich, near-stagnant water near the Thames and Cherwell. It had decreased in both vice-counties, and steeply in recent years. In GB, it is also found in grazing marshes. It is mostly S of Liverpool–Lincoln, with a gap in our area, and much decreased in the Midlands. HJK

23	O	Port Meadow with Wolvercote Common & Green	SAC, SSSI	SP494097	2011	AWM	Long pond
22	S	Hagbourne County Primary School Pond		SU525882	2008	RdA	New
22	V	Sandford Lock		SP529013	1997	HJK	
23	S	E of Abingdon		SU512967	1995	HJK	
23	O	Port Meadow with Wolvercote Common & Green	SAC, SSSI	SP495090	1992	PA	
22	V	Hinksey Stream Complex		SP494055	1989	NRA	

🔻 *Lemna gibba*
Native   **Fat Duckweed**

Scarce in Oxon and vc23

This is a small aquatic free floating plant. It is found in still to slow-moving water which is brackish to eutrophic. Although it appears to be showing a slight increase in distribution nationally, in Oxon it has declined. It was described as scarce in FlOx with 22 tetrads, mainly in the Thames Valley, but there are only four 2000–11 records in vc23 and one in vc22. SEE

23	C	Otmoor	SSSI	SP572137	2010	WC	Abundant
22	V	Meadow by Old Man's Bridge		SU301999	2009	SEE	Plentiful in old meander
23	S	Lord Philimore's Estate		SU736780	2007	RdA	
23	O	Trap Grounds	LWS	SP504082	2004	JE	
23	C	37 Acre Field	LWS	SP577136	2001	CRL	
22	V	Hinksey Stream Complex		SP494055	1989	NRA	

⬇ *Lemna trisulca* — Ivy-leaved Duckweed

With 30 2000–11 records in vc23 and 14 in vc22, there has been a slight decline from 43 tetrads in FlOx, but it is still Not Scarce, scattered across the county. SEE

⬇ *Baldellia ranunculoides*
Native

Lesser Water-plantain
Vulnerable ■ Rare in Oxon and vc23

(Peter Creed)

This attractive aquatic is usually rooted in the drawdown zone of still or slowly moving water, tolerating a range of alkalinity and some salt. It has declined in Europe where experiments have shown that it fails to thrive and sets few seed under nutrient-rich conditions (Kozlowski & Vallelian 2009). It is widespread in the British Isles, but has declined, mainly in the Midlands. Druce had seven sites and FlOx p. 256 four. The New Pill, a scrape which was dug at Otmoor by the EA in 1995, now has hundreds of plants, while the adjacent Fowls Pill has only eight. CRL

23	C	Otmoor	SSSI	SP572140	2006	FHW	c. 300
23	W	Gibraltar pit or canal		SP469189	1984	RWHS+	
22	V	Cothill Fen	SAC, NNR, SSSI	SU459997	1978	HJMB	Not re-found

➡ *Alisma lanceolatum*
Native

Narrow-leaved Water-plantain
Scarce in Oxon, Rare in vc23

Alisma lanceolatum is distinguished from *A. plantago-aquatica* by its narrow leaves, and by the short straight style arising from the side of the carpel, near the top. It is an emergent perennial herb of shallow water or exposed mud. It has only been consistently recognised as a separate species since 1952 so trends are difficult to assess, but all water related habitats are subject to loss due to drainage, with subsequent effect on species. It has been found scattered throughout Oxon where the right habitat occurs: eutrophic calcareous water, edge of ponds and canals, but now its main stronghold is in the Otmoor area. There are 16 FlOx tetrad records, (six N of Oxford) from some of which it has not been recently recorded, notably the Farmoor reservoir area. SEE

23	C	Otmoor	SSSI	SP572140	2010	WC	About 20
22	V	Pucketty Farm, Faringdon		SU311989	2007	SEE	2 ponds with 6 plants
23	S	RSPB Otmoor	pLWS, RSPB	SP565129	2006	RSPB	9 sites in area
22	O	Sandford Lock		SP50F	2001	HJK	
22	V	Farmoor		SP463072	1997	PA	
23	W	Old Gravel Pit nr Little Faringdon	LWS	SP219017	1985	JMC	

➡ *Butomus umbellatus* — Flowering-rush

In FlOx this was in 67 tetrads. Although there was concern about a possible decline, there have been 15 2000–11 records in vc23 and nine in vc22, so this is not considered Scarce. There are two problems, first that plants often lack flowers can be missed; secondly that as an attractive plant it is often planted, but the above records are well established and most go back several years. SEE

⬇ *Hydrocharis morsus-ranae*
Native

Frogbit
Vulnerable ■ Rare in Oxon and vc23

(Peter Creed)

This free-floating plant of still water likes neutral to base-rich conditions and tolerates high nutrients. It rarely sets seed, but spreads by vegetative buds. It is widespread in S England and Wales but has declined substantially with the loss of grazing marshes. Druce recorded it in 18 sites but there were only six FlOx tetrads including Otmoor and Port Meadow. Surviving at Otmoor, it has colonised the area re-wilded by the RSPB. The last FlBe record was in Wytham in 1918. CRL

23	C	Otmoor	SSSI	SP572139	2006	FHW	3 × 3 m
23	C	RSPB Otmoor	pLWS, RSPB	SP564146	2004	RSPB	New
22	V	Wytham Ditches and Flushes	SSSI	SP463098	1970	Doom	

→ *Stratiotes aloides* **Water-soldier**

We recorded this species because native populations, mainly in East Anglia, are declining in GB. We have newly seen it in 12 vc23 sites, but mostly in garden ponds. It is alien here so does not qualify for the Register. HJK

↓ *Triglochin palustre* **Marsh Arrowgrass**
Native **Near Threatened** ■ **Not Scarce in Oxon and vc23**

This inconspicuous perennial is widespread in the N and W, but has declined in central England. Braithwaite *et al.* (2006) found it had decreased significantly between 1987–8 and 2003–4. It requires marshy open conditions, tolerating some lime. It can survive under close mowing and grazing, but is difficult to find unless flowering. There are 32 localities in Druce, 42 tetrads in FlOx (p. 256), and 22 records in 2000–11. CRL

Potamogeton **Pondweeds**

As noted in FlOx (p. 256) pondweeds are hard to identify, especially the smaller ones; few have been critically named and records not backed by specimens may be errors, so conclusions are tentative. By the time of FlOx few genera had declined so greatly, due variously to pollution, turbidity, eutrophication, and disturbance by boats. FlBe had few recent records. As they are mostly submerged, some are difficult of access and probably under-recorded. HJK

↓ *Potamogeton polygonifolius* **Bog Pondweed**
Native **Last Oxon record 1986, in vc23 1979**

This rhizomatous perennial is common in Scotland, Wales and the heaths of S and SW England, but has declined in central and E England. It flourishes in shallow, acidic and very low-nutrient waters. Druce had seven sites and there were two FlOx tetrads; FlBe had it near S Hinksey in 1986. The decline is most likely due to eutrophication. CRL

23	S	Stag Hall Pond, Kingwood Cm		SU686834	1979	DJNH
23	S	Woodcote		SU6480	1977	VNP

→ *Potamogeton coloratus* **Fen Pondweed**
Native **Nationally scarce** ■ **Rare in Oxon, absent in vc23**

(Peter Creed)

Fen pondweed is perennial with translucent leaves, often totally submerged. In calcareous nutrient-poor fens, where spring-fed tufa-forming streams widen to form shallow pools; it can also survive on damp ground. From the 1950s we have a long run of records in vc22 (Oxon) at Dry Sandford Pit, Parsonage Moor and the Ruskin reserve. Here it is visible most years but its numbers and range vary with water levels. At Dry Sandford and Hitchcopse Pits the substrate is limestone; at Parsonage Moor it grows with *Chara* and *Utricularia* over peat, and in the Ruskin Reserve in a vegetation mat at the pool edge. It is at risk from successional changes but grazing has helped it at Parsonage Moor and Dry Sandford Pit. Its former Barrow Farm Fen site is overgrown. Holmes and Preston referred Gorman's atypical plant 8 km to the W, to this species. In BI its main strongholds are Norfolk and Cambs, where native populations are declining, and central Ireland. HJK, CRL

22	V	Parsonage Moor	SAC, SSSI, BBOWT	SU460997	2009	JAW	20, calc. valley fen
22	V	Dry Sandford Pit	SSSI, LGS, BBOWT	SU468994	2009	HJK	5x3 sq.m
22	V	Ditch south of Turf Pits Covert		SU374957	2008	SG	New conf. NTHH
22	V	Hitchcopse Pit	SSSI, BBOWT	SU452996	1981	HJMB+	

⬇ *Potamogeton lucens*
Native

Shining Pondweed
Scarce in Oxon and vc23

This robust, broad-leaved aquatic widespread in E England prefers calcareous water with moderate nutrient levels. Druce said it was common in all districts. FlOx had 34 tetrads. Now lost from the Thames, it was found during the 1990s extensively along the Windrush and the Evenlode and also in the Cherwell. River traffic may account for much of its decline. CRL

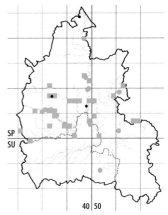

23	C	Broadfield Rd Pond, Yarnton		SP478129	2008	SG	New
23	W	Wychwood	NNR, SSSI	SP339168	2007	WOR	Many
23	C	Clattercote Reservoir		SP450485	2004	CRL	Druce
23	W	Windrush		SP299106	1996	JAT+	Downstream to 3904
23	W	Windrush (West Branch)		SP359092	1996	SJW	
23	C	Kidington, Cherwell		SP505148	1994	HJK	
22	S	West Hagbourne moor		SU535872	1992	HJMB+	
23	C	Evenlode		SP468398	1990	JFS	+ 1 km upstream
23	W	Evenlode		SP487198	1990	MHa	+ 1 km upstream
23	W	Evenlode		SP440148	1989	JFS	+ 1 km upstream
22	V	Hinksey Stream Complex		SP494055	1989	NRA	
23	S	Thame		SP611030	1978	PG	
23	C	Ray		SP613184	1978	EN	

⬇ *Potamogeton praelongus*
Native

Long-stalked Pondweed
Endangered ■ Last record in Oxon in 1988, in vc23 1975

This species is widespread in Scotland but rare in England following a huge decline. It requires deep water (>1 m), flowing or still, neutral pH and tolerates slightly raised nitrogen. In Oxon it is at the southwest edge of its range. Druce reported it locally common. In the Thames and Cherwell in the 1970s; FlOx had five tetrads. The decline is presumably due to eutrophication and river traffic. CRL

22	V	Kennington Pool	LWS	SP518034	1988	PA	Abs. CRL 2010
23	W	Farmoor		SP4206	1975	ML	FlOx
22	O	Port Meadow		SP4804	1974	HJMB	FlOx
23	O	Cherwell		SP5208	1968	MVFC	FlOx

⬇ *Potamogeton perfoliatus*

Perfoliate Pondweed

This rhizomatous perennial is widespread in England, Scotland and Wales. It has declined in the S. It prefers calcareous rivers with raised nutrients, but is also in ponds and reservoirs. Druce had it as common, FlOx had 31 tetrads in the Thames, canal, pits and new scrapes. We had six 2000–11 records, but recording along the Windrush (SP233137 to 391060) in 1996 revealed it in nine tetrads so it is Not Scarce. CRL

⬇ *Potamogeton friesii*
Native

Flat-stalked Pondweed
Vulnerable, Nationally Scarce ■ Last record in Oxon 1975, vc23 1973

This species is scattered in England, Wales and Scotland having suffered a huge decline. It grows in calcareous and slightly enriched water that is still or slowly flowing. FlOx p. 258 had five unconfirmed tetrads, none of them since 1973. FlBe cites a pool by Railway, South Hinksey **OXF** 1975, Palmer. CRL

⬇ *Potamogeton obtusifolius*
Native

Blunt-leaved Pondweed
Last record in Oxon 1994 and in vc23 1976

This species is distinguished by its linear leaves being c. 3 mm wide. It is widespread in England, Wales and Scotland, being found in neutral, mesotrophic, still or slowly flowing water. With us it was locally common in Druce's time and recorded in five FlOx tetrads. It appeared in a newly dug pond by the Thames at Farmoor. CRL

22	V	Farmoor Reservoir	LWS	SP443072	1994	PA
22	V	Sutton Courtenay Gravel Pits		SU518930	1985	HJMB
22	V	S of Standlake		SP3800	1976	AJR
23	W	Witney		SP3408	1969	AJR

↑ *Potamogeton pusillus*
Native

Lesser Pondweed
Not Scarce in Oxon, Scarce in vc23

This species is widespread in England and Scotland. It is told with difficulty from the commoner *P. berchtoldii* where the young stipules are not fused in a tube round the stem. It is found in ponds, gravel pits and new scrapes. It prefers neutral conditions and tolerates raised nutrients. Perhaps because of this, unlike most pondweeds, this one has seemingly increased. Druce had 29 sites and it was in seven FlOx tetrads. CRL

23	C	Bletchingdon Park		SP504183	2010	HJK	100 sq.m new conf. NTHH
23	W	Witney Lake & Meadows	Other	SP358083	2009	SEE	
22	V	Odstone Marsh, new pond		SU252871	2009	SEE	New
23	W	Linch Hill, fishing lake		SP418044	2007	SEE	2 areas
23	C	Cassington to Yarnton Gravel Pits	LWS	SP469108	2006	CRL	New, compartment 1.1
23	C	RSPB Otmoor	pLWS, RSPB	SP555130	2006	RSPB	5%, new
23	C	RSPB Otmoor	pLWS, RSPB	SP559140	2006	RSPB	Reedbed, new
22	V	Radley Gravel Pits	LWS	SU513971	2006	CRL	New
22	V	Radley Gravel Pits	LWS	SU521968	2006	CRL	New
22	V	Radley Gravel Pits Extension	pLWS	SU531974	2006	PJW	New
23	O	Part-used allotments		SP529086	2003	MaT	New
22	V	Farmoor Reservoir	LWS	SP443072	1997	PA	New scrapes
23	W	Marlborough Pool		SP453103	1988	PA	
22	V	Ashbury, new pond		SU253872	1988	PA	
23	W	Old Gravel Pit near Little Faringdon	LWS	SP219017	1984	JMC	
22	O	Oxon tetrad 5004		SP5004	1972	RCP	**OXF** Det. Dandy

↓ *Potamogeton trichoides*
Native

Hairlike Pondweed
Nationally Scarce ■ Rare in Oxon and vc23

This species is distinguished with difficulty from *P. pusillus* by leaf tips being acute (rather than abruptly narrowed) and not edged by a marginal vein, also its stipules are not fused; and from *P. berchtoldii* by its relatively rigid leaves with wide midribs (occupying >25% of the leaf). It is an annual which rarely flowers, reproducing by detachable buds. It is widespread in England and possibly increasing, but not here. It requires still or slowly moving water and tolerates raised nutrient levels. It colonises new sites. FlOx had five tetrads. CRL

23	C	RSPB Otmoor	pLWS, RSPB	SP559139	2006	RSPB	New
23	C	RSPB Otmoor	pLWS, RSPB	SP568134	2006	RSPB	2%, new
23	W	Steeple Barton		SP447253	1986	SW	
23	W	Evenlode		SP370168	1977	PG	
23	S	Rycote Park		SP665046	1976	FlOx	NMW

↓ *Potamogeton compressus*
Native

Grass-wrack Pondweed
s. 41, Endangered, Nationally Scarce ■ Last Oxon and vc23 record 1979

Distinguished by its flattened stems and leaves with thickened strands, this species is now very restricted in central England, Wales and East Anglia having suffered a big decline. It requires base-rich, but not eutrophic, water. While Druce had 15 sites, it was in the Thames at Iffley SP5202 in 1943, and at Nell Bridge SP4834 in 1947. The three tetrads since 1968 include Kiln Lane Pit, Oxford, by Bowen. Its decline is probably due to disturbance and eutrophication. CRL

⬇ *Groenlandia densa*
Native

(Peter Creed)

This submerged aquatic is widespread in E England, but has declined hugely. It requires still or slow-moving base-rich water and prefers quite high nitrates. Druce had 35 sites including Wychwood and FIOx 19 tetrads, while FIBe has it recently at Hagbourne and Radley Lakes. CRL

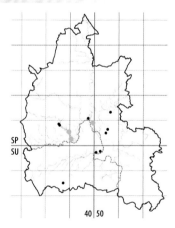

23	W	Ducklington, Emma's Dyke N of A40		SP354086	2004	JE	
23	O	Port Meadow with Wolvercote Common & Green	SAC, SSSI	SP492097	2004	JE	
23	W	Ducklington Mead	SSSI	SP363076	2003	CRL	1 patch
22	S	*West Hagbourne Moor*		*SU535872*	*1992*	*HJMB+*	
23	W	*Wychwood*	NNR, SSSI	*SP330165*	*1984*	*PS+*	
23	W	*Wychwood*	NNR, SSSI	*SP338170*	*1984*		
23	S	*Shiplake Marsh*	LWS	*SU760774*	*1984*	*GB+*	
22	V	*Radley Gravel Pits*	LWS	*SU513971*	*1979*	*PJK*	
23	C	*Oxford Canal*		*SP492130*	*1968*	*RJC*	

⬇ *Zannichellia palustris*
Native

This is a submerged aquatic with much branched slender stalks to 50 cm long, which prefers high-nutrient levels. Nationally, although it has been lost from some sites due to ditch clearance and drainage, it has been found in more, probably due to better recording. In Oxon it is probably declining, being lost from many of Druce's 26 sites.and from some of the 32 FIOx tetrads. SEE

23	W	Moors lake, ditch on west side		SP358081	2009	SEE+	Lots
22	V	Scrape in Long Mead		SU508973	2007	CRL	Lots
23	C	Cassington to Yarnton Gravel Pits	LWS	SP475109	2006	CRL	Rare
23	C	RSPB Otmoor	pLWS, RSPB	SP566133	2006	RSPB	
22	V	Radley Gravel Pits	LWS	SU525978	2006	CRL	
23	O	Lye Valley and Cowley Marsh	LWS	SP548050	2005	CWDG	
23	O	Stansfeld Field Study Centre	pLWS	SP555065	2005	RdA	
22	V	Letcombe Cressbeds	LWS	SU373851	2005	CRL	
23	W	Ducklington, Emma's Dyke		SP354086	2004	JE	
23	W	*Beard Mill channels*		*SP396055*	*1996*	*SJW*	
23	W	*Windrush*		*SP405026*	*1996*	*SJW*	
23	O	*Port Meadow with Wolvercote Common & Green*	*SAC, SSSI*	*SP495090*	*1992*	*PA*	

⬇ *Paris quadrifolia*

This plant of moist calcareous soils has 12 2000–11 records in vc23 and three in vc22 so is Not Scarce in Oxon, despite some losses. SEE

Colchicum autumnale
Native Iconic

Meadow Saffron, Autumn Crocus
GB Red List Near Threatened ■ Not Scarce in Oxon and vc23

(Camilla Lambrick)

This iconic perennial has declined, and is now largely confined to its stronghold in the Cotswolds, the S Welsh marches, Somerset and Wilts. It is an Ancient Woodland Indicator that prefers grassy rides. Being highly poisonous to stock it is often eradicated, though naturalised in gardens and used medicinally. Druce had 49 sites and FlOx had 35 tetrads. Wychwood may have the largest population in England (Mabey 1996). It is now present in good numbers at two sites and found at two new ones. FlBe had 11 sites, but only two in 2000–11 (Wytham SP 476076 c. 2006 and Appleton Upper Common). CRL

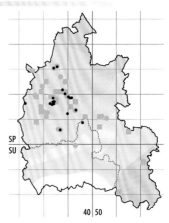

SP
SU

40 50

Gagea lutea
Native

Yellow Star-of-Bethlehem
Scarce in Oxon and vc23

(Peter Creed)

This cheery early-flowering bulb has leaves like bluebells and flowers like celandines. It is an Ancient Woodland Indicator which is commonest in the N of England. It prefers moist, high-nutrient and calcareous conditions. Mostly in the Cotswolds, it is also at Long Copse near Cumnor. Druce had c. 20 sites, FlOx nine tetrads, and FlBe two since 1950 and five pre-1920. Laney found it at Abel Wood SP409147 2016 and Maggots Wood in 2015. It may be under-recorded, as it sometimes fails to flower in shady conditions. CRL

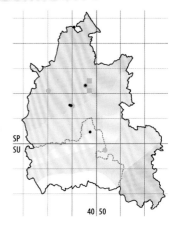

SP
SU

40 50

22	V	Long Copse	LWS	SP473047	2009	CRL	Approx 20, new
23	W	Whitehill Wood	SSSI	SP390154	2007	PEC	Approx 270, 10 fl
23	W	Steeple Barton		SP4422	2005	RWHS+	1000s
23	W	Sturt Copse	SSSI	SP396152	2004	BL	
23	W	Abel Wood		SP408146	2004	BL	New
23	W	Sarsgrove Wood	SSSI	SP304243	1998	AJD	
23	S	Furze Brake	LWS	SU535965	1977	HJMB	

Tulipa sylvestris
Neophyte, Iconic

Wild Tulip
Scarce in Oxon, Rare in vc23

(Peter Creed)

This is an attractive bulbous perennial, which was in cultivation by 1596. It is now mainly found in old orchards, open woodland or meadows (e.g. Challow) to the south of the Tees–Exe line though the core area has now retreated further east. This decline is probably caused by more intensive land use. The bulbs are long lived but seed set is poor. It is however doing well in its few locations in Oxon. In Coleshill Churchyard it thrives on a sympathetic mowing regime. At Chastleton House, where it has a long garden history and is known as the 'Catesby Lily' more than 140 have been found. Records are from old parkland and orchards; there are several sites in vc23 mentioned in FlOx before 1980. At Long Leys (22 V, SP4404 1993 Killick). SEE, HJK

23	W	Chastleton House	SP247291	2009	HJK	140 flowers
23	W	W Alvescot	SP275048	2009	SEE	Private land, 8
22	V	W Challow	SU366883	2009	HJK	>100 flowers
22	V	Coleshill Churchyard	SU235938	2008	SEE	3 large patches
22	V	Sparsholt, crossroads	SU349870	2007	SEE	Plants increasing
22	V	Wadley Manor	SU310960	1998	SEE	In old orchard

➡ *Fritillaria meleagris*
Neophyte, Iconic

Snake's-head Fritillary
Nationally Scarce ■ Not Scarce in Oxon, Scarce in vc23

(Peter Creed)

This iconic bulbous perennial is widespread; it had decreased by 1962 but losses since then have been limited by protection (Atlas 2002). Following a poll by Plantlife and *The Oxford Times* in 2002, Fritillary became Oxfordshire's County Flower. It is frequently planted as an ornamental and naturalises readily. It flourishes in damp or winter-flooded hay meadows, preferring alkaline conditions and tolerating moderate nutrients. It propagates freely by seed, but only a little vegetatively. Druce had c. 20 sites (as had FlOx) but noted that it was not recorded in the wild until 1780. Counts at Iffley by BBOWT show that numbers fluctuate considerably from year to year (Wolstenholme 2001), and it was set back by the summer floods of 2007–8. Killick guessed that a meadow at Ducklington had 100,000 flowers in 2009. Interestingly it is absent from Picksey Mead but recently appeared on West Mead. CRL, HJK

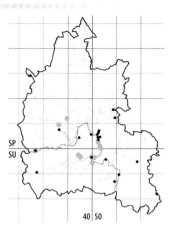

⬇ *Cephalanthera damasonium*
Native

White Helleborine
s. 41, Vulnerable ■ Not Scarce in Oxon and vc23

(Peter Creed)

Locally called the Poached-egg Orchid, this rhizomatous perennial is mostly restricted to the chalk and southern limestone and has suffered a big decline. It is typically found in beech woodland with little understorey, but occasionally grows in scrub or grassland. It is a calcicole and thrives with moderate nitrate levels. In Oxon it has colonised new and disturbed areas and survives in mown grass. Druce recorded 26 sites and FlOx had 52 tetrads. In 2000–11 at 27 localities in Oxon of which six are in vc22 (Oxon). FlBe had two sites and Bowen recorded it also at Buckland. CRL

22	V	Crog Hill and Scary Hill	LWS	SU323835	2011	JK	New
22	V	Wytham Woods	SSSI	SP462080	2010	AWM	
22	V	Radley Gravel Pits	LWS	SU518973	2010	RdA	New
23	S	Hartslock	SAC, SSSI	SU616795	2010	RdA	10+, BBOWT
23	S	Bottom Wood	LWS	SU665783	2010	JK+	6
23	S	Gutteridge Wood	LWS	SU667791	2010	JHW	1
23	S	Walk Shaw	pLWS	SU677791	2010	JHW	27
23	S	Warburg	SSSI, BBOWT	SU716877	2010	RdA	2
23	S	The Rabbit Banks, Hardwick		SU651779	2009	JHW	30 flowering, 66 non-flowering
23	S	Busgrove Lane Stoke Row		SU680835	2009	JHW	2 flowering, 2 non-flowering
23	S	Chazey Wood		SU685762	2009	JHW	10 flowering, new
23	S	Bear, Oveys & Great Bottom Woods	SSSI	SU702832	2009	JHW	19 flowering
23	S	Kents Hill	LWS	SU726808	2009	JHW	12 flowering
23	S	Crowsley Woods		SU740798	2009	JHW	3 flowering, 8 non-flowering
23	S	Hunts Green Harpsden		SU744804	2009	JHW	1 flowering, 1 non-flowering
23	S	Lucy's Copse		SU753806	2009	JHW	18
23	W	Ditchley	pLWS	SP308208	2008	AJD	1
22	V	Harwell Laboratories		SU476874	2008	MW	>100
22	V	Harwell Laboratories		SU482873	2008	MW	>100
23	S	Swyncombe Dean Wood		SU683914	2008	JHW	24
23	S	Lambridge Wood	SSSI	SU730839	2008	JHW	new
23	S	Old Elvendon Wood		SU629811	2005	SP	
23	W	The Barns Plantation		SP312242	2004	UF	
22	S	Unhill and Ham Woods	LWS	SU565827	2004	ShW	New
23	W	Milton Downs Windbreak		SP255151	2003	JMC	
23	S	Icknield Bank Plantation		SU670917	2000	LMC	

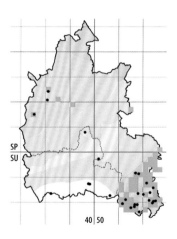

⬇ *Cephalanthera longifolia*   **Narrow-leaved Helleborine**
Native   **s. 41, Endangered, Nationally Scarce** ■ **Last record in Oxon and vc23 1970**

This long-lived perennial is curiously distributed being commonest along the western seaboard of Scotland. It has suffered a severe decline in Wales and the New Forest. It prefers open glades in calcareous woodland, but does not flourish under changing conditions such as coppice. Fitter recorded it in 1970 at Oakley Hill near Chinnor Hill, where it was known to Druce in 1917. CRL

➡ *Epipactis palustris*   **Marsh Helleborine**
Native   **Near Threatened** ■ **Scarce in Oxon, Rare in vc23**

(Peter Creed)

This rhizomatous species is found in neutral to calcareous, but nutrient-poor fens, especially those areas that are seasonally flooded. There has been a decline nationwide but not in Oxon, due to drainage and eutrophication. Druce 1886 and 1927 describe it as local, by the time of FlOx it was rare and lost from most of its old sites in vc23. It was still to be found in the Lye Valley, where it is flourishing and Spartum fen where it just survives. SEE

23	O	Lye Valley	SSSI	SP547051	2010	JAW	4 sites >1000
22	V	Parsonage Moor	SAC, SSSI, BBOWT	SU460998	2010	JAW	2 sites
22	V	Dry Sandford Pit	SSSI, LGS, BBOWT	SU468995	2009	HJK+	Large colony
22	V	Radley Gravel Pits	LWS	SU528976	2009	HJK	Many, new
22	V	Radley Gravel Pits	LWS	SU529981	2008	DG	1000's, new
23	S	Spartum Fen	SSSI	SP654016	2007	JAW	8 plants
22	V	Confidential	SSSI	SU49P	2007	JAW+	>100, present in 2011
23	S	Chinnor Hill	SSSI, BBOWT	SP7600	1989	HJMB	
23	S	Sydlings Copse	SSSI, BBOWT	SP550093	1987	HJMB	HJK/JAW 2008

⬇ *Epipactis purpurata*   **Violet Helleborine**
This ancient woodland indicator grows in closed beech woodland in southern England. Druce had 20 sites and FlOx had 41 tetrads. With about 20 2000–11 records in vc23, but no post-1987 records in vc22 (Oxon) in Atlas 2002, it is Not Scarce. CRL

⬇ *Epipactis leptochila*   **Narrow-lipped Helleborine**
Native   **Nationally Scarce** ■ **Rare in Oxon and vc23**

(Peter Creed)

This long-lived perennial takes at least four years to develop and then only appears sporadically. It is widespread in England and Wales and has increased recently. It is an ancient woodland indicator though also occurring in dune slacks. With us it requires beech woodland on chalk, usually with deep leaf litter, dense shade and little ground cover. Its erratic appearance and susceptibility to grazing make it likely to be under-recorded. It may have increased between the single record by Druce at Lambridge, the sparse pre-FlOx records for Ditchley (SP3820 1950 Bowen) and Maidensgrove (1941 Lousley) and FlOx. 2000–11 records have been fewer than the 25 tetrads in FlOx; FlBe has none since one at Streatley in 1955. CRL

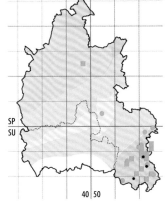

23	S	Warburg	SSSI, BBOWT	SU716878	2010	RdA	Approx 40, BBOWT
23	S	Lambridge Wood	SSSI	SU730840	2010	JHW	6 and 1
23	S	Walk Shaw	pLWS	SU677791	2009	JHW	New
23	S	Harpsden Wood	SSSI, WT	SU760807	1982	RMB	
23	S	Howe Wood	LWS	SU6991	1981	ND	
23	S	Aston Rowant	SAC, SSSI	SU724976	1981	SRD	
23	S	Aston Rowant	SAC, NNR, SSSI	SU728973	1981	MRH	
23	S	Stoneycroft Plntn, Whitchurch		SU6378	1974	EMT	
23	S	Bixmoor Wood	pLWS	SU652861	1974	HJMB	10
23	S	Watlington Park		SU7092	1974	anon	
23	S	Crowell Hill/Oakley Hill	LWS, BBOWT	SU7598		anon	

SP
SU

40 | 50

→ *Epipactis phyllanthes*
Native

Green-flowered Helleborine
Nationally Scarce ■ Scarce in Oxon and vc23

This rhizomatous perennial is restricted to areas with a calcareous substrate, and is only found in shady or damp beech, oak or alder woods on neutral soils where there is little ground cover. FlOx had nine tetrads. The flowers are usually self-pollinated, often not opening. It may be under-recorded as it is not easy to see, is often drought stressed before it is mature and is subject to deer grazing. CRL

22	S	Winterbrook, Wallingford Stream bank		SU601887	2010	RG	Approx 12 new
23	S	Bear, Oveys & Great Bottom Woods	SSSI	SU692841	2009	JHW	1
23	S	Lambridge Wood	SSSI	SU732843	2009	JHW	41 at 2 sites
23	S	Long Toll Road		SU651803	2007	JHW	4 flowering
23	S	Lackmore Wood		SU660813	2007	JHW	5
22	V	W of The Ark		SU391871	1999	FlBe	
23	S	Woodcote		SU6480	1997	RdA	
23	S	Sydlings Copse	SSSI, BBOWT	SP555096	1990	JZ+	
23	S	Harpsden Wood	SSSI, WT	SU760805	1987	SS+	
22	V	Ginge Brook		SU445870	1986	DJNH+	
23	S	Warburg	SSSI, BBOWT	SU720880	1986	NP	
23	S	Stoke Row		SU6884	1981		
22	V	Cothill Fen	SAC, NNR, SSSI	SU459997	1978	HJMB	
22	0	1 m south of Oxford Station entrance		SP5004	1972	RCP	Corpus cricket ground

↓ *Neottia nidus-avis*
Native

Bird's-nest Orchid
Vulnerable ■ Scarce in Oxon and vc23

This pale coloured plant is mycotrophic – depending on fungi for its nutrition. Though widespread in the BI, it had a considerable decline, especially 1930–70 in SE England. It is an Ancient Woodland Indicator with us, growing mostly in beechwoods with moderate nitrates, though formerly under hazel at Cothill. Druce listed 42 sites, 18 of them on the Cotswolds, and FlOx had 30 tetrads. Now it is mostly confined to the Chiltern plateau, though FlBe has it at Wytham. There are six records from the 1990s, so it may be Not Scarce. CRL

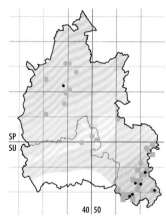

23	S	Harpsden Wood	SSSI, WT	SU758807	2010	SR	3
23	S	Gutteridge Wood	LWS	SU668791	2009	JHW	13
23	S	Busgrove Lane Stoke Row		SU680835	2009	JHW	2
23	S	Bear, Oveys & Great Bottom Woods	SSSI	SU702832	2009	JHW	12
23	W	Ditchley Ellen's Lodge		SP381224	2007	CE	1
23	S	Bottom Wood	LWS	SU657783	2001	RC	Beech
23	S	Warburg	SSSI, BBOWT	SU720879	2001	AB	
23	S	Crowell/Oakley Hill		SU7498	1998	RSRF	
22	V	Foxcombe End, Boars Hill		SP501022	1996	RGS	New
23	S	Witheridge Hill		SU695840	1995	RdA	
23	S	Kingwood Common	LWS	SU696825	1995	RdA	
23	S	Highmoor and Lower Common Wood	LWS	SU702850	1995	RdA	
23	S	Nettlebed Common	LWS	SU705871	1995	RdA	
23	W	Great Tew North Park		SP390313	1988	PJ	
23	C	New Halvers Wood		SP405312	1988	PJ	
23	S	Oakingham Bottom/Bush Wood		SU685845	1987	JHW	
23	S	Wyfold Wood/New Copse		SU690808	1987	JHW	
23	S	Gutteridge Wood	LWS	SU668787	1986	SS	
23	S	Howe Wood	LWS	SU703916	1986	VP+	
23	W	Holly Court Farm		SP386153	1985	HJMB	
23	W	Worton Wood	LWS	SP434278	1984	RPP	
22	V	Radley Large Wood	LWS	SP520008	1981	HJMB	
23	S	Park Wood		SU727886	1981	SS	
23	S	Lucy's Copse	pLWS	SU750806	1981	AJJ	
23	W	Sheers Copse/Ash Copse, Ditchley		SP391195	1980	JMC	
23	S	Waterperry Wood	SSSI	SP607090	1980	HJMB	
23	S	Wellgrove Wood		SU718868	1979	NP	
23	S	Doyley and Pishillbury Woods		SU727892	1979	NCC	
22	V	Cothill Fen	SAC, NNR, SSSI	SU459997	1978	HJMB	
23	S	Aston Rowant	SAC, NNR, SSSI	SU724976	1970	RSRF+	Also HJMB

Epipogium aphyllum
Native   **Ghost Orchid**
   Critically Endangered ■ Last certain Oxon and vc23 record 1979

Ghost Orchid has now been fully reviewed (Cole 2014). This tiny, easily overlooked orchid of leaf-litter in dark beech woods is dependent on fungi, notably *Inocybe*, and slug damage can hinder recognition. It was seen in Lambridge Wood in 1924–26. Paul recorded it in Bottom Wood and Oveys Wood between 1931 and 1979; of several unconfirmed records there since then, that of 1994 is the most probable, and there are some other unconfirmed Chiltern records. HJK

Spiranthes spiralis
Native   **Autumn Lady's-tresses**
   Near Threatened ■ Rare in Oxon and vc23

(Phil Cutt)

This slender inconspicuous orchid flowers late and sporadically. It is a species of the SW UK, and declined mostly before 1960. Druce listed 14 sites and FlOx three tetrads. It is confined to short sward on shallow, nutrient-poor, calcareous or acidic soils. It is grazed at one site by horses giving longish grass, at Hackpen by cattle, and at Kingwood it grows with heather on top of a covered reservoir managed by cutting. CRL

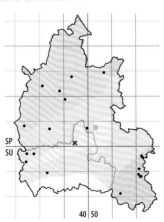

22	V	Hackpen Hill	SAC, SSSI	SU354848	2009	SEE	7, in 2 areas,
23	S	Confidential		SU67T	2009	JHW	143 new
23	S	Kingwood Common	LWS	SU696825	1995	RdA	Approx. 10
23	S	Nettlebed Common	LWS	SU705871	1995	RdA	
23	S	Peppard Commons		SU7080	1984		

Herminium monorchis
Native   **Musk Orchid**
   s. 41, Endangered, Nationally Scarce ■ Last Oxon and vc23 record 1979

This inconspicuous perennial grows on chalk and limestone in S England and has suffered a big decline. It likes short turf and very low nutrients. Druce had five sites. FlOx has a series of records at Bix until 1956 (Paul); it could have been ploughed in the 1950s. FlBe cites only Whitehorse Hill in 1964. CRL

23	W	Barton Abbey, Barton Grove	SP456234	1979	DJNH+

Platanthera chlorantha
Native   **Greater Butterfly-orchid**
   GB Red List Near Threatened ■ Not Scarce in Oxon and vc23

(Peter Creed)

This is a perennial which grows 30–40 cm high and differs from *P. bifolia* in that the pollinia diverge from each other. It is found in a wide range of habitats but usually on well-drained calcareous soils. It is commoner in S lowland GB than elsewhere in the UK; its decline during the 20th Century is possibly due to agricultural improvement and the coniferisation of woodland. Druce 1927 recorded it as widespread, but FlOx describes it as uncommon, seldom plentiful but surviving in its former sites, e.g. Wychwood, Ditchley and the Chilterns. These areas may well still have more sites than have been recorded in 2000–12. In TVERC there are 20 sites recorded between 1980 and 1999 as well as 12 different tetrads between 1970 and 1999 in vc23. During 2000–12 we found 18 localities in Oxon and 14 in vc23. SEE

⬇ *Platanthera bifolia*
Native

(Rod d'Ayala)

This perennial herb grows to 8 cm. It differs from *P. chlorantha* in that it is smaller and paler, but most reliably by the pollinia which lie parallel to each other. In *P. chlorantha* the pollinia diverge outwards. This species is remarkably tolerant of soil conditions, being found in acid bogs and calcareous fens as well as in drier woodland and grassland habitats which have low-nutrient values. In Oxon all records have come from tetrads which contain ancient woodland. It is probably this loss of woodland and increased fertilisation which has led to its decline. It has never been common in Oxon, Druce 1927 cited it as rare, and now there are only two major locations with 2000–11 records, Wychwood Forest and Cornbury Park in the W and Warburg reserve in the S. There is only one TVERC record dating from 1981 from Radley large wood in vc22 SEE

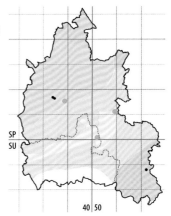

23	S	Warburg	SSSI, BBOWT	SU720880	2009	RdA	
23	W	Wychwood	NNR, SSSI	SP339169	2008	WOR	Rare
23	W	Wychwood	NNR, SSSI	SP346169	2008	WOR	Abundant
23	W	Hollycourt Farm		SP386153	1985	HJMB	
23	S	Menmarsh moat		SP592111	1985	HJMB	
22	V	Radley Large Wood	LWS	SP520008	1981	HJMB	

⬇ *Gymnadenia conopsea*
Native

This subspecies of the Fragrant Orchid prefers chalk downland, but is also found in low-nutrient base-rich bogs and marshes. *G. conopsea* s.l. was in 30 FlOx tetrads, below are records likely to be *G. conopsea* s.s., but confirmation is needed. In 2013 a few appeared at Hook Norton SP3531 Killick. CRL

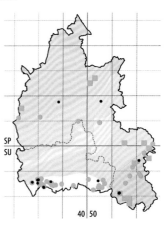

23	S	Holly Hill (Elmore Park Grassland)	LWS	SU631813	2011	JK	
22	V	Whitehorse Hill		SU298852	2010	SEE	Few, NW facing slope
23	S	Watlington and Pyrton Hills	SSSI	SU710942	2010	HJK	
23	S	Holly Hill (Elmore Park Grassland)	LWS	SU629813	2009	JHW	9
23	W	Reed Hill	SSSI	SP382176	2008	SEE+	3 west facing slope
23	C	Woodsides Meadow	SSSI, BBOWT	SP556178	2008	JAW	>100
22	V	Crog Hill and Scary Hill	LWS	SU323835	2007	SEE	BBOWT
22	V	Blewburton Hill	LWS	SU545861	2007	anon	New, 3 N side
22	V	Odstone Coombes	LWS	SU276856	2006	SEE	Frequent
22	V	Hackpen Downs		SU351858	2006	SEE	Few
22	V	Kingstone Warren Down (N)	LWS	SU305846	1991	NCC	
22	V	Pigtrough Bottom	LWS	SU345854	1991		
22	V	Ridgeway Path		SU525824	1991		
23	S	Swyncombe Downs	SSSI	SU682914	1991		
22	V	Ridgeway Path		SU298862	1990		
23	S	Nuffield Common	LWS	SU671879	1990		
23	S	Chinnor Hill	SSSI, BBOWT	SP766005	1989		
22	V	Cholsey Downs		SU564863	1988		
23	W	Asthall Leigh Valley	LWS	SP306115	1987		
23	S	Sydlings Copse	SSSI, BBOWT	SP550093	1987		
23	S	Little Cookley Hill		SU709889	1987		
22	V	Furze Wick Down (remains of)		SU395848	1986		
22	V	Fairmile to Kingstanding Hill		SU560834	1986		
23	S	Watlington and Pyrton Hills	SSSI	SU703936	1986		
23	W	Westwell Gorse	SSSI, BBOWT	SP219114	1985	HJMB	

Gymnadenia densiflora
Native

This Fragrant Orchid occurs scattered throughout the UK in low-nutrient but base-rich fens and occasionally north-facing calcareous slopes. In contrast *G. conopsea* prefers chalk downland. Only the records at Cothill have been reported as *G. densiflora*, the others were not identified, but are in suitable habitat, mostly on the Corallian Ridge. Killick found specimens at Parsonage Moor which did not fit the measurements given in Stace 2nd Ed. The plants at Woodsides Meadow BBOWT, Wendlebury SSSI need checking. CRL

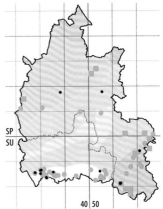

23	C	Woodsides Meadow	SSSI, BBOWT	SP556178	2009	JAW	163
22	V	Parsonage Moor	SAC, SSSI, BBOWT	SU460998	2009	JAW	11
22	V	Dry Sandford Pit	SSSI, LGS, BBOWT	SU468996	2009	JAW	28 in flower
22	V	Confidential	SSSI	SU49P	2007	SEE	
23	O	Lye Valley and Cowley Marsh	LWS	SP544049	1991	EN	
23	S	Sydlings Copse	SSSI, BBOWT	SP555096	1990	JZ+	
23	S	Spartum Fen	SSSI	SP655017	1988	NCC	Abs. JAW 2007
23	S	Sydlings Copse	SSSI, BBOWT	SP550093	1987	SJG	
22	V	Wytham Ditches and Flushes	SSSI	SP463098		Doom	Also HJMB
23	C	Arncott					>30

Coeloglossum viride
Native

(Peter Creed)

This is a small (4–20 cm) greenish-brown orchid, which favours calcareous, nutrient-poor pasture. It was distributed over lowland GB fairly evenly, but is now much more localised. The greatest loss has been in central England. The decline regionally and nationally is probably due to habitat loss, especially lowland meadows. It is also a species which is easy to overlook. It has been found along the chalk scarps of the Chiltern and Wessex downs, since Druce's time and some of his locations are still extant. It has never been common in Oxon, with Druce 1927 listing 24 locations. This was reduced to nine localities in FlOx all on the Chiltern scarp except for one at Wendlebury Meads. A new site at Juniper Valley was found by Dunford in 2012. Further searches on the downs, Nuffield to Chinnor and Ashbury to Streatley, could be worthwhile. SEE

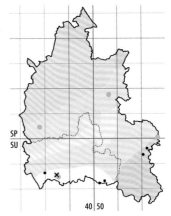

22	V	Whitehorse Hill	SSSI	SU298864	2008	MH	57 flowers
23	S	Watlington & Pyrton Hills	SSSI	SU706936	2008	JW	15 flowers
23	S	Aston Rowant	SAC, NNR, SSSI	SU722961	2007	HJK	50+ in 2011
22	V	Lower Chance Farm		SU523823	2002	CRL	
23	C	Wendlebury Meads and Mansmoor Closes	SSSI	SP560173	1998	PC	
22	V	Hackpen Hill	SAC, SSSI	SU352847	1997	KW+	Scattered over wide area
22	V	Pigtrough Bottom	LWS	SU346854	1991	NCC	Not found 2009 SEE
23	S	Chinnor Hill	SSSI, BBOWT	SP766005	1989	HJMB	
23	W	Bowham		SP277046	1988	GH	

Dactylorhiza maculata
Heath Spotted-orchid

This is widespread in the UK, except E central England where it has declined sharply. In Oxon it is found on acidic very low-nutrient soil in hay meadows of the Ray, and undisturbed pasture over clay; also on wet areas of the Corallian Ridge and commons of the Chiltern plateau. FlOx had 16 tetrads; with 12 2000–11 sites all in vc23, of which eight seem new, it is Not Scarce. CRL

Dactylorhiza incarnata
Early Marsh-orchid

This Orchid is Not Scarce in Oxon. The W district is still its stronghold. The number of sites for it has fluctuated widely. FlOx (33 tetrads) had three times the number in Druce 1927, but this has been reduced to 18 2000–11 records. A notable loss is at Dry Sandford where it has not been seen since 2008. SEE.

Dactylorhiza purpurella
Native

Northern Marsh-orchid
Only Oxon and vc23 record 1981

This tuberous perennial of open, very low-nutrient, acidic to base-rich, damp areas is widespread NW of the Severn–Wash line. Only two records are south of it – Wychwood 1981 by Woodell and Preston, and one in the New Forest. CRL

Dactylorhiza traunsteineriodes
Native

Narrow-leaved Marsh-orchid
Rare in Oxon, no vc23 records

(Rod d'Ayala)

The leaves of this species are 0.5–1.8 cm wide; there are usually three, the two basal are sheathing and the third is not. The labellum has a prominent central projection. This is a tuberous perennial which grows to 25 cm in neutral to base-rich flushes and fens. The population is scattered, local throughout GB, but stable, both in the UK and in Oxon. In Oxon it is found in two calcareous fens, which is a rare habitat. Numbers are not high in either location but a prolific year in 2015 saw 120 flowering spikes at the confidential site. The management is sympathetic at both sites, plants have been found regularly over several years of monitoring. However recent genetic work at Kew (Bateman 2011) suggests that many of the plants at both Oxon locations may be a subspecies of *D. praetermissa*. SEE

| 22 | V | Confidential | SSSI | SU49P | 2010 | SEE | 24 spikes |
| 22 | V | Parsonage Moor | SAC, SSSI, BBOWT | SU460998 | 2009 | HJK | |

Orchis purpurea
Native

Lady Orchid
Vulnerable, Nationally Scarce ■ Rare in Oxon and vc23

(Peter Creed)

This perennial favours basic to slightly acidic, grassland or woodland. In England it is largely stable and mostly confined to Kent with outliers round the Bristol Channel and the S coast. It was first found in the county in 1961 at a semi-shaded site in the Chilterns. Contrary to its big national decline, mostly due to habitat loss, it is increasing in our area. It appeared at Hartslock BBOWT reserve, first flowering in 1999 (C Raper pers. comm.). DNA studies indicated an origin in S France, though it is unclear whether it blew in or was brought. Later Raper found a hybrid with the closely related *O. simia* (Bateman 2010). A single large specimen flowered at Odstone Lane, in 2005 but was absent in following years. Seed from the Chiltern site was scattered at the Warburg BBOWT reserve in 1997 and plants have been flowering for three years. CRL

Orchis militaris
Native

Military Orchid
Schedule 8, Vulnerable, Nationally Rare ■ Last record in Oxon and vc23 1986

(Rod d'Ayala)

This tuberous perennial prefers highly calcareous grass or scrubland with very low nitrogen levels. While Druce listed 11 sites, it was considered extinct in the 1920s; it reappeared in Bucks where it is flourishing under careful management by BBOWT. FlOx details records at three sites in tetrad SU7484 (one at Eversdown), and SU7292 until 1984. The Eversdown plants, sporadic with few shoots, were unsuccessfully searched after 1986 by Fitter, and not found recently. In Suffolk a European var. *militaris* has appeared and is flourishing. It was introduced at Warburg in 1996 and newly found in West Oxfordshire in 2013. CRL

→ *Orchis simia*   Monkey Orchid
Native   Schedule 8, s. 41, Vulnerable, Nationally Rare ■ Rare in Oxon and vc23

(Peter Creed)

This delightful orchid was found in several southern counties in the 19th Century; Druce had three sites. It declined severely till it was thought extinct, and is now known at only two native sites – with us at Hartslock SSSI BBOWT reserve since 1960 and in Kent. It requires south-facing grassland which is highly alkaline and very low in nitrogen. During 1971–4 it also occurred in the combe between Bald Hill and Shirburn Hill (Fitter 1994). At Hartslock, under careful management by BBOWT, including protection of the flowering spikes, it has been spreading. Monitoring by C. Raper shows a maximum of c. 200 spikes, with individual plants surviving between one and 36 years. Attempts have been made, with some success, to augment the population with plants raised at Kew from seed from Hartslock. Since *O. purpurea* appeared at Hartslock, hybrids with that species have also appeared. CRL

→ *Orchis* (*Aceras*) *anthropophora*   Man Orchid
Native   s. 41, Endangered, Nationally Scarce ■ Rare in Oxon and vc23

(Peter Creed)

Restricted to calcareous and low-nutrient soils, this orchid is quite frequent in Kent and scattered N as far as Northants and W to Glos, though it has suffered a huge decline. Druce had two sites and FlOx two. Plants now in SU68 on the scarp slope of the Chilterns, have been hand-pollinated. Annual monitoring shows that individual plants are short-lived, with numbers fluctuating from 0 to 53. Sheep grazing has been discontinued, and the scrub is hand cut; fencing prevents deer and rabbit grazing. Horse grazing in an adjacent lower field has resulted in plants colonising the short sward. CRL

⬇ *Neotinea* (*Orchis*) *ustulata*   Burnt Orchid
Native   s. 41, Endangered, Nationally Scarce ■ Rare in Oxon, Last vc23 record ?1982

(Peter Creed)

This tuberous perennial prefers calcareous grassland with extremely low nitrogen levels. It used to occur widely in England but following a huge decline is now mostly in Wiltshire. It prefers south-facing chalk slopes with a short sward, but was apparently seen in river-side meadows at Yarnton, FlOx's only record. Druce had 12 sites. It flowers only sporadically, so is worth looking for at former localities. Flowering is mostly in late May, though there is also a July-flowering form. The one site in vc22 (Oxon) has up to three flowering stalks, and is being carefully grazed. CRL

⬇ *Anacamptis* (*Orchis*) *morio*   Green-winged Orchid
Native   Vulnerable ■ Not Scarce in Oxon and vc23

This tuberous perennial survives where grass is not too dense and nitrogen levels are low. It is widespread in England and Wales, but has suffered a big decline. It usually grows on base-rich soils, and occurs in well-drained conditions and also on heavy clays. With us it is mostly in hay meadows, but also in churchyards, undisturbed pasture and quarries. FlOx (p. 298) had 44 tetrads some almost certainly lost. We have only 12 records 2000–11 in vc23. Some losses may be due to deer, others to loss of grazing. Nine records are listed in FlBe; we had only four 2000–11 vc22 (Oxon) sites but they are all new. CRL

⬇ *Himantoglossum hircinum*   Lizard Orchid
Native   Schedule 8, GB Near Threatened, Nationally Rare ■ Rare in Oxon and vc23

This fantastic and erratic orchid was confined to Kent until the early 1900s when it started to expand reaching N Yorks, but has declined again. It is winter-green, and many of the plants flower once and then die. It requires highly calcareous and very low-nitrogen soils. Druce had it at Stow Wood, perhaps spread from Headington where plants from the Dordogne had flowered. FlOx reported it at Wick (Sydlings) Copse (1977–97) where it reached about 10 plants in two areas over 50 m apart, but has since dwindled despite fencing. In 2015 two plants appeared at separate sites in West and South Oxfordshire. CRL

↓ *Ophrys insectifera*
Native

Fly Orchid

s. 41, Vulnerable ■ Rare in Oxon and vc23

(Rod d'Ayala)

This is a tuberous herb which is shade tolerant. It is usually found on chalk or limestone on woodland edges. There has been a big decline nationwide in this orchid, probably due to scrubbing up of grassland, close to woodland. In Oxon the decline has been equally marked. Although it was never common, Druce 1886 described it as local and rather rare, Druce 1927 noted 17 localities including Maidensgrove, which remains its stronghold in the county. Here it was found in seven different compartments of the Warburg reserve in 2010. It is lost from vc22 (Oxon). SEE

23	S	Bottom Wood	LWS	SU665783	2010	SP	
23	S	Warburg	SSSI, BBOWT	SU719875	2010	RdA	
23	S	Gutteridge Wood	LWS	SU668787	1986	SS	
23	S	Warburg	SSSI, BBOWT	SU720880	1986	NP	
22	V	Uffington Wood	SSSI	SU302868	1981	HJMB	1998 SEE

↓ *Ophrys sphegodes*
Native

Early Spider-orchid

Schedule 8, Nationally Rare ■ Last Oxon and vc23 record 1975

This short-lived winter-green tuberous perennial of SE England has declined recently. It grows in tightly grazed, low-nutrient, calcareous grassland. It was seen in Kirtlington in 1975 by Pringle, unconfirmed, but not since. It was seen in 1920 at Stanton St John by Druce, who listed another nine sites. CRL

↑ *Leucojum aestivum*
Native/Neophyte

Summer Snowflake or Loddon Lily

Nationally Scarce ■ Not Scarce in Oxon and vc23

(Peter Creed)

This strikingly elegant plant was fittingly chosen as the Berkshire County flower. It is scattered in S England and Ireland, flourishing in wet woodland and less often in fen or wet grassland. It favours basic, extremely high nitrogen soils and is often associated with *Cardamine amara* (q.v.) Gerard wrote of it as wild in Italy and popular in 16th Century London gardens. In 1788 Curtis declared it wild "between Greenwich and Woolwich" (Mabey 1996). Druce said it was first recorded in Oxon just downstream of the city in 1821, though it is now lost in this area, FlOx cited 24 tetrads. It has buoyant seeds, dispersed by water-fowl, and still appears at new sites. It was seen in about 2000 at Lashford Lane, by Abingdon, and Crawley's survey along the Thames in 2012 located it near Chimney. A spectacular display can be appreciated at Withymead NR at Easter-time. *Leucojum aestivum* ssp. *pulchellum* is frequent in gardens, from which it may escape, and *L. vernum* is occasionally naturalised. CRL

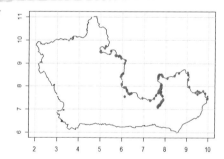
Map of vc22 (formerly Berks) showing *L. aestivum* along the Thames and Loddon. M J Crawley 2012

↓ *Narcissus pseudonarcissus* ssp. *pseudonarcissus*
Native and introduced in our area

Daffodil

Not Scarce in Oxon, Scarce in vc23

(Rod d'Ayala)

This beautiful plant is native in central, S and N England, but introduced in the E, with Oxon on the boundary. While often planted, it is an Ancient Woodland Indicator, growing in ash, oak and beech woods. It flourishes with coppicing, prefers neutral soils and tolerates raised nutrients, but not dry summers. Druce recorded 21 native sites, FlOx (p. 293) 51 tetrads and FlBe two recent records. There were 12 Oxon sites in 2000–11, seven in vc23. CRL

Convallaria majalis
Native and introduced

Lily-of-the-valley
Last record in the wild in Oxon and vc23 ?1987

This fragrant rhizomatous perennial is frequently planted and naturalised, as are all our post-1990 records. It is widespread in England and is an ancient woodland indicator. It favours acidic soils in the S but limestone woodlands from the Chilterns northwards, tolerating raised nitrate levels. Druce had 11 sites and FlOx (p. 290) 13 tetrads. FlBe has no recent wild records but it was "abundant" in Bagley Wood in 1813. CRL

22	V	Letcombe Cressbeds	LWS	SU372851	2005	CRL+
23	W	Acrey Pits	LWS	SP456111	2003	CRL still present 2009 SG+
23	W	Vicarage Pit		SP401056	1999	JAW

Polygonatum multiflorum
Native and introduced

Solomon's-seal
Scarce in Oxon and vc23

(Peter Creed)

This rhizomatous perennial is often planted and also can be confused with the Garden Solomon's-seal *P.* × *hybridum*, which has larger flowers (15–22 (-25) × 3–6 mm) and stems ridged. It is native mostly in central S England and has seemingly increased but some of the records could be the hybrid. It is usually found in ash woodlands on lime and nutrient-rich soils. Druce had five sites including Berrick Trench, known since 1797. In FlOx p. 290 it was recorded in 14 tetrads. Six of the 12 2000–11 records are at new sites, perhaps naturalised. CRL

23	S	Greenmoor Hill Woods		SU647810	2010	JHW	50 new
23	S	Drawback Hill		SU757815	2010	SR	1 new
23	S	Coldmoor Wood		SU698833	2009	JHW	New
23	S	Berrick Trench	LWS	SU703881	2009	SG	Locally Frequent
23	W	Whiteways Quarry	LWS, LGS	SP420246	2008	AW	New
23	S	Warburg	SSSI, BBOWT	SU713878	2008	RdA	
22	S	Unhill and Ham Woods	LWS	SU561821	2004	ShW	
23	S	Kingwood Common	LWS	SU693823	2003	VR+	New
23	C	Cradle and Grounds Farm Banks	LWS	SP371332	2000	RWHS	New
22	V	Woodley Manor		SU310959	1996	SEE	
23	S	Shirburn Wood		SU717947	1988	HJMB	Also in Druce
23	W	Black Moat, Caswell Farm		SP320078	1987		
23	S	Harpsden Wood	SSSI, WT	SU760805	1987	SS	
23	W	Rabbits Piece Copse (Brize Norton)		SP314084	1986	GH	
22	S	Woodland nr Downs Farm		SU572837	1986		
23	S	Cowleaze Wood		SU728955	1975	HC	

Muscari neglectum
Neophyte, Iconic   s. 41, GB Red List Vulnerable, Nationally Rare ■

Grape-hyacinth
Scarce in Oxon and vc23

This attractive bulbous plant is considered native only in East Anglia. The blue-black fertile flowers distinguish it from the common royal blue *M. armeniacum*. It was known to Druce at Chadlington and now survives in a headland of the field in which it was once abundant. It used to grow in allotments, and when they were 'developed', bulbs were saved by the CRPG who put them back in the landscaping around these allotments and into the headland. These sites are now monitored by the WFG. Druce had it in four sites and FlOx 11 tetrads. Following Dunn's observation that it happened to grow in some gardens (at Spelsbury for 40 years), the recording was improved by the CRPG in 1994 and this aspect was featured by Killick and *The Oxford Times* on 31 March 2006. Planted *M. armeniacum* bulbs can frequently include some *M. neglectum* and both can spread, though in one FlOx site *M. neglectum* was less vigorous. The species seems not at risk in Oxon. CRL, HJK

23	W	Chadlington Allotment site		SP327220	2009	CMcN+ 2000
23	W	Verge off Green Lane		SP332237	2009	CMcN+

⬇ *Typha angustifolia*   Lesser Bulrush

This tall emergent plant prefers water about 50 cm deep, neutral pH and tolerates high nutrients. It is commonest in the S and E of England, and has increased in recent years. In Oxon it is on the Thames, Cherwell, the canal, Otmoor, and introduced in garden ponds. FlOx had 35 tetrads; it is now in 12 sites in vc23 it is Not Scarce. Some Swere records (Meagher and Sheasby 2005) are *T. latifolia*. CRL

⬇ *Juncus subnodulosus*   Blunt-flowered Rush

This rhizomatous perennial is local but widespread in England and Wales. It forms dense stands in base-rich fens, but does not tolerate raised nutrients. It is in 33 FlOx tetrads and 22 sites in 2000–11 (12 in vc23) so is Not Scarce. CRL

⬇ *Juncus acutiflorus*   Sharp-flowered Rush

Druce found this rush common in wet acidic places, FlOx had 94 tetrads; with 29 2000–11 records in Oxon (26 in vc23) it is Not Scarce. CRL

⬇ *Juncus bulbosus*   Bulbous Rush
Native   **Rare in Oxon and vc23**

This small, tufted, bright green rush is found on wet heaths and pond margins, heathy woodland rides on peaty, acid, very infertile soils, often on bare soil or peat. It is widespread in W and N GB, but has declined in the S Midlands probably owing to habitat loss. While easily overlooked it often has a bulbous base and viviparous flower heads. In shallow water the stems can be very long and much branched. On Nettlebed Common it grows on winter-flooded areas under a light canopy of birch with few associated species, mainly *Lythrum portula* or *Sphagnum*. At Binfield it occurs on a damp woodland path with *Stellaria uliginosa*, *Sagina procumbens*, *Potentilla erecta* and *Galium palustre*. Druce had 15 sites, FlOx had 22 tetrads and FlBe says it has gone from the Corallian Ridge. JHW, CRL

23	S	Nettlebed Common	LWS	SU700873	2009	JHW	3 areas @ 1 sq.m
23	S	Binfield Heath The Common		SU739786	2009	JHW	6 areas @ 1 sq.m new
23	C	Stratton Audley Quarry	LWS	SP605246	2008	SG+	New
23	S	Witheridge Hill		SU695840	1995	RdA	
23	S	Kingwood Common	LWS	SU696825	1995	RdA	
23	S	Highmoor and Lower Common Wood	LWS	SU702850	1995	RdA	
23	C	Lower Heyford Canal		SP4824	1993	HJK	
23	O	Lye Valley	SSSI	SP547052	1990	EN	
22	V	Confidential	SSSI	SU49P	1990	EN	
23	W	North Leigh Common	LWS	SP401136	1987	Doom	

➡ *Juncus squarrosus*   Heath Rush
Native   **Rare in Oxon and vc23**

(Rod d'Ayala)

This small tufted perennial is common in the N and W, flourishing with very acidic and very low nutrients. It is abundant in Scotland and the N, but has declined substantially in S and E England. Druce didn't find it though there had been two records in the county from the 18th Century. FlOx gave the site where it just survives. FlBe had Boars Hill, 1938. CRL

23	S	Kingwood Common	LWS	SU698824	2007	JHW	1

Juncus compressus
Native

(Peter Creed)

This rhizomatous perennial is told from the maritime *J. gerardii* by anthers <1–2× length of filaments and <1 mm long, and styles <0.4 mm. It was in 37 tetrads (FlOx p. 261) in short damp grass especially in meadows on alluvium or near rivers, notably the Thames and Ray. Many were not re-found, and the N is inadequately covered, but there are 16 sightings in vc23, 12 new. FlBe cited records at Marcham, Radley gravel pits, Buckland Warren and Bablockhythe, plus older undated ones; there are eight recent sightings, two since lost.

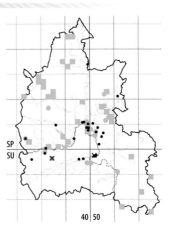

Records at Manor Farm Marcham include both *J. compressus* (plants at SU453960 from 1990s assumed to be this) and *J. gerardii* (SU454961, until 1954). Killick has checked some Oxon plants elsewhere but found no *J. gerardii*. In GB (but not Oxon, where it has appeared in new sites) it has declined owing to drainage and loss of permanent grass. It is most widespread in the East Midlands. HJK

22	V	Bablockhythe		SP435042	2010	HJK	East bank of river, 1 clump
23	O	Binsey Green	LWS	SP493076	2010	SEE+	Large patch
23	O	New Marston Meadows	SSSI	SP525069	2010	JAW	Flood plain meadow, 12 flower heads
22	V	Abingdon Common		SU472962	2010	HJK	Widely in 4 scrapes, new
23	O	Port Meadow with Wolvercote Common & Green	SAC, SSSI	SP486087	2009	JAW	Flood plain meadow, 6
23	O	Cutteslowe lower recreation field		SP512104	2009	JAW	Meadow, new
23	O	Marsh Lane/Elsfield Rd meadow	OPT	SP532087	2009	JAW	Wet hay meadow, new
22	V	Radley Gravel Pits	LWS	SU525977	2009	HJK	Grassy margin
23	O	Port Meadow with Wolvercote Common & Green	SAC, SSSI	SP494086	2008	SEE+	Unimproved grass, corner
23	W	Langel Common	Other	SP360097	2006	CRL	New
23	C	Cassington to Yarnton Gravel Pits	LWS	SP469108	2006	CRL	New
23	C	Cassington to Yarnton Gravel Pits	LWS	SP475109	2006	CRL	New
22	V	Pucketty Farm		SU314984	2006	SEE	2 flowering clumps
23	C	Cherwell Valley Somerton to Nell Bridge, compartment 10		SP492339	2005	CRL	New
23	O	Oxford Science Park, Balancing Ponds		SP537020	2005	anon	New
23	O	Lye Valley and Cowley Marsh	LWS	SP548050	2005	CWDG	New
23	O	Stansfeld Field Study Centre	pLWS	SP555065	2005	RdA+	New
23	W	The Bog	LWS	SP235043	2004	CRL	New
23	C	Meadow on Blackthorn Hill		SP615212	2003	CRL	New
22	V	Buckland Marsh	LWS	SP318004	2002	CRL	New
22	V	Badbury Forest – Eaton Wood	LWS	SU2696	2002	SEE	New
23	O	Canalside Meadow North of Wolvercote		SP492102	2001	AM	
22	V	*Radley Gravel Pits*	*LWS*	*SU517974*	*2001*	*HJK*	*Under fly-ash*
22	V	*Marcham Salt Spring*	*LWS*	*SU454960*	*2000*	*SEE*	*SEE new*

⬇ *Juncus ranarius* (*J. ambiguus*)

Frog Rush

In 1833 Professor J S Henslow gathered this rush from damp ground at Cholsey (SU5985; FlBe p. 1012); not seen since. D R McKean named it in 2002 from a mixed gathering in **E** with *J. bufonius*. HJK

➡ *Luzula multiflora*

Heath Wood-rush

Heath Wood-rush favours acid heaths, a habitat decreasing in Oxon. In 2000–11 it was in 16 Oxon sites (12 in vc23 including several in the Chilterns plus Foxholes, Cogges Wood, Eynsham Park and Shotover), so it is Not Scarce. HJK

⬇ *Luzula sylvatica*
Native

Great Wood-rush
Seemingly Scarce in Oxon and vc23

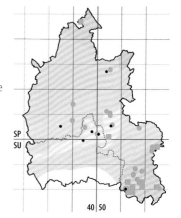

Great Wood-rush is a robust rhizomatous clump-forming perennial of damp often acidic, shaded habitats including ancient woodland, streamsides and banks. FlOx (p. 262) had 23 tetrad records; of 17 in the Chilterns surprisingly few have been re-found, but in 2014 at Nettlebed (SU711876 Killick). FlBe gave no dated records and reported it decreasing. We have only nine recent records (including Youlbury SP479031 in 2012, and Nettlebed), five in vc23. In GB it is common and widespread with stable distribution except for a decline in central and SE England. HJK, JHW

23	C	Ardley Cutting and Quarry	SSSI, LGS, BBOWT	SP538271	2011	HJK	2 sq.m, new
22	V	Tubney Woods	LWS	SU443996	2010	JK	Few, new
22	V	Bagley Wood	LWS	SP507021	2009	HJK	Few
23	W	Claywell Farm, nr Witney		SP350052	2007	RdA	By pond, new
23	S	Brasenose Wood and Shotover Hill	SSSI	SP558054	2007	RR	
23	S	Great Chalk Wood		SU620802	2006	JHW	Many, new
22	V	Bagley Wood	LWS	SP505016	2004	HJK	Few
23	S	Stow Wood		SP555105	1999	HJK	
22	V	Foxcombe End Boar's Hill		SP501022	1996	HJK	Coppice

⬇ *Eriophorum latifolium*
Native

Broad-leaved Cotton-grass
Rare in Oxon and vc23

(Peter Creed)

This is a perennial of calcareous marshes. It differs from *E. angustifolium* in having rough forward-pointing bristles on the spikelet stalks. It is declining generally in lowland GB, where drainage and fertilisation have taken place. It is rare in Oxon. It has been lost from Spartum Fen, Stow Wood and Headington Wick since Druce's records, though it was described by him as rare in both the 1886 and 1927 editions of his Flora. SEE

22	V	Confidential	SSSI	SU49P	2010	SEE	40+
22	V	Parsonage Moor	SAC, SSSI	SU460997	2010	JAW	2
23	O	Lye Valley	SSSI	SP548052	2008	JAW	5 2 sites

Eriophorum angustifolium
Native

Common Cotton-grass
Vulnerable ■ **Scarce in Oxon, Rare in vc23**

(Peter Creed)

This perennial of wet acid grassland and marshes differs from *E. latifolium* in having smooth stalked spikelets and narrow leaves. Though still plentiful in upland GB, it is declining in the lowlands. It is declining due to loss of habitat as wetland becomes drained and is fertilised. In Druce's floras it is described as local in 1886 but by 1927 it was local but decreasing. In FlOx it was noted as being lost from most of its sites and only four remain. SEE, HJK

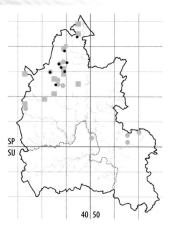

23	O	Lye Valley	SSSI	SP547056	2010	JAW	2 locations
22	V	Parsonage Moor	SAC, SSSI, BBOWT	SU460999	2010	JAW	
23	W	Manor Farm Meadow, Crawley	LWS	SP338120	2007	WOR	
22	V	Confidential	SSSI	SU49P	2007	SEE	Increasing in 2012
23	W	Coombe Fen	LWS	SP408150	1983	WOR	2008

SP / SU — 40 | 50

Bolboschoenus maritimus
Native

Sea Club-rush
Rare in Oxon, absent in vc23

(Peter Creed)

Sea Club-rush, mainly in saline marshes around much of GB's coasts, spreads by tubers, rhizomes and seed. It was known from 1897 to 1967 at Marcham salt spring (SU453960), and appeared in a small reservoir at Frilford (SU434977) in 1978. Wetland scrapes were made in Abingdon Common set-aside field (22 V, SU470962) in 1999–2000 and it was there in 2005–2012, a patch spreading steadily to 5 × 3 m, except in one year when herbicides were used to control willows and bulrush. Erskine found it introduced by lake in Folly Park SU295949 in 2008. HJK

Scirpus sylvaticus
Native

Wood Club-rush
Probably Scarce in Oxon and vc23

(John Killick)

The big rhizomatous Wood Club-rush forms stands in swamps, streams and wet shady places; typically on rather eutrophic silt, often iron-rich. In vc23, it was in 20 tetrads (FlOx p. 263) mostly in the NW, and eight sites in 2000–11; FlBe has only South Hinksey. In the Swere catchment it was well documented by Meagher and Sheasby (2005) but we did not re-visit all northerly locations. In GB it is widespread and stable except in E England and the Midlands, with local losses in SE England. HJK

23	C	Cradle and Grounds Farm Banks	LWS		SP369330	2009	SG	
23	C	S. Newington			SP403335	2007	HJK	20, NE of pond, new
23	W	Priory Mill Ponds	LWS		SP333297	2002	PS+	Tufa pond
23	W	Lidstone Bottom	LWS		SP356247	2002	CRL	West
23	W	Little Bridge Marsh	pLWS		SP378316	2002	PS+	Island marsh, new
23	C	Tadmarton			SP392382	2002	PS	Meadow
23	W	near Great Tew			SP393300	2002	PS	
23	C	Hanwell Gorse			SP445438	2001	PS	New

SP / SU — 40 | 50

→ *Schoenoplectus tabernaemontani*
Native

Grey Club-rush
Rare in Oxon, last vc23 record 1997

This emergent wetland perennial is frequent in coastal marshes and has increased in GB recently especially inland and often around gravel pits. We cannot judge whether it has spread here. It was in four FlOx tetrads and prefers margins of still or moving calcareous water and high-nutrient levels. CRL

22	S	Dorchester Town Meadow		SU567950	2010	JHW	New
22	V	Radley Gravel Pits	LWS	SU517975	2000	CRL	New
22	S	Mowbray Fields	LNR	SU523887	1999	GH	
23	S	*Spartum Fen*	*SSSI*	*SP655017*	*1997*	*HJK*	*? Abs. JAW*
23	W	Windrush		SP312115	1996	JAT	
23	C	Stratton Audley		SP6024	1994	HJK	
23	C	Fernhill Weir		SP5818	1979	FlOx	
23	W	N of Furzy Breach, S. Leigh		SP3808	1973	RCP	Conf. Tutin

Eleocharis

Spike-rushes

Spike-rushes are native perennial herbs of various wet habitats. Our scarcer species are easy to overlook, and their small solitary terminal spikelets are easily confused. As few records have been confirmed by experts, errors are possible. CRL, HJK

? ↑ *Eleocharis uniglumis*
Native

Slender Spike-rush
?Scarce in Oxon, Scarce in vc23

The small rhizomatous Slender Spike-rush is told, sometimes with difficulty, by the lower glume, which encircles virtually all the spike, but less than ¾ of it in the more frequent *E. palustris*. Both kinds have two stigmas. It grows in base- (notably sodium-) rich marshes and calcareous wet meadows. In vc23 it is at 10 sites, seven of them new, and was in eight tetrads (FlOx p. 263). In vc22 (Oxon), recently at Radley Lakes and Iffley Meadows, at Radbrook Common in 1988 (FlBe) and pre-1968 at Marcham salt spring. Of the 13 Oxon records, only three, from Alvescot and two by Palmer (all **OXF**) are confirmed; specimens from Crawley, Ferry Hinksey, Wytham Meads and Marcham are also in **OXF**. In GB it is mainly a coastal plant of salt marshes and brackish grassland but is now also better recorded inland. HJK

23	O	Almonds Farm and Burnt Mill Fields	LWS	SP519090	2010	JAW	Few, new
23	W	Manor Farm Meadow, Crawley	LWS	SP339119	2009	SEE+	Few
23	O	Park Farm Meadows	SLINC	SP521075	2009	JAW	
22	V	Radley Gravel Pits	LWS	SU525977	2009	HJK	1 sq.m, new
23	O	Port Meadow, Wolvercote Common & Green	SAC, SSSI	SP492095	2008	SEE+	2 patches, new
23	C	Woodsides Meadow	SSSI	SP556177	2008	HJK	Few, new
23	S	Otmoor	SSSI	SP572127	2008	CRL+	Few
23	W	Manor Farm Meadow, Alvescot	LWS	SP272049	2007	HJK	Scattered
23	W	Minster Lovell Marsh	LWS	SP313119	2007	WOR	Few, new
23	W	Crawley Mead	LWS	SP334112	2007	CRL	Frequent
22	O	Iffley Meadows	SSSI, BBOWT	SP522038	2005	RdA	
23	W	Grimes Meadow and Little Grimes	LWS	SP360099	2001	GH	New
23	W	Alvescot Meadows	SSSI	SP273050	1998	HJK	**OXF**, conf. Jermy

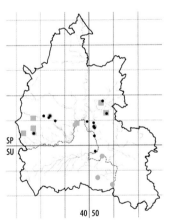

⬇ *Eleocharis multicaulis*
Native

Many-stalked Spike-rush
Last Oxon and vc23 record 1968

The lower glume of this tufted Spike-rush is only ¼ as long as the spikelet; it is half as long in *E. acicularis* and *E. quinqueflora*. All three species have three stigmas, and this one grows in wet heaths and acid bogs with minimal nitrates. Simmonds' record at Caversham (SU7274) was accepted for FlOx but may have lacked the preferred habitat. It is widespread in Scotland, Wales and the SW, but disappearing in England. An increase between 1987 and 2004 (Braithwaite *et al.* 2006) is due to better recording. HJK, CRL

Eleocharis quinqueflora
Native

Few-flowered Spike-rush
Rare in Oxon and vc23

This Spike-rush differs from *E. acicularis* by its round stem 0.5 mm or more diameter; the lowest glume 2.5–7 mm. In short turf, calcareous flushes and base-rich fens and water meadows; it needs grazing or cutting to produce open ground and cannot tolerate raised nitrogen levels. It was at Lye Valley N and S in 2008, previously in 1968 (Palmer) and 1985 (Creed). Here it sets seed thanks to management by the Oxford City Council and the Friends of the Lye Valley. In Frilford Fen (SU4595, 1961) and Cothill Fen (SU4497, FlBe undated); was at Hinksey in 1880 (**OXF**). In GB it was lost from many lowland sites in the 19th Century onwards and is now mainly in the N and W. HJK, JAW, CRL

23	0	Lye Valley	SSSI	SP548052	2008	JAW	>50
23	0	Lye Valley	SSSI, LNR	SP548057	2008	JAW	

Eleocharis acicularis
Native

Needle Spike-rush
Near Threatened ■ Last confirmed vc23 record 1978

This Spike-rush is told from *E. quinqueflora* by its slender four-ridged stem <0.5 mm diameter; the lowest glume 1.5–2.5 mm. This very slender perennial grows in shallow water or in the drawdown zone and is said to set seed freely when above water. It prefers alkaline water and tolerates raised nitrogen levels. Found at Blenheim Park (23 W, SP435165, 1978 Bowen). Unconfirmed FlOx tetrads were SP5828 (1982), SP5004 (1972), in SP4008 where Sibthorp had found it, SP2212 and SP5402. It had been in Oxford Canal (Druce). It is widespread in England but has declined. HJK, CRL

Isolepis setacea

Bristle Club-rush

This is an easily overlooked small plant of wet habitats. There were 16 records in FlOx and 14 2000–11 records in vc23 and two in vc22. It is scattered across the county. With fewer recorders for the register, it could be this species is increasing. HJK

Eleogiton fluitans
Native

Floating Club-rush
Last Oxon and vc23 record pre-1927

This small perennial or annual grows mostly in the W of the BI being rare in central England. It is mainly in peaty, acidic, and very low-nutrient conditions in or by slow-flowing water. It declined mainly before 1930, and is now better recorded. Druce listed four localities and FlOx gave only one record, introduced at Nuneham Courtenay SU5498. A sighting on Port Meadow in the 1980s seems unlikely as the habitat is too alkaline and nutrient-rich. CRL

Cyperus longus

Galingale

This is an aquatic, native in parts of Britain but introduced into Oxon. In Druce 1927 it is described as an alien, which has not yet become established. There has been an increase in sites in Oxon due to planting but the authors do not consider there is sufficient evidence to show that the species has become established away from introductions. There are no TVERC records before 2001. SEE

Blysmus compressus
Native

Flat-sedge
s. 41, Vulnerable ■ Rare in Oxon and vc23

(Peter Sheasby)

This inconspicuous, rhizomatous monocot is commonest in the N. It has suffered a huge decline due to habitat loss and eutrophication. It grows in damp calcareous and low-nutrient short sward, mostly wet flushes. Druce had five sites including Marston and Wychwood. FlOx p. 264 cited six tetrads and "typical of the transition zone between some contrasting habitats: salt to fresh, dry to wet, nutrient-rich to nutrient-poor". It is tolerant of low salt levels – Druce and Bowen recorded it at the Marcham salt spring, see under *Apium graveolens*. FlBe: not seen since 1992. CRL

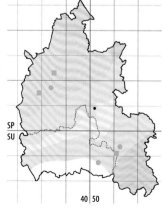

23	0	Almonds Farm and Burnt Mill Fields	LWS	SP519090	2009	JAW+	
23	W	Wychwood	NNR, SSSI	SP3416	1993	RSRF	
22	S	W Hagbourne Moor		SU535872	1992	HJMB+	Abs. GH
23	S	Rokemarsh		SU625936	1985	WS+	Abs. JAW
23	W	Wychwood	NNR, SSSI	SP338170	1975	PS	Till 1993
23	W	South Lawn, Burford		SP2814	1971	RCP	**OXF**

⬇ *Schoenus nigricans*
Native

Black Bog-rush
Scarce in Oxon, Last vc23 record 1983

(Peter Creed)

This is a tufted perennial of calcareous fens. Nationally there has been a decline, especially in lowland sites due to habitat destruction. This has always been a rare habitat in Oxon. Even in Druce 1886 it was rated rare. In FlOx it was 'surviving only at Headington Wick', but gone from Bullingdon Bog. It was found at Weston Fen (1983). It has not been seen in vc23 since 1983, but it remains in the fens of the Corallian Ridge. It is more successful in vc22, but has long since disappeared from the Buckland sites; some but not all colonies at Dry Sandford have died. It was recently re found at Lashford Lane fen after scrub clearance. All the extant sites have some level of conservation protection. SEE

22	V	Lashford Lane Fen	SAC, SSSI, BBOWT	SP467012	2010	JAW+	8 clumps
22	V	Parsonage Moor	SAC, SSSI, BBOWT	SU460999	2009	JAW	Frequent
22	V	Dry Sandford Pit	SSSI, LGS, BBOWT	SU468996	2009	HJK	
22	V	Confidential	SSSI	SU49P	2008	SEE	Several clumps
23	C	Weston Fen	SSSI	SP526194	1983	HJMB	
23	S	Sydlings Copse	SSSI, BBOWT	SP553094	1979	PC	

➡ *Cladium mariscus*
Native and planted

Great Fen-sedge
Last wild Oxon record 1988, planted in Oxon and vc23

(Peter Creed)

This large rhizomatous perennial of swampy paces and by ponds is, in vc23, only in the Oxford Parks, planted. In vc22 (Oxon) it was formerly wild at Cothill (in 1988 FlBe) and in a wood near Pusey (1988 Bowen), and is ?planted at Cumnor. In GB it is widespread but very scattered in England except, its stronghold, East Anglia. HJK

22	V	Cumnor Pond		SP459042	2010	HJK	2 sq.m, planted?, new
23	0	University Parks	LWS	SP517076	2006	HJK	20x7 m planted
22	V	Ruskin Reserve	SAC, NNR, SSSI	SU459997	1988	HJMB+	Abs.
22	V	Peat Bottom Wood		SU3495	1966	HJMB	Abs. SEE 1997

Carex

Sedges

Our 34 sedges, a major component of our wetter habitats, belong to three subgenera: *Vignea*, *Carex* and *Psyllophora* (*Primocarex*). Over half qualify for the Register. All those under review are perennial herbs, so this is not repeated in the species accounts. Many depend on protected, managed wet habitats, which have declined and could be threatened by climate change. The ligule (where the leaf-blade joins the stem) can help in identification. The fruit is a "utricle" often bottle-shaped; its dimensions include the beak where present. The account in FlOx had included advice from R W David. HJK

Subgenus *Vignea*

⬇ *Carex paniculata*

Greater Tussock-sedge

With only 11 2000–11 records for vc23 and 12 for vc22, this reveals a great loss since FlOx (40 tetrads in vc23) but it is Not Scarce. It is scattered across the county in ditches, river banks and wet meadows, but recent sightings would still be welcomed. SEE.

⬇ *Carex diandra*
Native

Lesser Tussock-sedge
Vulnerable ■ Last Oxon and vc23 record 1968

Like *C. paniculata*, but it lacks tussocks (despite its name); fruits wingless with beaks >½ their length. It is in wet, peaty places. RW David was surprised (pers. com.) by Simmonds' 1968 records at Sonning (SU7274) and Shiplake (7878) and Druce had doubted an earlier one. It was at Frilford bog (SU4497) in 1912 **OXF**. In GB mainly in the N and W, scattered and much decreased in England by drainage and overgrowth. HJK

➡ *Carex vulpina*   True Fox-sedge
Native   s. 41, Vulnerable, Nationally Rare ■ Scarce in Oxon and vc23

(Ron Porley)

This large, tufted perennial of calcareous flood-meadows, ditch edges and damp woodland tolerates high nitrates. Poor specimens can be mistaken for *C. otrubae* which was only distinguished in the 1920s. *C. vulpina* has a truncate ligule, whose edges overlap the leaf edge, and the inner face of the sheath is wrinkled. In *C. otrubae* the ligule is sharply acute and no wider than the leaf; the inner face of the leaf sheath is smooth. *C. vulpina* is also found in Bucks, Kent, Sussex and Glos. In 2004 Graves discovered several new sites in the Ray catchment. In 2005 NEng contracted her to monitor these. The RPG has found that the single original plant at Asham Meads flowers quite regularly and sets abundant seed, but declined in 2012. C. Smith germinated some seed which was used in 2004 to reinforce the population at Asham Meads BBOWT NR; of 38 new plants, eight survived in 2011. It has been lost from two ditches at Fox Covert which became shaded, and flowered better after tree clearance in its woodland site. In 2007 seed from eight plants in Bucks and Oxon was collected by Aylesbury Vale District Council Biodiversity Team and BBOWT. In 2008–11 1,100 plants were planted out in Bucks by Aylesbury Vale District Council in six sites, and 1,027 survived in 2011. CRL

23	C	Asham Meads	SSSI, BBOWT	SP593140	2008	CRL+	1 + 8 intr
23	C	Otmoor	SSSI	SP577128	2005	RPG	11
23	C	Arncott Bridge Meadows	SSSI	SP608185	2005	HG	2 new
23	C	Meadow Farm Meadows	LWS, BBOWT	SP631192	2005	HG	9 new
23	C	Fox Covert & Heath Br, Blackthorn		SP636202	2005	HG	6
23	C	Essex Farm, Marsh Gibbon		SP638206	2005	HG	8 new
23	C	Westbury Farm, Blackthorn		SP627194	2004	HG	2 new
23	*0*	*Port Meadow with Wolvercote Common & Green*	*SSSI*	*SP495097*	*1975*	*HJMB*	*Now abs.*

Carex muricata group
This group comprises three species, two of them with subspecies. *C. muricata* and *C. spicata* are often confused and Druce combined them. David's comments based on Nelmes (1947) are cited here with additions from FlBe. The ripe fruits of the widespread *C. spicata* are greenish, 4–5 mm with corky bases and beaks 1–2 mm; in *C. muricata* mostly shorter, truncate at base, blunter and browner, and less spreading. The ligules are respectively longer than wide (more or less pointed) and short (rounded). HJK

⬆ *Carex muricata* ssp. *muricata*   Prickly Sedge
Native   Nationally Rare, Near Threatened ■ Rare in Oxon and vc23

Its fruits are 4–4.6 mm, dark red-brown; it grows on dry calcareous soil. After an unconfirmed sighting in SP5022 in 1973, the first confirmed vc23 record was by Showler in 2002 in the Warburg Reserve, SU718878, confirmed by M. Porter, and re-found by Welsh in 2007. It grows only in scattered sites in England, notably Glos. HJK

Ssp. *pairae* (ssp. *lamprocarpa*) has fruits <4 mm, paler brown; in 57 tetrads (FIOx p. 265). It is still widely scattered on dry acid soils; with 20 2000–11 records in Oxon (16 in vc23) it is Not Scarce. HJK, SEE

➡ *Carex divulsa* ssp. *divulsa*   Grey Sedge
Carex divulsa has a long interrupted inflorescence; the two subspecies are obvious in their extreme forms but intermediates exist. Ssp. *divulsa* was in 71 FIOx tetrads, 45 of them in the Chilterns, and it is not Scarce. HJK

➡️ *Carex divulsa* ssp. *leersii*
Native

Leers' Sedge
Seemingly Scarce in Oxon and vc23

(Rod d'Ayala)

Leers' Sedge differs from ssp. *divulsa* by the gap between the 2–4 lower spikes being <2 cm, and reddish brown ripe utricles. On dry grassy banks and wood margins on lime-rich soils, mostly in the SE (SU7191 added in 2012), also Wychwood and Ditchley; more could be expected. It was in 14 tetrads (FIOx p. 266); confirmed by David in SP3616 (**OXF**); none in FIBe. It is scattered in lowland GB, mostly in SE England. HJK

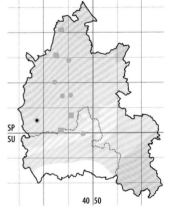

23	S	Sonning Common		SU711806	2009	RH-B	1 clump
23	W	Wychwood	SSSI	SP327159	2007	WOR	Frequent, new
23	W	Wychwood	NNR, SSSI	SP338170	2007	WOR	Frequent, new
23	W	Ditchley Estate		SP382222	2007	AJD	2 sites
23	S	Pishill		SU725899	2004	JE	Several
22	V	Radley Large Wood	LWS	SP520009	2003	HJK	New
23	S	Bozedown		SU6478	1999	SP	Det. HJK
23	Be	Caversham St Peters Churchyard		SU709749	1983	FIOx	
23	W	Ditchley Park Complex		SP376230	1979	AMS	

🔻 *Carex leporina* (*C. ovalis*)

Oval Sedge

This sedge. of low-nutrient, poorly drained habitats, has declined since FIOx (p. 266) reported 57 tetrads. With 34 2000–11 sites in Oxon (29 in vc23) it is Not Scarce. SEE, HJK.

🔻 *Carex echinata*
Native

Star Sedge
Near Threatened ■ Rare in Oxon and vc23

The spikelets of Star Sedge are no longer than wide, with <10 spreading fruits, but it has sometimes been misidentified. Small, in a variety of marshy and boggy areas, waterlogged at least seasonally. Druce recorded 13 vc23 localities, some from the early 19th Century, FIOx (p. 266) had eight tetrad records, mostly not re-found, and FIBe lists four "extinct" sites. In GB, widespread especially in the N and W; it has declined owing to farming and drainage. HJK

23	W	Alvescot Meadows	SSSI	SP273050	2011	SEE+
23	W	Coombe Fen	LWS	SP408150	1983	HJMB+
22	V	Cothill Fen	SAC, NNR, SSSI	SU459997	1978	HJMB+
23	W	by Limb Brook		SP4006	1973	RCP

➡️ *Carex dioica*
Native

Dioecious Sedge
Rare in Oxon and vc23

(Judy Webb)

C. dioica has round smooth stems and a single spikelet, is usually dioecious and inhabits very wet, neutral to base-rich mires. The last in FIBe was Frilford (SU4497) in 1946; in FIOx it was last seen at Sydlings Copse (SP5498) in 1926. It was recently at Lye Valley, perhaps benefiting from recent management, and Frilford. In GB mostly in the N and W; it declined sharply in lowland England before 1930. HJK

23	O	Lye Valley	SSSI	SP547058	2011	FHW	17 female spikes
22	V	Confidential	SSSI	SU49P	2011	JAW	5 male spikes

Subgenus *Carex*

➡ *Carex pseudocyperus*
Cyperus Sedge

C. pseudocyperus is Not Scarce in Oxon, even after noting that at some of 17 sites it may have been planted. HJK

⬇ *Carex rostrata*
Native

Bottle Sedge
Scarce in Oxon and vc23

C. rostrata has long-stalked green upright female spikes with widely spreading fruits 3.5–6.5 mm contracted into a short (1–1.5 mm) beak; female glumes acute. It forms stands in peaty or boggy areas or edges of water bodies, often acidic and nutrient-poor.

Among 15 tetrads (FlOx p. 267), three of eight from SP20 northwards were re-found; five undated FlBe records. Widespread and stable in GB, it is sparser and decreasing in central and SE England. HJK

23	O	Lye Valley	SSSI	SP547052	2010	JAW	<10
22	V	Parsonage Moor	SAC, SSSI, BBOWT	SU460997	2010	JAW	Many
23	W	Manor Farm Meadow, Crawley	LWS	SP339119	2009	SEE+	Frequent, new
23	W	Marsh, W of Worcester Hill		SP426199	2009	CRL+	
23	W	Glyme Farm		SP327264	2008	HJK+	
23	C	Enslow Marsh	LWS	SP487185	2008	GH	
23	C	Trow Pool	LWS	SP547250	2008	SG	
22	V	Confidential	SSSI	SU49N	2007	SEE	20, new
23	W	Ditchley Estate		SP380222	1990	AJD	2 sites
22	V	Barrow Farm Fen	SSSI	SU467975	1990	EN	
23	S	Spartum Fen	SSSI	SP655017	1985	NCC	
23	C	Weston Fen	SSSI	SP526194	1983	HJMB+	

⬇ *Carex vesicaria*
Native

Bladder-Sedge
Vulnerable ■ Scarce in Oxon and vc23

Bladder-sedge has yellow-green leaves, long-pointed female glumes, and big fruits 5–8 mm tapering into a 1.5–2.5 mm beak. It grows in wet, mesotrophic, slightly basic, meadows and marshes liable to flooding, and ditches. Lost from many of Druce's 27 localities; half the 16 FlOx tetrads were near the Ray, but some NE of Oxford were not re-found. There were new sightings and FlBe's record on Wytham Meads was re-found. Widespread in the BI, especially the N and W but has decreased in England since 1962. HJK

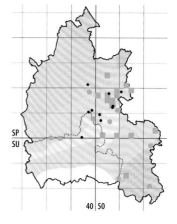

23	C	Arncott Bridge Meadows	SSSI	SP608185	2011	JAW	Several patches, new
23	O	New Marston Meadows	SSSI	SP522071	2010	JAW	New
23	W	Tackley Heath	LWS	SP468214	2009	RdA	New
23	O	Burnt Mill meadow SLINC	SLINC	SP518093	2009	JAW	2 m patch, new
23	C	Woodsides Meadow	SSSI, BBOWT	SP556178	2008	HJK	Frequent
23	S	Otmoor	SSSI	SP573128	2008	SEE+	
23	S	Otmoor		SP571123	2006	JE	
22	V	Tubney Woods	LWS	SP444003	2005	FHW+	New
23	V	Pixey and Yarnton Meads	SAC, SSSI	SP471101	2005	AWM	New
23	C	Wet Wood and Swamp near Yarnton	LWS	SP485111	2005	CRL+	New
23	C	SE of Warmugh Copse		SP5416	1971	RCP	

→ *Carex strigosa*
Native

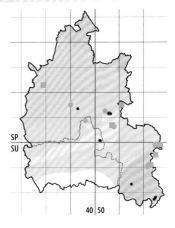

C. strigosa is told from the common *C. sylvatica* by its broad 6–10 mm wide leaves and its fruits almost without beaks. It grows in damp, base-rich, often clayey, deciduous woods; here often in or by rides, or by seepages or streams. Among 10 tetrads in FlOx, some Chiltern ones were not repeated; in vc22, FlBe had three undated records and it was recently seen in Boars Hill (Lambrick) and Wytham Woods (Watkins). In GB it is mostly in England and Ireland, better recorded than in the past, but has declined in Kent and Sussex. HJK

22	V	Radley Large Wood	LWS	SP520008	2010	HJK	80 m of track
23	S	Dunsden Round Wood		SU744773	2010	JHW	20 m of stream, new
23	S	Hammonds Wood and North Grove	LWS	SU650833	2006	CRL+	New
23	S	Beckley Pasture	LWS	SP565115	2003	CRL	New
23	W	Pinsley Wood	LWS	SP429135	2002	CRL	Re-found 2015 JK
23	C	Noke Wood & Sling Copse	LWS	SP557116	2001	CRL+	
23	S	Holmwood and Shiplake Copse		SU750781	2000	JAW	
23	S	Greenfield and College Woods		SU719910	1988	VP+	
23	C	Prattle Wood	LWS	SP541126	1985	HS	
23	S	Shotover Spinney		SP578063	1984	RH-B	

Carex distans group

Distant Sedges

These are tufted, with a terminal male spike with 0–1 of the female spikes close to it. They have a flap opposite the blade of the upper leaves. HJK

⬇ *Carex binervis*
Native

C. binervis fruits have scabrid beaks and two prominent ribs; the obtuse female glumes have a short bristle-like tip. It grows in various habitats on acidic nutrient-poor soils, which however some of the 10 tetrads in FlOx (p. 268) lack; some good recent records. FlBe has none. It is widespread and stable especially in N and W GB; perhaps decreasing in central England. HJK

23	S	Nettlebed Common	SSSI, LWS	SU700872	2009	JHW	20, new
22	V	Coxwell Wood	LWS	SU261952	2003	SEE	from 1999, 2 in 2003, not seen 2006

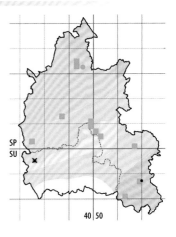

Carex distans
Native

Distant Sedge
?Scarce in Oxon and vc23

C. distans is told with difficulty from *C. hostiana* by leaf blades and lowest bract gradually contracted to the apex; female glumes pale, acuminate, with narrow papery margins. As both species have been recorded from Alvescot, Lye Valley, Parsonage Moor and Woodsides there could be errors. In marshes, wet meadows and fens; mainly on mineral-rich soils and it seems to depend less on managed sites than *C. hostiana*. The 54 mostly lowland tetrads in FlOx (p. 268), many more than in Druce (three sites), are not mapped here as some could have been *C. disticha* or *C. hostiana*; we have re-found some undated records in FlBe. It has long-lived seeds so more may turn up. In many coastal habitats in GB; also, but decreasingly, inland in the S. HJK

23	W	Alvescot		SP272050	2010	SEE	
23	O	Lye Valley and Cowley Marsh	LWS	SP547051	2010	JAW	
23	O	Lye Valley	SSSI	SP547058	2010	JAW	
22	V	Ruskin Reserve	SAC, NNR, SSSI	SU460996	2010	JAW	
22	O	Iffley Meadows	SSSI, BBOWT	SP521038	2008	HJK	Tens
23	C	Woodsides Meadow	SSSI	SP556177	2008	HJK	Few
22	V	Radley Gravel Pits	LWS	SU519970	2008	HJK	
23	W	Standlake		SP397024	2005	CRL	
23	C	Branson's Lake and Scrub	pLWS	SP506146	2005	CRL	few
23	W	The Bog	LWS	SP235043	2000	CRL+	
22	V	Lashford Lane Fen	SAC, SSSI, BBOWT	SP467012	1998	HJK+	
23	W	Old Gravel Pit near Little Faringdon	LWS	SP219017	1997	HJK	
23	S	Henton Marsh		SP768028	1994	RSRF	
22	S	W. Hagbourne Moor		SU535872	1992	HJMB+	
23	W	Newbarn Farm Pastures	LWS	SP393189	1989	AJD	
23	S	Otmoor	SSSI	SP575128	1981	HJMB	2015 JAW
23	C	Curbridge		SP5824	1974	RCP	Nr Coral spring

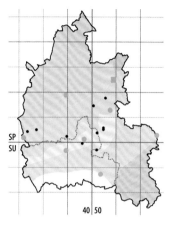

SP
SU

40 50

(Peter Creed)

Carex hostiana
Native

Tawny Sedge
Scarce in Oxon and vc23

C. hostiana is told with difficulty from *C. distans* (see above) by leaf blades and lowest bract rather abruptly contracted to the apex (a narrow parallel-side point); female glumes dark, acute, with broad papery margins. In vc23, only in a few sedge-rich sites on mildly acid but base-rich, nutrient-poor fens and marshes, in eight FlOx tetrads (three re-found); FlOx cites earlier records and some disappearances. Spartum Fen (SP6400) and Barrow Lane Fen are long overgrown, but we have new records. In GB mainly in the N and W, and has decreased in S and central England since 1950. HJK

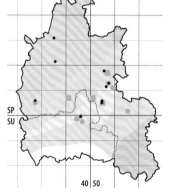

23	O	Lye Valley and Cowley Marsh	LWS	SP547051	2010	JAW	100 in fr
22	V	Ruskin Reserve	SAC, NNR, SSSI	SU460996	2010	JAW	
23	C	Woodsides Meadow	SSSI, BBOWT	SP556178	2008	JAW	New
23	S	Otmoor	SSSI	SP575129	2008	SEE+	30–50
23	C	Swere Bank	LWS	SP350309	2006	CRL	Frequent, new
23	W	Taston Brook and Springs	LWS	SP355215	2006	CRL+	Frequent, new
23	O	Lye Valley	SSSI	SP548059	2004	JAW	Frequent
23	S	Beckley Pasture	LWS	SP565115	2003	CRL	
23	W	Willow Meadows	LWS	SP273060	2000	SEE	

SP
SU

40 50

The Yellow-sedges (previously *Carex viridula*) are small with yellow-green leaves and utricles: at least half the male spikes are close to the single female spike. The three kinds have probably been confused; two are claimed from the same five FlOx tetrads and all three at Dry Sandford Pit. We have more recent records of, and more of the base-rich fen sites favoured by, *C. lepidocarpa* than of the damp acid bogs and flushes typical of *C. demissa*. All are at risk from drainage and overgrowth. HJK

Carex lepidocarpa (C. viridula ssp. brachyrrhyncha)

Long-stalked Yellow-sedge

Native

Scarce in Oxon and vc23

(Peter Creed)

This is told from *C. demissa* by the three-angled leaf tip and stalked male spike; utricles curved, with 1.5 mm beaks. It favours damp base-rich seasonally flooded fens. It is in 12 tetrads (FlOx p. 269), and in **OXF** from Cumnor SP4500, Bagley Wood SP5002. A long-recorded colony in Dry Sandford pit died in 2009; at Barrow Hills (SU5198, **OXF**) now lost, but it is still at Parsonage Moor and in set-aside. It is mostly in nature reserves and SSSIs dependent on suitable management. In GB, mainly in the N and W; its decrease in S England is probably due to modern farming and drainage. HJK

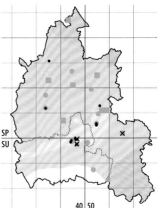

23	S	Nettlebed Common		SU700873	2009	JHW	4 clumps conf Chater
23	O	Lye Valley	SSSI	SP547051	2010	JAW	Many
23	O	Lye Valley	SSSI	SP547058	2010	JAW	Many
23	C	RSPB Otmoor	pLWS, RSPB	SP561129	2010	HJK	Few, new
22	V	Confidential	SSSI	SU49P	2010	SEE+	>50 clumps
22	V	Parsonage Moor	SAC, SSSI, BBOWT	SU460998	2010	JAW+	Many
22	V	Confidential		SU49T	2010	HJK	3 clumps
23	W	Manor Farm Meadow, Crawley	LWS	SP338119	2009	SEE	10 × 5m patch
22	V	Confidential	SSSI	SU49P	2009	SEE	>50 clumps
22	V	*Dry Sandford Pit*	*SSSI, LGS, BBOWT*	*SU468995*	*2008*	*HJK*	*Few; abs. 2009*
23	W	Swere Bank	LWS	SP352308	2004	PS+	New
23	S	*South Stoke Marsh (south)*	*LWS*	*SU595833*	*1993*	*SJG*	
22	S	*West Hagbourne Moor*		*SU535872*	*1992*	*HJMB+*	
22	V	*Barrow Farm Fen*	*SSSI*	*SU467975*	*1990*	*EN*	*Absent 2003*
23	S	*Spartum Fen*	*SSSI*	*SP655017*	*1988*	*NCC*	*Absent 1997*
23	C	*Weston Fen*	*SSSI*	*SP526194*	*1983*	*HJMB+*	
23	W	*Wychwood*	*NNR, SSSI*	*SP338170*	*1972*	*HJMB*	

Carex demissa (C. viridula ssp. oedocarpa)

Common Yellow-sedge

Native

Rare in Oxon and vc23

This differs from *C. lepidocarpa* in its straight 1 mm beak; the lowest female spike is often far below the others. Its various habitats are mostly on acidic soils in bogs and flushes. Apart from Palmer's (SP6008, **OXF**) many of the 13 tetrads (FlOx p. 269) lack these habitats, but we have two good recent records. No FlBe records. Widespread in GB and stable especially in N and W, but decreasing in central and S England, probably owing to modern farming and drainage. HJK

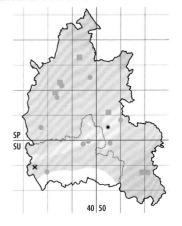

23	O	Lye Valley	SSSI	SP548052	2007	JAWp	
23	W	*Alvescot Mead*	*SSSI*	*SP273050*	*1988*	*HS+ m*	
23	S	*Waterperry Wood*		*SP6008*	*1974*	*RCPOXFp*	

Carex oederi (C. viridula ssp. viridula)

Short-fruited Yellow-sedge

Native

Rare in Oxon, Last vc23 record 1946

This differs from *C. demissa* by smallness, the close lowest female spike, beak 0.3–1 mm, and sessile male spike. In damp or wet places; once in vc23, in temporarily flooded turf at the S end of Port Meadow (SP 4806) by Brenan in 1946. In vc22 (Oxon) seen by Palmer at Cothill (SU467997, 1976, **OXF**) and FlBe has it from Dry Sandford Pit (467995) in 1997–2004 but not seen by us. In GB it is mainly on the wetter coasts, on dune slacks or the top end of salt marshes, and has decreased slightly; occasionally in wet habitats inland. HJK

Carex pallescens
Native

Pale Sedge
Scarce in Oxon and vc23

(Peter Creed)

Pale Sedge is told by lowest leaf sheaths and blades hairy, lowest bract crimped at base and green beakless female spikes. In open woods and hay meadows. In 26 tetrads in FlOx (p. 269) plus SP6109, SU7384 and 7288, mainly on clays; it had declined to the NE of Oxford. It is in vc22 (Oxon), at Radley Large wood (1981) and below. In GB widespread especially in the N and W, but has decreased in many areas since 1950 especially in England. HJK

23	W	Foxholes	SSSI, BBOWT	SP254206	2009	WOR	1
23	C	Woodsides Meadow	SSSI, BBOWT	SP556178	2009	JAW	1 clump
23	S	Otmoor	SSSI	SP573126	2009	CRL	Few
23	W	Ditchley Estate		SP388198	2007	CRPG	New
23	C	Stoke Wood	LWS, WT	SP554276	2007	CRL	1 clump, new
23	S	Brasenose Wood and Shotover Hill	SSSI	SP560054	2006	ShW	Small patch, new
22	V	Tubney Woods	LWS	SP4400	2003	JW	
23	S	Sydlings Copse	SSSI, BBOWT	SP555096	1990	JZ+	
23	W	Mouldens Wood & Davis Copse	LWS	SP340070	1986	CRL+	Re-found 2015 JK
22	V	Bagley Wood	LWS	SP512023	1986	RH-B	
23	S	Warburg	SSSI, BBOWT	SU720880	1986	NP	
22	V	Appleton Lower Common	SSSI	SP425007	1982	HJMB+	
23	W	Foxholes	SSSI, BBOWT	SP250205	1981	HJMB+	

Carex caryophyllea

Spring-sedge

We found this small early flowering sedge of calcareous grasslands in 23 2000–11 sites in Oxon (18 in vc23) so it is Not Scarce. HJK, SEE

Carex filiformis
Native

Downy-fruited Sedge
Nationally Rare ■ Scarce in Oxon, Rare in vc23

(Peter Creed)

This sedge has rhizomes and hairy fruits, bigger than those of the tufted *C. caryophyllea* and *C. pilulifera*. In calcium-rich, damp or dry grassland, where it has a curious distribution and can be plentiful, woodland rides and road verges. In FlOx at Westwell since 1923, where RW David in 1982 reported threats from scrub, but active management by K and B Betteridge increased the population from few to 80,000 (K Betteridge, pers. comm). The grass can readily overgrow it. It was seen in wet pastures in Otmoor in 1927 and is still abundant near the rifle range. It was confirmed from Hartslock in 1971 and still there in hundreds. A FlBe Grafton Meadow 1982 record was re-found. In GB only in a few places; it is still widespread in Glos. HJK

23	W	Westwell Gorse	SSSI, BBOWT	SP219113	2009	DeL	
22	V	Grafton Lock Meadow	SSSI	SU271991	2009	SEE+	>100
23	S	Otmoor	SSSI	SP575128	2008	SEE+	150
23	S	Hartslock	SAC, SSSI, BBOWT	SU617794	2008	RdA	600

Carex pilulifera

Pill Sedge

This is scattered across the county, but mainly in S on low-nutrient acidic soils. There are 17 2000–11 records for vc23 and three for vc22 so it is Not Scarce. SEE

→ *Carex elata*   Tufted-Sedge
Native   **Near Threatened, Nationally Scarce** ■ **Rare in Oxon and vc23**

(Margaret Killick)

This big plant is told from *C. acuta* by its dense tussocks and the leaf-sheaths splitting into ladder-like fibres at the back. It is in marshy habitats, often calcium-rich and seasonally flooded. FlOx cited it by two lake margins near Cottisford (SP5931, 1996 Killick; SP6131, 1975), Shiplake (SU7878); at Spartum Fen (SP6400) Druce had reported it dying out. FlBe believed it extinct. In GB it is scattered with local strongholds e.g. East Anglia, but has decreased in England following drainage. HJK

23	C	Cottisford		SP593311	2009	HJK	>10 clumps
23	S	South Stoke Marsh (south)	LWS	SU596833	2006	CRL	Many, new
23	O	Long Meadow	LWS	SP522055	1991	EN	
23	C	Kirtlington Park Lake (north)	LWS	SP512202	1979	DJNH	

Subgenus *Psyllophora*

→ *Carex pulicaris*   Flea Sedge
Native   **Near Threatened** ■ **Scarce in Oxon, Rare in vc23**

(Peter Creed)

This small sedge has a single terminal spikelet with hanging utricles. It grows in mineral-rich soils in damp meadows and fens. It declined in Oxon before Druce (1927); FlOx had four tetrad records (SP5612, re-found and SP5408, 5604, and 6400 not re-found). FlBe lists six undated sites. HJK saw none in 1998 in Spartum Fen where in 1969 it was "common" (Palmer), or in 2003 in Barrow Farm Fen; both are overgrown. However, we have four new records. In GB it is fairly widespread, but much decreased with drainage and loss of habitat in lowland England. HJK

23	0	Lye Valley	SSSI	SP547052	2010	JAW	4 seeding, new
22	V	Parsonage Moor	SAC, SSSI, BBOWT	SU460998	2010	JAW	49 seeding
22	V	Confidential	SSSI	SU49P	2009	SEE	>50 clumps
23	S	Otmoor	SSSI	SP573128	2008	CRL+	Many
23	W	Alvescot Meadows	SSSI	SP273050	2007	HJK	1 × 1 m, new
23	S	Sydlings Copse	SSSI, BBOWT	SP555096	1990	JZ+	
23	S	Spartum Fen	SSSI	SP655017	1990	EN	Not seen 1998
22	V	Barrow Farm Fen	SSSI	SU467975	1990	EN	Abs. HJK, 2003
23	S	Brasenose Wood and LGS Shotover Hill	SSSI,	SP567057	1981	DTS	
23	S	Otmoor	SSSI	SP575128	1973	HJMB+	

↓ *Nardus stricta*   Mat-grass
Native   **Near Threatened** ■ **Last Oxon and vc23 record 1987**

This densely tufted grass is common in the N and W, but had a big decline in the S. Braithwaite *et al.* (2006) found it declined significantly between 1987–8 and 2003–4. It thrives with light grazing and acidic, very low-nutrient conditions. Druce had seven sites including Shotover where it was noted in 1980, and North Leigh Common, where it was seen in 1975 by Bowen and again in 1987. FlOx had two tetrads by North Leigh. This common is managed by WODC, but is ungrazed and the vegetation has become quite dense. Druce also had Cumnor Hurst, now an SSSI and open space. CRL

⬇ *Lolium temulentum*   Darnel
Archaeophyte   **Critically Endangered, Nationally Rare** ■ **Last Oxon and vc23 record 1977**

A poisonous and formerly persistent annual grass of arable crops, it probably declined through better seed cleaning and by the 1920s occurred mostly from seed for bird feeding. Formerly it was widespread in England but since 1950 it was mostly a casual of waysides and tips. It prefers alkaline soils and tolerates high nutrients. Druce had six sites and FIOx p. 272 seven tetrads; FIBe records were all pre-1960. CRL

23	0	S Oxford tip		SP5204	1977	HJMB
23	S	Thame Park and New Park	pLWS	SP716038	1972	RSRF
23	S	Binfield Heath		SU7478	1969	HJMB

⬇ *Festuca filiformis*   Fine-leaved Sheep's-fescue
Native   **Scarce in Oxon, Rare in vc23**

This very fine-leaved fescue is widespread in the BI, though restricted to acidic and very low-nutrient soils. Any changes in frequency are obscured by name changes. Druce had seven widespread sites, but we have only four 2000–11 records. Its decline from 12 tetrads in FIOx may reflect a lack of grazing and recording on the commons. Bowen cited Cumnor Hurst and Bagley, but it has not been re-found in FIBe. CRL

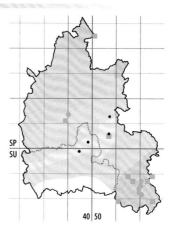

22	V	Memorial Garden	LWS, OPT	SP483026	2010	CRL	few, conf. A Copping
23	S	Otmoor	SSSI	SP573128	2009	CRL	100s
22	V	Confidential	SSSI	SU49P	2007	SEE	Several
23	S	Brasenose Wood and Shotover Hill	SSSI, LGS	SP570059	2006	SW	
23	S	Witheridge Hill		SU695840	1995	RdA	
23	S	Kingwood Common	LWS	SU696825	1995	RdA	
23	S	Highmoor and Lower Common Wood	LWS	SU702850	1995	RdA	
23	S	Nettlebed Common	LWS	SU705871	1995	RdA	
23	S	Peppard Common	LWS	SU706817	1981	HJMB+	
23	W	North Leigh Common	LWS	SP401136	1969	HJMB	

Vulpia myuros   Rat's-tail Fescue
This annual archaeophyte of dry, poor, slightly acidic soils has increased in GB but probably not in Oxon since FIOx. Druce had 34 sites and FIOx (p. 272) 70 tetrads; 27 sites were found in 2000–11 in Oxon (15 in vc23) so it is Not Scarce. HJK

➡ *Vulpia unilateralis*   Mat-grass Fescue
Neophyte   **Nationally Scarce** ■ **Scarce in Oxon, Rare in vc23**

This small annual fescue is inconspicuous and potentially overlooked. It grows in dry bare well-drained, sometimes disturbed, ground such as thin chalk grassland, sandpits, railways and walls; first seen at Bald Hill in 1955 and still there. Very scattered in vc23 (FIOx cited tetrads SP3430, 3632, SU7092, 7294 and 7296 between 1955 and 1969). In vc22 (Oxon), it was at Moulsford Fair Mile (SU5583) in 1956, Hitchcopse Pit (SU452996) in 1967 and since and newly noted by Webb and Killick at and near SU457990 in 2014. It was at Dry Sandford Pit in 1980 and seen by Erskine in 1999, cited below. First seen in GB in 1903, it is widely scattered SE of a line Lincoln–Worcester–Exeter. HJK

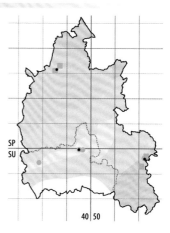

23	C	Hook Norton Cutting & Banks	SSSI, BBOWT	SP357315	2009	HJK+	Rock wall 2 clumps
22	V	Hitchcopse Pit	SSSI, BBOWT	SU451996	2009	SEE	Frequent
23	S	Aston Rowant	SAC, NNR, SSSI	SU724959	2007	GS	
22	V	Coxwell Pit	LGS	SU285943	1999	SEE+	Not since FIBe

⬆ *Poa infirma*
Native

Early Meadow-grass
Rare in Oxon and vc23

This little annual differs from the abundant *Poa annua* in more erect inflorescences and very short (0.5 mm) anthers. It is frequent in trampled coastal grassland in SW England and is recently spreading more widely in road verges, pavements and gutters. It was first seen here in Witney (SP337093) by P Stanley in 2007, det. E J Clement, **OXF**, and can be expected elsewhere. HJK

⬇ *Poa humilis*
Native

Spreading Meadow-grass
Not Scarce in Oxon, Scarce in vc23

This rhizomatous grass was only recently recognised as a separate species to *P. pratensis*, from which it can be distinguished by usually having hairs around the ligule, extensive rhizomes and solitary flowering stems. It is widespread and under-recorded in the BI on a variety of soils, some quite nitrate-rich. In Oxon it is found both on the chalk and in acidic grassland as well as neutral roadsides and damp meadows. Druce had it (as a variety) at 24 sites; FlOx p. 274 had 15 tetrads, and FlBe seven sites. We studied it but almost all of the 11 records in 2000–11 are new, so it could have been under-recorded. CRL

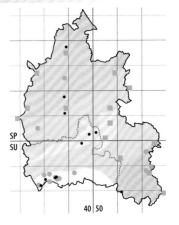

22	V	Hill End	SSSI	SP466070	2010	SEE	
22	V	Picketts Heath		SP484026	2010	CRL	
22	V	Confidential	SSSI	SU49N	2010	HJK	5 locations
22	V	Dry Sandford Pit	SSSI, BBOWT	SU468995	2010	HJK	
23	C	Ardley lay-by		SP536251	2009	CRL	
22	V	Black Horse field		SU466983	2009	HJK	
23	W	Westwell Gorse	SSSI, BBOWT	SP219113	2007	WOR	
23	W	Dix Pit	LWS	SP408050	2005	HJK	
23	S	Pishill verges		SU724899	2003	CMJ-H	

⬇ *Poa angustifolia*
Native

Narrow-leaved Meadow-grass
Seemingly scarce in Oxon, Scarce in vc23

This is a perennial grass, which can be distinguished from other Meadow-grasses by its very narrow tiller leaves (0.8 mm). It also tends to be the earliest to flower. Found throughout GB, but chiefly east of a line from Humber to Exe. It grows in thin less fertile soils than *P. pratensis*. It was in 50 FlOx tetrads. Due to confusion with others in the *P. pratensis* group it is probably recently under-recorded; especially as 18 FlOx tetrads were north of 10 northing. Agricultural changes may also account for some losses. It thrives in set-aside fields near Frilford in vc22. Recent records collected since 2011 suggest that this species would no longer be classed as scarce. SEE

22	V	Hill End	SSSI	SP466070	2010	SEE	
22	V	Picketts Heath		SP484026	2010	CRL	
22	V	Confidential	SSSI	SU49N	2010	HJK	5 locations
22	V	Dry Sandford Pit	SSSI, BBOWT	SU468995	2010	HJK	
23	C	Ardley Lay-by		SP536251	2009	CRL	
22	V	Black Horse field		SU466983	2009	HJK	
23	W	Westwell Gorse	SSSI, BBOWT	SP219113	2007	WOR	
23	W	Dix Pit	LWS	SP408050	2005	HJK	
23	S	Pishill verges		SU724899	2003	CMJ-H	

Catabrosa aquatica
Native

Water Whorl-grass
Vulnerable ■ Rare in Oxon and vc23

This water-side perennial flourishes in neutral conditions and tolerates high nutrients. While it is still common in central and E England, it has had a big decline – perhaps fewer wet places where cattle congregate. Although Braithwaite *et al.* (2006) recorded an increase between 1987–8 and 2003–4, it has declined steeply from 50 tetrads in FlOx. The only entry in Meagher and Sheasby (2005) is Horse Pasture (SP3933). But it may also be under-recorded as 35 of these tetrads were N of Oxford. Druce had 25 sites but declining. CRL

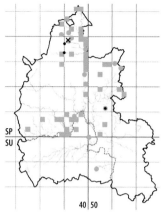

23	C	Horse pond, Swere		SP400336	2004	PS	New
23	S	Upper Park Farm	LWS	SP572114	2001	CRL	
23	C	Wetland west of Tadmarton		SP401372	2000	PS	New
23	C	Thrupp		SP4816	1995	HJK	Canal
23	C	Cherwell & canal, L Heyford		SP485249	1993	HJK	
22	S	West Hagbourne Moor		SU535872	1992	HJMB+	
23	S	Beckley		SP5610	1991	HJK	In flush
23	C	Godington		SP636275	1991	RCP+	Stream
23	C	Broughton Park		SP418382	1987	HJK	Abs. HJK 2010
22	V	Swinford Meadow	OPT	SP442082	1985	WS	
22	V	Sugnell Copse		SU503999	1985	HS+	
23	C	Pool Spinney	LWS	SP611293	1979	BBOWT	
23	C	Wroxton Park		SP418415	1977	AN	
23	C	The Bretch, Banbury		SP430394	1975	PS+	Abs. CRL

Avenula pratensis (Helictotrichon pratense)
Meadow Oat
This calcicole grass is near-stable in GB. It was in 99 tetrads (FlOx p. 276) which seemed over-recorded, and frequent on chalk in vc22 (Oxon). With 26 2000–11 records in Oxon (16 in vc23) it is Not Scarce; the change is hard to assess. HJK

Aira caryophyllea
Native

Silver Hair-grass
Scarce in Oxon, Rare in vc23

(Peter Creed)

Silver Hair-grass, a small spring annual, likes dry open places on porous, mostly sandy, soils. Its numbers fluctuate greatly. It was in 37 FlOx tetrads, most seemingly now lost. Of these 21 were N of Northings 30 and in one of four sites re-visited it was re-found. As the other 17 northerly sites were not re-visited, the species may *not* be rare, unless scrub growth has eliminated former railway sites mentioned in FlOx. In vc22 (Oxon), it is in five sites, two new, since 2000 but was not re-found in one. In GB it is widespread but has declined throughout, especially in the SE and since 1950. HJK

22	V	Confidential		SU49N	2010	HJK	10
22	V	Hitchcopse Pit	SSSI, BBOWT	SU452996	2010	HJK	1 sq.m
22	V	Confidential		SU49P	2009	HJK	Hundreds
22	V	Jespers Hill		SU297950	2006	SEE	Frequent, new
22	V	Southmoor, roundabout		SU387977	2006	SEE	3 places, new
23	C	Hangland Farm Railway Cutting	LWS	SP511450	2000	PS	
23	C	Tadmarton Heath		SP390356	1993	HJK	Abs. 2008 HJK
23	C	Hook Norton Cutting & Banks	SSSI, LGS, BBOWT	SP358315	1977	HJMB+	Abs. 2009 HJK
23	C	The Bretch, Banbury		SP430394	1975	PS	Not seen 2009 HJK

⬇ *Aira praecox*
Native

This winter annual of dry open sunny places on sandy acid soils was in 32 tetrads (FlOx p. 278). It was not re-found at Tadmarton Heath but we have not checked the other 19 N of Oxford. It had perhaps not been seen since the 1970s near Chadlington, Leafield and Freeland which were former hot-spots. In vc22 (Oxon), it was commoner than *A. caryophyllea* but is not so now. It is at risk from competitors and scrub; it may have benefited from set-aside. The numbers fluctuate. In 22 V Killick's Cumnor Hurst record (SP477042 1998), was repeated in 2015 (Lambrick). Its modest decline in England was perhaps worst near our area. HJK

22	V	Confidential	SSSI	SU49P	2010	SEE+	2 patches
22	V	Ripon Hall OU offices		SP490020	2008	CRL	c. 20
22	V	Confidential		SU49P	2008	HJK	>100
23	S	Sydlings Copse	SSSI, BBOWT	SP555096	2007	HJK	Sparse
23	S	Peppard Common	LWS	SU704814	2007	JHW	8 m length
23	S	Crowsley Park	LWS	SU729796	2007	JHW	
23	S	Shotover		SP5604	2006	ShW	Widely
23	S	Shotover		SP5606	2006	ShW	Widely
22	V	Tubney Woods	LWS	SP445001	2005	AWM+	
22	V	Birch Copse set-aside	pLWS	SP488032	2003	CRL	
23	S	Monks Wood Grassland	LWS	SP567066	2001	CRL	
23	S	Kingwood Common	LWS	SU694825	1995	RdA	
23	S	Shirburn Hill	SSSI	SU715955	1986	HJMB+	
23	W	Cogges Wood	LWS	SP380110	1975	JMC	
23	C	Hangland Farm Railway Cutting	LWS	SP509449	1975	HJMB+	

⬆ *Agrostis curtisii* (*A. setacea*)
Native

A. curtisii is a perennial tufted fine-leaved grass of poor, acid, sandy soils in heaths or open woodland. Small quantities have been newly seen at Tadmarton Heath and also by Helm in the heathy part of Sydlings Copse (SP?554096) where management machinery may have brought it from Berkshire. These extend by 60 km its published national range, which lies within SW and S England (including heaths in vc22 (Berks), and S Wales. HJK

23	S	Sydlings Copse	SSSI, BBOWT	SP554096	2009	SJH	New
23	C	Tadmarton Heath Golf Course		SP393355	2007	HJK	Few, new, OXF

➡ *Agrostis canina*
Native

A. canina is perennial with creeping stolons and tufts of fine (1–3 mm wide) leaves and narrow ligules; the palea in the spikelets is minute. It is found in damp places and pond-sides on infertile acid often peaty soils – habitats rare in Oxon, and Druce (1927) found it rare. Inclusion of *A. canina* in the FlOx tick-list attracted many records in improbable areas and habitats, and FlOx reported that after consultation many of these were deleted from the FlOx dot map. Only three tetrads were kept, Palmer's at Whitecross Green Wood, SP5814 and 6014, and Waterperry wood, SP6008. More records have since been received: the most plausible are cited. Its inclusion in future tick-lists may attract more errors. In GB it is widespread except in the Midlands. HJK

23	S	Otmoor	SSSI	SP572127	2008	CRL+	New
23	S	Waterperry Wood	SSSI	SP605089	2008	HJK	Many locally
23	S	Nuneham Arboretum	LWS	SU553986	2007	HJK	
23	C	Quarry Spring meadow		SP388332	2003	PS+	
23	C	The Meanders and Peat Marsh	LWS	SP398335	2003	PS+	Meanders meadow
23	W	North Leigh Common	LWS	SP401136	1998	GH	
23	S	Kingwood Common	LWS	SU696825	1994	JHW	
23	S	Sandford Brake	LWS	SP562016	1993	SJG	
23	S	Emmer Green Reservoir		SU727774	1992	EN	
23	W	Foxholes	SSSI, BBOWT	SP251204	1986	HJMB	
23	S	Russell's Water Common		SU716892	1972	HJMB	
23	C	Weston-on-Green		SP533178	1971	RCP	

⬇ *Agrostis vinealis*
Native

Brown Bent
Rare in Oxon and vc23

This perennial grass was formerly treated as *A. canina* ssp. *montana*, but is now considered a full species by being rhizomatous rather than stoloniferous, having the ligule on the second culm leaf at most 1.5 × as long as wide, and the flowering spike strongly contracted at fruiting. It is widespread and common especially in the N and W, on dry acidic sandy soils with extremely low nutrients. Druce has no mention and FlOx two tetrads; FlBe has records at Buckland Warren SU344956 and Hurst Hill LWS, SP476042. CRL

23	W	North Leigh Common	LWS		SP401135	2006	GH	Locally abundant

➡ *Calamagrostis epigejos*
Wood Small-reed

We recorded this tall perennial grass, but in 2000–11 had seen it 31 times (25 times in vc23) so is Not Scarce. HJK

➡ *Calamagrostis canescens*
Native

Purple Small-reed
Rare in Oxon, absent in vc23

FlBe reported this smaller relative of *C. epigejos*, in shady carr at Colliers Copse near Besselsleigh (SP449011), in 1969 (**OXF**) and subsequently. HJK

⬇ *Apera spica-venti*
Loose Silky-bent
Archaeophyte   GB Near Threatened, Nationally Scarce ■ Rare in Oxon, last vc23 record 1998

(Brian Laney)

This elegant annual used to be grown as an ornamental. It is a plant of E England that has declined, growing on light soils in arable and waste places, and is usually transient. At Dry Sandford Pit it came up following cultivation, just to the right of the entrance gate, inside rabbit fencing. Druce had five sites and FlOx 12 tetrads (p. 280). CRL

22	V	*Dry Sandford Pit*	*SSSI*	*SU4699*	*2004*	*MJC*	*10 in 2005*
22	V	**Kingston Bagpuize**		**SU4098**	**2003**	**FlBe**	**Many**
23	S	Shotover, Manor Farm Yard		SP571051	1998	ShW	
23	V	Sandy field W of Culham Lab		SU5294	1992	RCP	
23	S	Nineveh Farm, Nuneham Courtenay		SP5400	1972	RCP	
23	S	E of Bayswater Farm		SP5606	1968	RCP	

⮕ *Apera interrupta*   **Dense Silky-bent**
Neophyte, possibly introduced in Oxon Nationally Scarce ▪ Scarce in Oxon, only vc23 record 1924

This annual appeared wild in GB in 1848; it does best in East Anglia and is possibly increasing. Usually in arable margins, verges and wasteland, it can also grow on hard-grazed grass. It needs disturbance to flourish, but has a long-lived seed bank. It has high local interest because of its fluctuating appearance on light soils on the southern margins of the Corallian Ridge from Marcham to Faringdon. Big plants thrived in 1995 in a nutrient-rich Marcham bean field (SU448969); in 1996 myriads grew in the first year of set-aside in a Frilford field but in less disturbed conditions, monitored for 15 years, decreased to almost nil. Moles and rabbits may have sometimes helped its seeds to germinate. It appeared previously at Culham in 1924 and in vc22 (Oxon) in 1900 (at Marcham), 1923 and 1939. HJK

22	V	Tubney		SU439996	2010	SEE
22	V	Confidential		SU49T	2010	HJK
22	V	Confidential		SU49N	2009	HJK
22	V	Confidential		SU49P	2009	HJK	Also 447987
22	V	Confidential		SU49U	2007	HJK
22	V	Folly Hill, Faringdon		SU295956	2006	SEE
22	V	Fyfield allotments		SU418986	2006	SEE
22	V	Confidential	SSSI	SU49J	2005	SEE+
22	V	Tubney Woods	LWS	SU445995	2003	ShW
22	V	Tubney Woods Sandpit	LGS	SP448008	1997	OS	+ more sites
22	V	Besselsleigh, arable margin		SP459019	1995	HJK	Arable margin
22	V	Radley		SU526977	1993	DGr	Det. RM Payne
22	V	*Hitchcopse Pit*	*SSSI, BBOWT*	*SU452996*	*1980*	*HJMB*	*Not recently*

⮕ *Polypogon monspeliensis*   **Annual Beard-grass**
Native on the coast, but not in Oxon   Nationally Scarce ▪ Rare in Oxon and vc23

A casual of bird-seed (including pheasant feed) and a garden escape. It prefers neutral soils and raised nutrient levels. In Oxon it seems to colonise pits, tips, verges and open areas. Druce had three sites, all in Oxford. FlOx had three tetrads, none far from Oxford. FlBe five sites, and Erskine saw it at Shellingford Pit in 2014. CRL

23	W	Dix Pit	LWS	SP407054	2005	HJK	
22	V	Upper Sledge Pit		SP452000	2004	HJK	Pond
22	V	Abingdon Common		SU470962	2002	HJK	Pond
22	V	Hitchcopse Pit	SSSI	SU4498	1995	HJK	FlBe
22	V	Radley		SU5296	1994	RCP	FlBe
23	O	Headington bypass		SP5406	1992	CMJ-H	
23	O	*N Oxford Tip*		*SP5008*	*1978*	*HJMB*	*FlOx*
22	V	Drayton		SU4692	1978	RCP	
22	V	Steventon		SU4690	1978	FlBe	**OXF**
23	W	Stanton Harcourt Tip		SP4004	1977	HJMB	FlOx
22	V	Appleford Halt		SU524935	1976	RCP	

⬇ *Alopecurus aequalis*   **Orange Foxtail**
Native   Nationally Scarce ▪ Rare in Oxon and vc23

A. aequalis is a small annual grass of wet places, most often muddy pond edges. In vc23 at Clattercote Reservoir in 1885, 1927 and 1981 (SP450485); in 1969 Palmer found it non-flowering, but was not re-found in 1994 when the site had much scrub. It was near Peppard in 1932 (**RDG**); unconfirmed from tetrad SP3402 in 1972. Webb has newly found it in Otmoor SP572139, conf. T A Cope. FlBe has none in our area. The patchy distribution in GB shows a gap in Oxon but greater abundance in the Midlands and SE. HJK

23	C	Clattercote Reservoir		SP450485	1981	MJW	HJK not seen 1994

⬇ *Glyceria declinata*
Native

Small Sweet-grass
Scarce in Oxon and vc23

This perennial is told by its small size, glaucous leaves and three-lobed lemma with the bifid palea protruding under its tip. It grows in marshy fields, waterside mud and shallow water. It tends to replace *G. fluitans* in heavily trampled sites and base-poor mire (Grime *et al.* 1988, p. 310); because base-poor sites are relatively few in Oxfordshire Killick mistrusted many of the 46 tetrads (FlOx p. 275) and his 1993 record surprised him. It is also easy to overlook. FlBe more plausibly cites only three records, undated, and reports its decline due to drainage. Recent and selected pre-2000 records are cited here. Widespread in GB, but there are many gaps in the S Midlands; it has declined, especially in the SE and since 1950. HJK

23	S	Garsington		SP584017	2007	RH-B	New
23	W	Shifford Chimney Meadows	LWS, BBOWT	SP356004	2004	SEE+	New
23	C	Gavray Drive Meadows (non LWS)		SP599221	2002	CRL	New
23	S	Nuffield Common	LWS	SU673876	2002	JHW	
23	W	Newbridge Cut		SP406024	1996	AJL	
23	C	Lower Heyford canal		SP485249	1993	HJK	
23	O	New Marston Meadows	SSSI	SP522074	1992	EN	
23	W	Cassington		SP446119	1987	HJMB	
23	W	Taynton Quarries	SSSI	SP236151	1986	HJMB+	
23	O	Almonds Farm and Burnt Mill Fields	LWS	SP519092	1986	RH-B	

Bromus racemosus

Smooth Brome

Druce had this native grass of damp hay meadows as locally common, and FlOx had 57 tetrads. In 2000–11 we found 42 sites in Oxon (37 in vc23) so it is Not Scarce. CRL

⬇ *Bromus interruptus*

Interrupted Brome

Neophyte, Endemic   s. 41, Extinct in the Wild ■ Last Oxon and vc23 record in the Wild 1931

This annual of arable fields is of unknown origin; it appeared in 1849 in Beds, spread widely and then declined; the last record is from Cambs in 1972 (Marren, 1999). It reached Oxon in 1888, increasing to 10 sites by 1927, but was last seen in 1931 at Taynton **OXF**. Seed collected in Cambs was bulked up by the Millennium Seed Bank at Wakehurst Place and sown by EN into an ex-arable field at Aston Rowant (and in Cambs). More than 100 plants set seed in 2005; but due to difficult weather, ploughing was late, and only tens were present the following year; the vegetation was dominated by tougher grasses and less open. In 2007 sheep ate all the young seed heads. Ploughing and monitoring in subsequent years failed to reveal any *B. interruptus,* Graham Stevens (pers. comm.) reports that the plant is very palatable and that the seed has limited dormancy. CRL

⬆ *Bromus secalinus*

Rye Brome

Archaeophyte   Near Threatened ■ Scarce in Oxon and vc23

(Judy Webb)

This tall annual to biennial brome probably evolved as a weed of cereal fields, though its country of origin is not known. It is widespread in S England and Druce listed 39 sites, but it has undergone a huge decline nationally and was in only two FlOx tetrads. It grows on neutral soils and tolerates moderate nutrients. The undated record in FlBe N of Childrey B4001 SU356888 was by Erskine in 1998. In 2000–11 it is mostly in arable field margins. Recent records collected since 2011 suggest that this species would no longer be classed as scarce. CRL

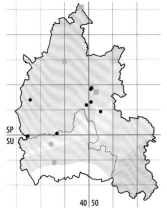

23	W	Dean Bottom	LWS	SP257140	2010	JK+	New
23	C	Meadows west of the Oxford Canal	LWS	SP490119	2010	JK+	New
23	C	Bletchingdon		SP508182	2010	HJK	1 & FlOx
23	C	Field off Water Eaton Lane		SP509131	2010	JAW	Lots, new
23	C	Bletchingdon		SP511187	2010	HJK	Lots
23	W	Field margin, nr Kelmscott		SU247996	2010	SEE	New
23	S	Track to Sydlings Copse		SP549093	2009	RH-B	c. 50 new
23	W	Shifford Chimney Meadows	LWS, BBOWT	SP367006	2004	SEE+	New
22	V	Buckland Warren	SSSI	SU343963	1999	SEE	
23	C	SE of Kirtlington		SP5018	1993	HJK	Conf. Trist

⬇ *Anisantha madritensis*
Neophyte

Compact Brome
Last Oxon and vc23 record 1998

This annual of waste places on light soils especially by railways (notably, plenty by Swindon station (vc7) in 1978–83), is limited to Oxford where it first appeared in 1909. Palmer saw it at Rewley Road (SP5107) in 1984 and Upper Fisher Row in 1991. In 1991–98 he and Killick independently found it spreading in cinders, at the former LMS station in Oxford, SP505063, but it was lost when this became the Said Business School. Not in FlBe. In GB it was known wild by 1716 and is mostly S of a line Swansea–Gloucester–London. HJK

⬇ *Bromopsis benekenii*
Native

Lesser Hairy-brome
Nationally Scarce ■ ?Scarce in Oxon and vc23

This tufted perennial is scattered in GB. It could be scarce but is under-recorded due to its similarity to *B. ramosa*, with which it often grows. An intermediate was found near Nettlebed (see FlOx p. 282). It prefers beech woods, and all 10 records in FlOx are from the Chilterns. One at Stonesfield in 2002 was not re-found in 2010. Druce also had 10 sites in vc23, and there are none from vc22 (Oxon). While requiring humus-rich alkaline soils, it tolerates moderate nutrient levels. CRL

23	S	Nr Bozedown Ho, Whitchurch-on-Thames		SU6278	1994	NE	
23	S	Ipsden, Yewtree Brow		SU6484	1992	RCP	**OXF**
23	S	Chinnor Hill	SSSI, BBOWT	SP766007	1979	RSRF	
23	S	Warburg	SSSI, BBOWT	SU716879	1979	VNP	
23	S	Hartslock	SSSI	SU67E	1972	Cobb	**RDG**
23	S	Maidensgrove		SU7286	1971		Conf. Hubbard

⬇ *Hordelymus europaeus*
Native

Wood Barley
Nationally Scarce ■ Not Scarce in Oxon and vc23

This grass is almost only found in the Chiltern woods, from which there are 26 2000–11 records: it is Not Scarce. In FlOx it was in 44 tetrads. The only vc22 (Oxon) record was from Radley Large Wood. SEE

➡ *Danthonia decumbens*
Heath-grass
Although its main habitat, grassy heaths, is sparse in Oxon, Heath-grass was in 26 FlOx tetrads, and found in 12 places in Oxon, all in vc23, in 2000–11, so is Not Scarce. It is also at Frilford. HJK

⬇ *Molinia caerulea*
Native

Purple Moor-grass
Scarce in Oxon and vc23

Moor-grass is a deciduous tufted perennial, mostly on rather acid peaty soils, damp or wet but not waterlogged. It was in 19 FlOx tetrads (eight N of Oxford not re-visited) but has decreased owing to habitat destruction and scrub growth; timely scrub clearance has since revived it at Lashford Lane Fen. It was not re-found at The Slade (SP4234). It is now in seven vc23 sites and three in vc22 (Oxon). In GB it is widespread in seasonally wet peaty or mineral soils, and grows in a wider range of habitats including moors, heaths and birch woods. HJK

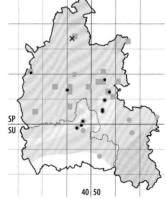

23	O	Lye Valley	SSSI	SP547051	2010	JAW	Many, some dominant
23	O	Lye Valley	SSSI	SP547058	2010	JAW	Frequent
22	V	Ruskin Reserve	SAC, NNR, SSSI	SU460996	2010	JAW	Frequent
23	W	Foxholes	SSSI, BBOWT	SP252205	2009	HJK	By path
23	W	North Leigh Common	LWS	SP401136	2009	JAW+	Dominant in 80 × 5m 2012
23	C	Woodsides Meadow	SSSI, BBOWT	SP556178	2009	JAW	
22	V	Lashford Lane Fen	SAC, SSSI	SP466012	2008	HJK	2011 few
23	S	Otmoor	SSSI	SP575128	2008	SEE+	Rifle range
22	V	Confidential	SSSI	SU49P	2007	SEE	Near dominant
23	S	Sydlings Copse	SSSI, BBOWT	SP556096	2006	HJK	Few in fen
23	S	Spartum Fen	SSSI	SP655017	1997	HJK	
23	W	Worcester Hill Bank & Marshes	LWS	SP428199	1996	AWM	
23	S	*Henton Marsh*		*SP768028*	*1994*	*RSRF*	*Destroyed*
22	V	*Barrow Farm Fen*	*SSSI*	*SU467975*	*1990*	*EN*	*None recent*
23	S	Easington Fen		SU667966	1990	EN	

Charophytes – Stoneworts

P.E. Cutt

The Stoneworts (Characeae) are structurally complex freshwater green algae that resemble aquatic vascular plants. They have great value as indicators of pristine water-bodies because of their sensitivity to pollution and even low levels of enrichment.

They derive the common name from the crust of calcium carbonate. This is deposited on their surface as a result of metabolic processes and fizzes or crackles in contact with dilute acid such as vinegar.

Of the 33 British species, 12 (one extinct) have been recorded in Oxfordshire. Within the county there are two important Stonewort areas – Otmoor to the NE of Oxford along the River Ray, and the Lower Windrush Valley, south of Witney, comprising many gravel pits (Stewart 2004).

The lead organisation for the conservation of all the Red listed stoneworts is Plantlife, with the Environment Agency for *Tolypella intricata*.

To identify a stonewort, it is best to use one of the keys in the standard texts, but a **simplified key to Oxfordshire genera** follows:

1. Encrusted with calcium carbonate; stem with multicellular ridges	*Chara*
Unencrusted and with a smooth stem, only one cell wide	**2**
2. Branchlets divided into unequal, multi-celled rays (appears lop-sided)	*Tolypella*
Branchlets divided without a dominant axis (similar structure to *Chara*)	*Nitella*

Chara vulgaris   Common Stonewort
The many varieties of *C. vulgaris* have now been combined into one species (John *et al.* 2002). With 24 records mostly in the Lower Windrush it is not scarce.

Chara contraria   Opposite Stonewort
C. contraria is not scarce here. It is mainly found in East Anglia and the Thames region; the flooded gravel pits of the Lower Windrush valley account for 27 of our 32 records.

Chara hispida   Bristly Stonewort
Scarce (four sites) in Oxon, and rare (2) in vc23

This moderately encrusted species is easily distinguished by its long spines and thick (3 mm) stem. It is widespread throughout the British Isles in a range of habitats, though in Oxfordshire a rare plant of calcareous springs and pools. In deeper water it can form dense, perennial stands as at Stratton Audley.

Chara globularis   Fragile Stonewort
Scarce, 5 sites in Oxon

A cosmopolitan species found throughout the UK, mainly in still water-bodies of various sizes. It seems to prefer slightly higher nutrient levels than most other stoneworts. It can exist as a perennial in deeper water, but in normal situations will disappear over winter.

Chara virgata (= C. globularis var. virgata)   Delicate Stonewort
This widespread species is found in a variety of habitats, though often in more acidic water than other species of stonewort; it can also survive brackish water and in pools which dry out over summer. Found in 24 Oxfordshire sites, it is Not Scarce.

Chara curta (= C. aspera var. curta)   Lesser bearded Stonewort
Rare, 3 sites in Oxon, 1 in vc23

Growing to about 40 cm, this is a slender spiny plant with long internodes. Spine cells are typically in groups of two or more. It spreads mainly by bulbils, rarely fertile. Distribution internationally centred on Britain with only a few records from the continent. Within the UK it is found along the west coast and also in East Anglia stretching into central England. Preferring calcareous water, in Oxfordshire it is found in flooded gravel pits, typically at 1–2 m depth.

Nitella flexilis

Smooth Stonewort
Scarce, 8 sites in Oxon

This monoecious species is hard to separate from *N. opaca*, so there are relatively few records. It is only during early summer when mature oospores are visible that anything other than *N. flexilis* agg. (which includes *N. opaca*) may be recorded. It occurs in fairly nutrient-rich lakes and pools, and sometimes in temporary pools such as vehicle ruts.

Nitella opaca (= *N. flexilis*)

Smooth Stonewort
Rare, 2 sites in Oxon

This dioecious species can only be separated reliably from *N. flexilis* in early summer with the mature oospores and antheridia. When sterile it should be recorded as *N. flexilis* agg. Plants may be summer or winter annuals, or in deeper water may survive as perennials. *Nitella opaca* can be found in any water-body that lacks nutrient enrichment. It is widespread throughout the British Isles and in Europe.

Nitella mucronata

Pointed Stonewort
Near Threatened ■ Rare, 2 sites in Oxon

This species differs from *N. flexilis*, in having branchlet tips made of two or three cells tapering to a fine or mucronate point. It seems to prefer sites which have a moderate level of disturbance and low-nutrient enrichment, e.g. canals. It is confined to S and E England. Previously found in Oxfordshire in the River Thames (Druce 1886), in a site which now seems unsuitable, it was recorded in 2004 in a nearby ditch.

Var. *gracillima,* in which the final two cells of the branchlets are of equal length, is becoming the dominant form throughout the UK, possibly due to introductions via garden centres and ornamental ponds. The second Oxfordshire location is at Youlbury Lake (vc22) about 5 km from the Thames site.

Tolypella intricata

Tassel Stonewort
s. 41, Endangered ■ Scarce, 5 sites in Oxon

Tolypella intricata is lightly encrusted, yellow-green with fertile whorls forming bird's nest-like heads. These can be felt for using fingertips in likely locations beneath floating vegetation. The end cells of the branchlets are acutely tipped. This annual first appears in January/February, producing oospores in April/May. It is dead and gone by the end of July. A plant mostly of SE England, in Oxfordshire *T. intricata* grows in shallow pools and ancient channels, being very slow to spread. It is very vulnerable to habitat degradation and competition from surrounding vegetation.

Tolypella prolifera

Great Tassel Stonewort
s. 41, Vulnerable ■ Last Oxon record 1886

T. prolifera, a spring or summer annual, can occur in cleared ditches or in other slow moving alkaline water-bodies. Scattered in southern England, only once recorded in Oxfordshire, from the Thames in Oxford, close to the University boat-house (Druce 1886).

Tolypella glomerata

Clustered Stonewort
Rare ■ 3 sites in Oxon, 2 in vc23

This monoecious annual has obtuse branchlet end-cells. It prefers open habitats and has a scattered distribution in SE England. In Oxon there was one temporary colony near the rifle range in Otmoor, and other sightings elsewhere in Otmoor. Also found at Pinkhill (SP469067) in 2002 (Crawley 2005).

List of Recorders

The list of recorders is tabled in two ways:
- First in alphabetical order of surname, indicating how they are coded in the tables
- Second in order of codes, indicating to whom the code refers.

Abbreviations in surname order

Name	Code	Name	Code	Name	Code	Name	Code
W Adams	WA	R D'Ayala	RdA	R Heath-Brown	RH-B	Martin	JM
EJ Adnams	EJA	C Dalton	CDa	SV Hedger	SH	Maycock	RM
JA Allen	JAA	RWD David	RWD	SJ Helm	SJH	AW McDonald	AWM
S Antrobus	SA	R Davies	RD	R Helyar	RH	C McNab	CMcN
N Barber	NB	G Davy	GD	DJN Hind	DJNH	W Meagher	WM
R Barber	RB	G Dawe	GDa	M Hodgkiss	MH	M Middleton	MM
Bateman	RMB	HV Dawkins	HVD	A Hollands	AH	JNB Milton	JNBM
BBOWT	BBONT	S Denley	SD	NTH Holmes	NTHH	PGM Morris	PGMM
G Bellamy	GB	N Diserens	ND	RJ Hornby	RJH	J Morritt	JMo
K Betteridge	KB	S Diserens	SRD	CE Hubbard	CEH	G Morrison	GM
B Betteridge	BB	Doomsday	Doom	MR Hughes	MRH	J Muddeman	JMu
J Bevan	JBe	HB Douglas	HBD	L Hunt	LH	A Muldal	AM
R Bevan	RBa	GC Druce	GCD	Hunts Fauna	HFFS	A Nash	AN
JP Bolam	JPB	C Duncan	CD	CR Huxley	CRL	Nat Mus Wales	NMW
HJM Bowen	HJMB	A-J Dunn	AJD	NS Isaacs NS	NSI	Nat Rivers Auth	NRA
S Braeley	SB	A Duranel	AD	P Jackson	PJ	Natural England	NE
British Museum	BM	D Edgington	DE	CM Jackson-Houlston		Nature Con C	NCC
R Brocklehurst	RBe	J Edgington	JE		CMJ-H	P Nicolet	PN
CM Brotherton	CMB	D Elton	Del	R Jacques	RJ	E Norman	ENo
Broughton	DB	EN Oxon Grass	ENOGS	Johnston	AJJ	M North	MN
J Buchanan	JB	English Nature	EN	A Jones	AJ	JA Norton	JAN
A Burdock	ABu	SE Erskine	SEE	EW Jones	EWJ	G O'Donovan	GO'D
Burrow	CB	P Evans	PE	BE Juniper	BEJ	S O'Leary	SO'L
R Buxton	RBUX	SJ Everett	SJE	QON Kay	QONK	C O'Toole	CO'T
A Byfield	AB	T Fairfield	TF	S Kay	SK	S Ottway	SO
B Campbell	BJC	U Fenton	UF	M Keith-Lucas	MKL	Ox Coun Museum	OCMR
JM Campbell	JMC	D Ferguson	DF	D Kempster	KD	Oxon Fungus Svy	OFS
WD Campbell	WDC	RA Finch	RAF	D Kenny	DK	Ox Urban WG	OUWG
H Carter	HHC	J Finn	JF	J Kerans	JK	Oxford Canal p	OCP
L Carter	LC	RSR Fitter	RSRF	HJ Killick	HJK	L Palfreman	LP
JC Cartmell	JC	R Fitzgerald	RF	R Knight	RK	RC Palmer	RCP
RJ Chancellor	RJC	Flynn	FLY	L Knipe	LKn	RJ Pankhurst	RJP
JH Chapman	JHC	Flora Berks	FlBe	P Knipe	PJK	S Parkinson	SP
R Christian	RC	Flora Oxon	FlOx	AJ Lack	AJL	AC Partridge	ACP
S Christian	SC	TH Fowler	THF	T Laflin	TL	J Partridge	JWP
W Clarke	WC	W Foyt	WF	D Lamb	DLm	VN Paul	VP
M Clist	MC	M Gascoigne-P	MG-P	C Lamberth	CL	RP Payne	RPP
L Clowes	LCl	CWD Gibson	CWDG	CR Lambrick	CRL	AR Perry	ARP
LE Cobb	LEC	S Gimson (nee Kay)	SK	S Lane	SL	GF Peterken	GP
MM Cochrane	MMC	P Goodhind	PaG	B Laney	BL	N Phillips	NP
J Collier	JCo	P Goriup	PG	D Langston	DL	D Piggott	DP
B Collins	BC	S Gorman	SG	A Larkman	ALk	Pond Action	PA
S Conn	SP	H Graves	HG	EM Lee	EL	Pond Cons Trust	PA
E Cooper	EC	J Greenall	JG	D Lewis	DeL	RD Porley	RDP
I Corbyn	IC	SJGregory	SJG	A Lincoln	ALi	S Rankin	SR
MFV Corley	MFVC	S Gresham	SGr	Little Wittenham NR	LWNR	T Rayner	TR
L Cornwallis	LCo	F Griffith	FG	AJ Lockton	AJLo	D Rear	DR
Cotswold RPG	CRPG	D Guyoncourt	DG	R Louch	RL	T Reynolds	TRe
P Creed	PC	C Hardiker	CH	M Loukes	ML	TCG Rich	TCGR
J Crewe	JCR	C Hare	CHr	JR Makepeace	JRM	AJ Richards	AJR
M Crick	MCr	R Harrison	RHa	C Malone-Lee	CM-L	Ridgeway volunteer	RV
R Crossley	RCr	M Harvey	MHa	P Mansfield	PaM	L Ridout	LR
I Curtis	ICu	TR Harvey	TRH	B Marcan	BMa	W Ritter	WR
PE Cutt	PEC	G Hawker	GH	Marsack	PM	Road verge svy	RVNR

Abbreviations in surname order, continued

M Rodgers	MR	Simmonds R	RMS	WL Theobald	WLT	SJ Whild	SJW
R Roslyn	RR	Skidmore	Ski	JA Thompson	JAT	P Whitton	PW
RSPB	RSPB	H Smith	HS	MA Townsend	MaT	MJ Wigginton	MJW
V Ruane	VR	W Smyth	WS	MI Townsend	MT	M Wilkins	MW
R Russel R	RRu	N Snell	NS	EM Trembath	EMT	Williams	PJW
AM Sandels	AMS	RF Souster	RFS	J Trinder J	JT	PJ Wilson	PhJW
R Sanderson	RS	JF Southey	JFS	A Urwick	AU	A Winter	AW
S Sandford	SSa	A Spicer	ASp	W Oxon Recorders	WOR	SRJ Woodell	SRJW
MA Saunders	MAS	CA Spinage	CAS	HP Waldy	HPW	J Wright	JW
MG Schultz	MGS	GM Spooner	GMS	RM Walls	RMW	I Wright	IW
A Scott	AS	AI Spriggs	AIS	Ward	LKW	J Yeoman	JY
S Scroggins	SS	H St John	HStJ	Warden	KW	T Young	TY
RWH Scroggs	RWHS	DT Steel	DTS	Watkins	FHW	J Zwannenberg J	JZ
J Sheasby	JSh	P Sterry	PSt	S Watkinson	SWa	R Zwannenberg R	RLZ
P Sheasby	PS	G Steven	GS	JA Webb	JAW	Jocelyn Allard	JA
Shotover Wildlife	ShW	RG Stevens	RGS	Webber	EW	B Pollard	BP
AJ Showler	AJS	J Stretton	JS	JH Welsh	JHW	D Green D	DGr
Simmonds A	AMS	O Sutcliffe	OS	S Westwood	SW		

Abbreviations ordered by code

AB	Byfield	CMB	Brotherton	GDa	Dawe	JNBM	Milton
ABu	Burdock	CMcN	McNab	GH	Hawker	JPB	Bolam
ACP	Partridge A	CMJ-H	Jackson-Houlston	GM	Morrison	JRM	Makepeace
AD	Duranel	CM-L	Malone-Lee	GMS	Spooner	JS	Stretton
AH	Hollands	CO'T	O'Toole	GO'D	O'Donovan	JSh	Sheasby J
AIS	Spriggs	CRL	Lambrick	GP	Peterken	JT	Trinder J
AJ	Jones A	CRL	Huxley	GS	Steven	JW	Wright J
AJD	Dunn	CRPG	Cotswold	HBD	Douglas	JWP	Partridge J
AJJ	Johnston	CWDG	Gibson	HFFS	Hunts Fauna	JY	Yeoman
AJL	Lack	DB	Broughton	HG	Graves	JZ	Zwannenberg J
AJLo	Lockton	DE	Edgington D	HHC	Carter H	KB	Betteridge K
AJR	Richards	Del	Elton	HJK	Killick	KD	Kempster
AJS	Showler	DeL	Lewis	HJMB	Bowen	KW	Warden
ALi	Lincoln	DF	Ferguson	HPW	Waldy Mrs HP	LC	Carter L
ALk	Larkman	DG	Guyoncourt	HS	Smith	LCl	Clowes
AM	Muldal	DGr	Green	HStJ	St John	LCo	Cornwallis
AMS	AM Sandels	DJNH	Hind	HVD	Dawkins	LEC	Cobb
AMS	AM Simmonds	DK	Kenny	IC	Corbyn	LH	Hunt
AN	Nash	DL	Langston	ICu	Curtis	LKn	Knipe L
ARP	Perry	DLm	Lamb	IW	Wright I	LKW	Ward
AS	Scott	Doom	Doomsday	JAA	Allen	LP	Palfreman
ASp	Spicer	DP	Piggott D	JA	Allard J	LR	Ridout
AU	Urwick	DR	Rear	JAN	JA Norton	LWNR	Little Witt NR
AW	Winter	DTS	Steel	JAT	Thompson	MAS	Saunders
AWM	McDonald	EC	Cooper	JAW	Webb	MaT	Townsend Ma
BB	Betteridge B	EJA	Adnams	JB	Buchanan	MC	Clist
BBONT	BBOWT	EL	Lee	JBe	Bevan J	MCr	Crick
BC	Collins	EMT	Trembath	JC	Cartmell	MFVC	Corley
BEJ	Juniper	EN	Eng. Nature	JCo	Collier	MG-P	Gascoigne-P
BJC	Campbell B	ENo	Norman	JCR	Crewe	MGS	Schultz
BL	Laney	ENOGS	EN Ox Grass	JCR	Crewe	MH	Hodgkiss
BM	British Museum	EW	Webber	JE	Edgington J	MHa	Harvey
BMa	Marcan	EWJ	Jones E	JF	Finn	MJW	Wigginton
BP	Pollard B	FD	Ferguson	JFS	Southey	MKL	Keith-Lucas M
CAS	Spinage	FG	Griffith	JG	Greenall	ML	Loukes
CB	Burrow	FHW	Watkins	JHC	Chapman	MM	Middleton
CD	Duncan	FlBe	Flora Berks	JHW	Welsh	MMC	Cochrane
CDa	Dalton	FlOx	Flora Oxon	JK	Kerans	MN	North
CEH	Hubbard	FLY	Flynn	JM	Martin	MR	Rodgers
CH	Hardiker	GB	Bellamy	JMC	Campbell JM	MRH	Hughes
CHr	Hare Mrs C	GCD	Druce GC	JMo	Morritt	MT	Townsend Mi
CL	Lamberth C	GD	Davy	JMu	Muddeman	MW	Wilkins

Abbreviations ordered by code, continued

NB	Barber N	PSt	Sterry	RPP	Payne	SP	Conn
NCC	Nature Con C	PW	Whitton	RR	Roslyn	SR	Rankin
ND	Diserens N	QONK	Kay Q	RRu	Russel R	SRD	Diserens S
NE	Natural England	RAF	Finch RA	RS	Sanderson	SRJW	Woodell
NMW	Nat Mus Wales	RB	Barber R	RSPB	RSPB	SS	Scroggins
NP	Phillips	RBa	Bevan R	RSRF	Fitter	SSa	Sandford
NRA	Nat Rivers Auth	RBe	Brocklehurst	RV	Ridgeway	SW	Westwood
NS	Snell N	RBUX	Buxton		volunteer	SWa	Watkinson
NSI	Isaacs NS	RC	Christian R	RVNR	Road verge svy	TCGR	Rich
NTHH	Holmes	RCP	Palmer	RWD	David	TF	Fairfield
OCMR	Oxf County	RCr	Crossley	RWHS	Scroggs	THF	Fowler
	Museum	RD	Davies	SA	Antrobus	TL	Laflin
OCP	Oxford Canal P	RdA	D'Ayala	SB	Braeley	TR	Rayner
OFS	Oxon Fungus Svy	RDP	Porley	SC	Christian S	TRe	Reynolds Tom
OS	Sutcliffe	RF	Fitzgerald	SD	Denley	TRH	Harvey
OUWG	Ox Urban WG	RFS	Souster	SEE	Erskine	TY	Young
PA	Pond Action	RGS	Stevens	SG	Gorman	UF	Fenton
PA	Pond Cons Trust	RH	Helyar	SGr	Gresham	VP	Paul
PaG	Goodhind	RHa	Harrison	SH	Hedger	VR	Ruane
PaM	Mansfield	RH-B	Heath-Brown	SH	Hedger	WA	Adams W
PC	Creed	RH-B	Heath-Brown	ShW	Shotover Wild	WC	Clarke
PE	Evans	RJ	Jacques	SJE	Everett	WDC	Campbell W
PEC	Cutt	RJC	Chancellor	SJG	Gregory	WF	Foyt
PG	Goriup	RJH	Hornby	SJH	Helm	WLT	Theobald
PGMM	Morris PGM	RJP	Pankhurst	SJW	Whild	WM	Meagher
PhJW	Wilson P	RK	Knight	SK	Gimson	WOR	W Oxon
PJ	Jackson	RL	Louch	SK	Kay S		Recorders
PJK	Knipe P	RLZ	Zwannenberg R	Ski	Skidmore	WR	Ritter
PJW	Williams P	RM	Maycock	SL	Lane	WS	Smyth
PM	Marsack	RMB	Bateman	SO	Ottway		
PN	Nicolet	RMS	Simmonds R	SO'L	O'Leary S		
PS	Sheasby P	RMW	Walls	SP	Parkinson		

Bibliography

Amano T, Smithers RJ, Sparks TH, Sutherland WJ. 2010. A 250-year index of first flowering dates and its response to temperature changes. *Proc. R. Soc. B* **277(1693)**: 2451–7.

Amphlett A. 2013. Distance from recorder's home as a source of bias in plant recording. *BSBI News* **124**: 61.

Bateman R. 2010. Where does Orchid conservation End and Gardening begin? *Journal of the Hardy Orchid Society* **7**: 119–133.

Bateman R. 2011. Two steps forward, one step back: Deciphering British and Irish Marsh Orchids. *Journal of the Hardy Orchid Society* **8**: 48–59.

Bowen HJM. 1968. *The Flora of Berkshire*. Oxford: [the author].

Braithwaite ME, Ellis RW, Preston CD. 2006. *Change in the British Flora 1987–2004*. London: Botanical Society of the British Isles.

Brenan JPM. 1946. Notes on the Floras of Oxfordshire and Berkshire. *Report of the Botanical Society and Exchange Club of the British Isles for 1943–4*: 781–802.

Butterfly Conservation. 2014. http://butterfly-conservation. org/48-4912/climate-change-sees-butterflies-move-north.html.

Cheffings CM, Farrell L. 2005. The Vascular Plant Red Data List for Great Britain. *Species Status* **7**: 1–116. Peterborough: Joint Nature Conservation Committee.

Clapham AR, Tutin TG, Warburg EF. 1962. *Flora of the British Isles*. 2nd ed. Cambridge: Cambridge University Press.

Cole SR. 2014. History and Status of the Ghost Orchid (*Epipogium aphyllum*: Orchidaceae) in England. *New Journal of Botany* **40**: 1–13.

Coleman M, Hollingsworth ML, Hollingsworth PM. 2000. Application of RAPDs to the critical taxonomy of the English endemic elm *Ulmus plotii* Druce. *Bot. J. Linn. Soc.* **133**: 241–262.

Crawley MJ. 2005. *The Flora of Berkshire*. Harpenden, Herts: Brambleby Books.

Department for Environment, Food and Rural Affairs. 2010. *Open Mosaic Habitats on Previously Developed Land*. DEFRA July 2010.

Department for Environment, Food and Rural Affairs. 2013. defra-stats-foodfarm-landuselivestock-june-results-nationalcharacterareas-12nov14.xls

David RW. 1958. An introduction to the British species of *Callitriche*. *Proceedings of the Botanical Society of the British Isles* **3**: 28–32.

Druce GC. 1886. *The flora of Oxfordshire*. Oxford: Parker and Co.

Druce GC. 1927. *The flora of Oxfordshire*. 2nd Ed. Oxford: Clarendon Press.

Druce GC. 1897. *The flora of Berkshire*. Oxford: Clarendon Press.

Dunn AJ. 1993. *The Flora of Ditchley. The Wild Flowers of an Oxfordshire Estate*. Sandford St Martin: Catherine Wills.

Dunn AJ. 1997. Biological Flora of the British Isles 196. *Stachys germanica* L. *J. Ecol.* **85**: 531–539.

Fitter RSR. 1994. The second Oxfordshire *Orchis simia* site. *BSBI News* **66**: 17.

FlBe = Crawley MJ. 2005. *The Flora of Berkshire*. Harpenden, Herts: Brambleby Books.

FlOx = Killick J, Perry R, Woodell S. 1998. *The Flora of Oxfordshire*. Pisces Publications.

French C. 2014. Applying the 2014 Red List to Cornwall and comparing it with the 2005 Red List. *BSBI News* **127**: 47–50.

Gent G, Keech TJ, Sutherland DS, Wilson R.1995. *The Flora of Northamptonshire and the Soke of Peterborough*. Robert Wilson Designs.

Glickman TS. 2000. *Glossary of Meteorology* 2nd Ed. American Meteorological Society. Boston. ISBN 1-878220-34-9.

Grassly NC, Harris SA, Cronk QCB. 1996. British *Apium repens* (Jacq.) Lag. (Apiaceae) status assessed using random amplified polymorphic DNA (RAPD). *Watsonia* **21**: 103–111.

Grime JP, Hodgson JG, Hunt R. 1988. *Comparative plant ecology: A functional approach to common British species*. London: Unwin Hyman.

Grose D. 1957. *The Flora of Wiltshire*. Devizes: Wiltshire Archaeological and Natural History Society.

Huxley-Lambrick CR. 2002. Introduction to the valley-head fens of Oxfordshire. *Fritillary* **3**: 3–7.

John DM, Whitton BA, Brook AJ. (Eds) 2002. *The freshwater algal flora of the British Isles. An identification guide to freshwater and terrestrial algae*. Cambridge University Press, The Natural History Museum, London and the British Phycological Society.

Killick HJ. 1975. The decline of *Vicia sativa* L. *sensu stricto* in Britain. *Watsonia* **10**: 288–289.

Kozlowski G, Vallelian S. 2009. Eutrophication and endangered aquatic plants: an experimental study on *Baldellia ranunculoides* (L.) Parl. (Alismataceae). *Hydrobiologia* **635**: 181–187.

Mabey R. 1996. *Flora Britannica*. London: Chatto and Windus.

Mabey R. 2010. *Weeds: How Vagabond Plants Gatecrashed Civilisation and Changed the Way We Think About Nature*. London: Profile Books.

Marren P. 1999. *Britain's Rare Flowers*. T & AD Poyser.

McDonald AW, Lambrick CR. 2006. *Apium repens* Creeping Marshwort Species Recovery Programme 1995–2005. *English Nature Research Report* **706**.

Meagher WL, Sheasby P. 2005. *Portrait of a River: The River Swere in Oxfordshire*. English Landscapes Bloxham Oxfordshire.

Mitchell RJ, Morecroft MD, Acreman M, Crick HQP, Frost M, Harley M, Maclean IMD, Mountford O, Piper J, Pontier H. *et al.* 2007. *England biodiversity strategy – towards adaptation to climatic change*. DEFRA report CRO327. http://www.defra.gov.uk

Moser B, Thompson K. June 2014. Self-incompatibility will slow climate-driven northward shift of two dominants of calcareous grasslands. *Biological Conservation* **169**: 297–302.

Nelmes E. 1947. Two Critical Groups of British Sedges. *The Botanical Society and Exchange Club of the British Isles. Report for 1947* **13**: 95–105.

Palmer M. 2006. Fen violet *Viola persicifolia* Schreber: A review of conservation work carried out under English

Nature's Species Recovery Programme: 1993–2005. *English Nature Research Report* **676**.

Perring FH, Walters SM. 1962. *Atlas of the British Flora*. London: Thomas Nelson & Sons.

Plot R. 1677. *The Natural History of Oxfordshire being an essay toward the Natural History of England*. Oxford.

Poland J, Clement E. 2009. *The Vegetative Key to the British Flora*. Southampton: J Poland and Botanical Society of Britain and Ireland.

Preston CD, Pearman DA, Dines TD. 2002. *New Atlas of the British and Irish Flora*. Oxford University Press.

Rackham O. 1986. *The History of the Countryside*. London: Dent and/or Phoenix Press.

Rackham O. 1999. The woods 30 years on: where have the primroses gone? *Nature in Cambridgeshire* **41**: 73–87.

Rackham O. 2008. Ancient Woodlands: modern threats. *New Phytologist* **180**: 571–586.

Rich TCG, Jermy AC. 1998. *Plant Crib 1998*. London: Botanical Society of the British Isles.

Scott A. 1989. The Ecology and Conservation of *Salvia pratensis*. MSc Thesis. Corporation of London Commons.

Spinage C. 2000. The Wild Pear Tree – one of Britain's rarest trees or a garden escape? *British Wildlife* **11(5)**: 313–318.

Stace CA. 1997. *New Flora of the British Isles*. 2nd ed. Cambridge: Cambridge University Press.

Stace CA. 2010. *New Flora of the British Isles*. 3rd ed. Cambridge: Cambridge University Press.

Stewart NF. 2004. *Important stonewort areas: An assessment of the best areas for stoneworts in the United Kingdom*. Plantlife International, Salisbury, UK.

Stroh PA, Leach SJ, August TA, Walker KJ, Pearman DA, Rumsey FJ, Harrower CA, Fay MF, Martin JP, Pankhurst T, Preston CD, Taylor I. *A Vascular Plant Red Data List for England*. Bristol: Botanical Society of Britain and Ireland.

Sutcliffe O, Kay Q. 2000. Changes in the arable flora of central and southern England since the 1960s. *Biological Conservation* **93**: 1–8.

Watkins FH. 2011. *Veronica praecox*, Breckland Speedwell: 2010: Twelve years on. www.fritillary.org.uk/fritr/veronica.pdf

Wentworth JE, Gornall RJ. 1996. Cytogenetic evidence for autopolyploidy in *Parnassia palustris*. *New Phytologist* **134 (4)**: 641–648.

Wheeler BD. 2002. Controls on the composition of vegetation of valley-head fens in the Oxford region. *Fritillary* **3**: 37–46.

Wicks & Cloughley, 1998. The Biodiversity of SE England: an audit and assessment. Wild Oxfordshire.

Wigginton M J. 1999. British Red Data Books. Volume 1. *Vascular Plants* 3rd ed. Peterborough: Joint Nature Conservation Committee.

Wolstenholme RS. 2011. The History of North Meadow Cricklade. *Fritillary* **5**: 35–40

www.VisionofBritain.org.uk. 2001. Uses historical material which is copyright of the Great Britain Historical GIS Project and the University of Portsmouth.

Young A. 1813. *General view of the agriculture of Oxfordshire*. London: Sherwood, Neely and Jones.

Glossary

We have used technical terms fairly sparingly but some that we have used frequently are cited here; a full glossary of botanical terms is in Stace (2010, p. 1077.)

Archaeophyte A species associated with human activity, established in the Britain Isles before 1500.

Base-rich Soil or water rich in salts of alkali metals, notably calcium carbonate.

Bract A leaf-like blade.

Calcicole A species occurring only on calcareous (lime-rich) soils.

Chiltern slopes The Chiltern Hills have scarp slopes (steep, towards the northwest), and the much shallower dip slopes facing southeast.

Corallian Ridge An intermittent line of hills running from near Faringdon northeastwards towards Oxford and Beckley.

Eutrophic Rich in plant nutrients especially nitrates and phosphates.

Glumes Leaflike structures enclosing the flowers (spikelets) of grasses and sedges.

Internode The length of stem between a leaf (or pair of leaves) and the next above it.

MG4 Meadows characterised by Greater Burnet and Meadow-foxtail, as defined by the National Vegetation classification.

Native A species that colonised the Britain Isles by natural means.

Neophyte A species which became established by human agency in the Britain Isles after 1500.

pH A logarithmic measure of acidity, neutral = 7. acidity below it and alkalinity above it.

Sepal A part of the outer covering of a flower, usually green.

Tetrad A square area of 2 × 2 km of the National Grid – the unit of mapping in The Flora of Oxfordshire (1998).

Tufa A concretion of calcium carbonate forming over rocks and objects in lime-rich streams.

Turbidity Of water, opacity due to suspended mud.

Vc22 The Watsonian vice-county of Berkshire, mostly the pre-1974 county of Berkshire.

Vc23 The Watsonian vice-county of Oxfordshire, mostly the pre-1974 county of Oxfordshire, north of the Thames.

Index